Open this book and you will find... thinking and shrinking, dreaming and scheming, creek crossing and brother bossing, biscuit baking, ice-cream making, time traveling, mystery unraveling, blizzarding, lizarding, snoring, choring, roaring... and DINOSAURING! All in

HOUGHTON MIFFLIN
The Literature Experience
READING

Acknowledgments appear on page 493.

Printed in the U.S.A.

ISBN: 0-395-51923-3

FGHIJ-VH-998765432

DINOSAURING

Senior Author
John J. Pikulski

Senior Coordinating Author
J. David Cooper

Senior Consulting Author
William K. Durr

Coordinating Authors
Kathryn H. Au
M. Jean Greenlaw
Marjorie Y. Lipson
Susan Page
Sheila W. Valencia
Karen K. Wixson

Authors
Rosalinda B. Barrera
Ruth P. Bunyan
Jacqueline L. Chaparro
Jacqueline C. Comas
Alan N. Crawford
Robert L. Hillerich
Timothy G. Johnson
Jana M. Mason
Pamela A. Mason
William E. Nagy
Joseph S. Renzulli
Alfredo Schifini

Senior Advisor
Richard C. Anderson

Advisors
Christopher J. Baker
Charles Peters

HOUGHTON MIFFLIN COMPANY BOSTON
Atlanta Dallas Geneva, Illinois Palo Alto Princeton Toronto

Fantasy Close to Home

BOOK 1

THEME BOOK
Flat Stanley
by Jeff Brown

NONFICTION
77

THEY WALKED THE EARTH

BOOK 2

FICTION
127

BOOK 3

AUTHOR
191

Laura Ingalls Wilder

BOOK 4

THEME BOOK
Farmer Boy
by Laura Ingalls Wilder

MYSTERY

271

The Mystery Hour

BOOK 5

BIOGRAPHY

335

The Dreamers

BOOK 6

FICTION
407

Dear Diary

BOOK 7

FANTASY

BOOK 1

Fantasy Close to Home

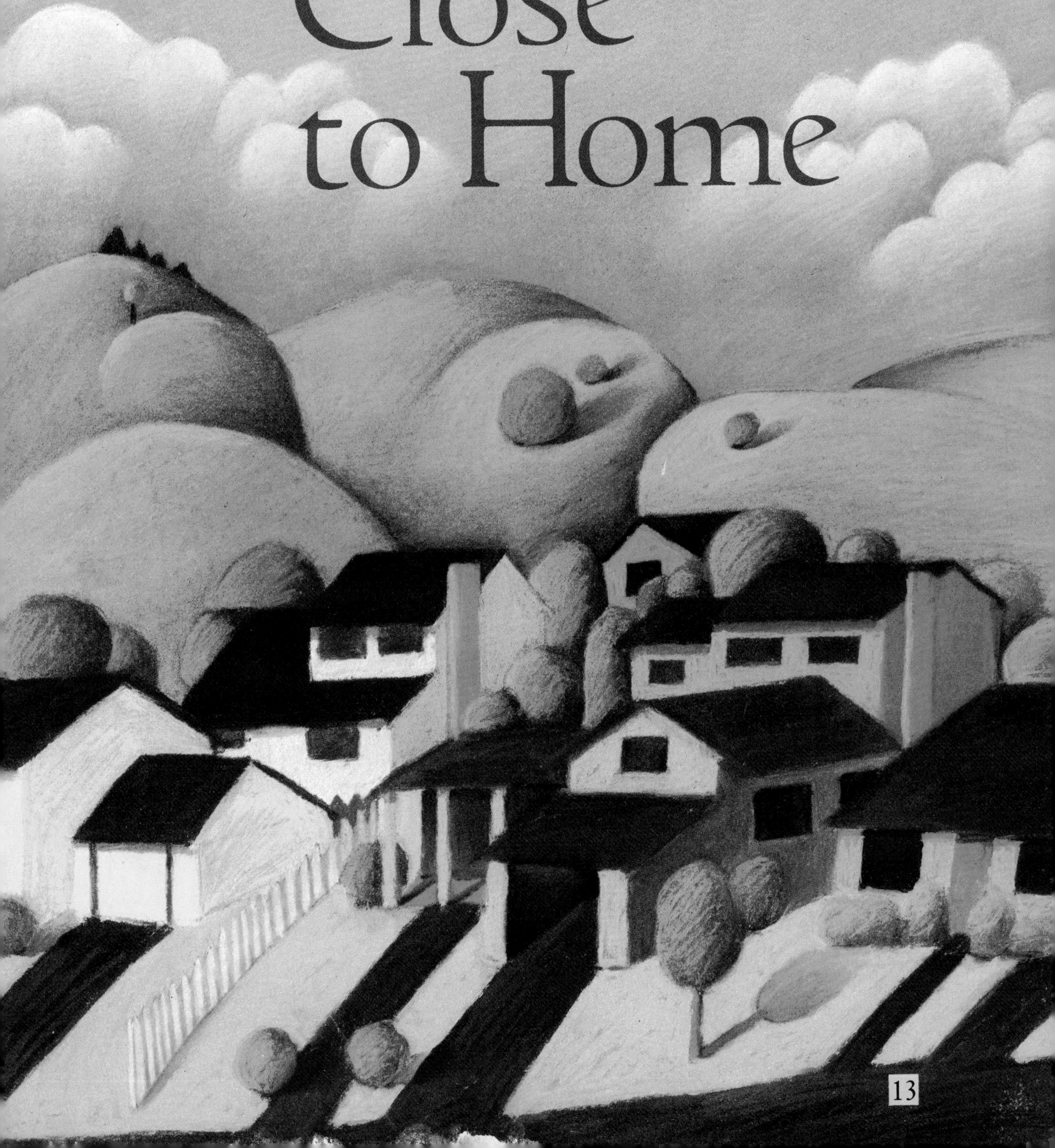

What makes everyday life seem ordinary and boring? Is it doing the same things day after day? Is it thinking that exciting and strange adventures happen only in books or on TV? But what if you were suddenly faced with a game complete with disaster, a ghost from the past, or a decrease in size? Ordinary life might seem safe and pleasant by comparison.

The characters in this book learn that an adventure in fantasy doesn't always take place in a faraway, make-believe land. Sometimes fantasy occurs very close to home.

CONTENTS

JUMANJI

written and illustrated by Chris Van Allsburg

"Now remember," Mother said, "your father and I are bringing some guests by after the opera, so please keep the house neat."

"Quite so," added Father, tucking his scarf inside his coat.

Mother peered into the hall mirror and carefully pinned her hat in place, then knelt and kissed both children good-bye.

When the front door closed, Judy and Peter giggled with delight. They took all the toys out of their toy chest and made a terrible mess. But their laughter slowly turned to silence till finally Peter slouched into a chair.

"You know what?" he said. "I'm really bored."

"Me too," sighed Judy. "Why don't we go outside and play?"

Peter agreed, so they set off across the street to the park. It was cold for November. The children could see their breath like steam. They rolled in the leaves and when Judy tried to stuff some leaves down Peter's sweater he jumped up and ran behind a tree. When his sister caught up with him, he was kneeling at the foot of the tree, looking at a long thin box.

"What's that?" Judy asked.

"It's a game," said Peter, handing her the box.

" 'JUMANJI,' " Judy read from the box, " 'A JUNGLE ADVENTURE GAME.' "

"Look," said Peter, pointing to a note taped to the bottom of the box. In a childlike handwriting were the words "Free game, fun for some but not for all. P.S. Read instructions carefully."

"Want to take it home?" Judy asked.

"Not really," said Peter. "I'm sure somebody left it here because it's so boring."

"Oh, come on," protested Judy. "Let's give it a try. Race you home!" And off she ran with Peter at her heels.

At home, the children spread the game out on a card table. It looked very much like the games they already had. There was a board that unfolded, revealing a path of colored squares. The squares had messages written on them. The path started in the deepest jungle and ended up in Jumanji, a city of golden buildings and towers. Peter began to shake the dice and play with the other pieces that were in the box.

"Put those down and listen," said Judy. "I'm going to read the instructions: 'Jumanji, a young people's jungle adventure especially designed for the bored and restless.

> " 'A. Player selects piece and places it in deepest jungle. B. Player rolls dice and moves piece along path through the dangers of the jungle. C. First player to reach Jumanji and yell the city's name aloud is the winner.' "

"Is that all?" asked Peter, sounding disappointed.

"No," said Judy, "there's one more thing, and this is in capital letters: 'D. VERY IMPORTANT: ONCE A GAME OF JUMANJI IS STARTED IT WILL NOT BE OVER UNTIL ONE PLAYER REACHES THE GOLDEN CITY.' "

BALDWAY

"Oh, big deal," said Peter, who gave a bored yawn.

"Here," said Judy, handing her brother the dice, "you go first."

Peter casually dropped the dice from his hand.

"Seven," said Judy.

Peter moved his piece to the seventh square.

" 'Lion attacks, move back two spaces,' " read Judy.

"Gosh, how exciting," said Peter, in a very unexcited voice. As he reached for his piece he looked up at his sister. She had a look of absolute horror on her face.

"Peter," she whispered, "turn around very, very slowly."

The boy turned in his chair. He couldn't believe his eyes. Lying on the piano was a lion, staring at Peter and licking his lips.

The lion roared so loud it knocked Peter right off his chair. The big cat jumped to the floor. Peter was up on his feet, running through the house with the lion a whisker's length behind. He ran upstairs and dove under a bed. The lion tried to squeeze under, but got his head stuck. Peter scrambled out, ran from the bedroom, and slammed the door behind him. He stood in the hall with Judy, gasping for breath.

"I don't think," said Peter in between gasps of air, "that I want . . . to play . . . this game . . . anymore."

"But we have to," said Judy as she helped Peter back downstairs. "I'm sure that's what the instructions mean. That lion won't go away until one of us wins the game."

Peter stood next to the card table. "Can't we just call the zoo and have him taken away?" From upstairs came the sounds of growling and clawing at the bedroom door. "Or maybe we could wait till Father comes home."

"No one would come from the zoo because they wouldn't believe us," said Judy. "And you know how upset Mother would be if there was a lion in the bedroom. We started this game, and now we have to finish it."

Peter looked down at the game board. What if Judy rolled a seven? Then there'd be two lions. For an instant Peter thought he was going to cry. Then he sat firmly in his chair and said, "Let's play."

Judy picked up the dice, rolled eight, and moved her piece. " 'Monkeys steal food, miss one turn,' " she read. From the kitchen came the sounds of banging pots and falling jars. The children ran in to see a dozen monkeys tearing the room apart.

"Oh boy," said Peter, "this would upset Mother even more than the lion."

"Quick," said Judy, "back to the game."

Peter took his turn. Thank heavens, he landed on a blank space. He rolled again. " 'Monsoon season begins, lose one turn.' " Little raindrops began to fall in the living room. Then a roll of thunder shook the walls and scared the monkeys out of the kitchen. The rain began to fall in buckets as Judy took the dice. " 'Guide gets lost, lose one turn.' " The rain suddenly stopped. The children turned to see a man hunched over a map.

"Oh dear, I say, spot of bad luck now," he mumbled. "Perhaps a left turn here then . . . No, no . . . a right turn here . . . Yes, absolutely, I think, a right turn . . . or maybe . . ."

"Excuse me," said Judy, but the guide just ignored her.

". . . around here, then over . . . No, no . . . over here and around this . . . Yes, good . . . but, then . . . Hm . . ."

Judy shrugged her shoulders and handed the dice to Peter.

". . . four, five, six," he counted. " 'Bitten by tsetse fly, contract sleeping sickness, lose one turn.' "

Judy heard a faint buzzing noise and watched a small insect land on Peter's nose. Peter lifted his hand to brush the bug away, but then stopped, gave a tremendous yawn, and fell sound asleep, his head on the table.

"Peter, Peter, wake up!" cried Judy. But it was no use. She grabbed the dice and moved to a blank. She rolled again and waited in amazement. " 'Rhinoceros stampede, go back two spaces.' "

As fast as he had fallen asleep, Peter awoke. Together they listened to a rumble in the hallway. It grew louder and louder. Suddenly a herd of rhinos charged through the living room and into the dining room, crushing all the furniture in their path. Peter and Judy covered their ears as sounds of splintering wood and breaking china filled the house.

Peter gave the dice a quick tumble. " 'Python sneaks into camp, go back one space.' "

Judy shrieked and jumped up on her chair.

"Over the fireplace," said Peter. Judy sat down again, nervously eyeing the eight-foot snake that was wrapping itself around the mantel clock. The guide looked up from his map, took one look at the snake, and moved to the far corner of the room, joining the monkeys on the couch.

Judy took her turn and landed on a blank space. Her brother took the dice and rolled a three.

"Oh, no," he moaned. " 'Volcano erupts, go back three spaces.' " The room became warm and started to shake a little. Molten lava poured from the fireplace opening. It hit the water on the floor and the room filled with steam. Judy rolled the dice and moved ahead.

" 'Discover shortcut, roll again.' Oh dear!" she cried. Judy saw the snake unwrapping himself from the clock.

"If you roll a twelve you can get out of the jungle," said Peter.

"Please, please," Judy begged as she shook the dice. The snake was wriggling his way to the floor. She dropped the dice from her hand. One six, then another. Judy grabbed her piece and slammed it to the board. "**JUMANJI**," she yelled, as loud as she could.

The steam in the room became thicker and thicker. Judy could not even see Peter across the table. Then, as if all the doors and windows had been opened, a cool breeze cleared the steam from the room. Everything was just as it had been before the game. No monkeys, no guide, no water, no broken furniture, no snake, no lion roaring upstairs, no rhinos. Without saying a word to each other, Peter and Judy threw the game into its box. They bolted out the door, ran across the street to the park, and dropped the game under a tree. Back home, they quickly put all their toys away. But both children were too excited to sit quietly, so Peter took out a picture puzzle. As they fit the pieces together, their excitement slowly turned to relief, and then exhaustion. With the puzzle half done Peter and Judy fell sound asleep on the sofa.

"**W**ake up, dears," Mother's voice called.

Judy opened her eyes. Mother and Father had returned and their guests were arriving. Judy gave Peter a nudge to wake him. Yawning and stretching, they got to their feet.

Mother introduced them to some of the guests, then asked, "Did you have an exciting afternoon?"

"Oh yes," said Peter. "We had a flood, a stampede, a volcano, I got sleeping sickness, and —" Peter was interrupted by the adults' laughter.

"Well," said Mother, "I think you both got sleeping sickness. Why don't you go upstairs and put your

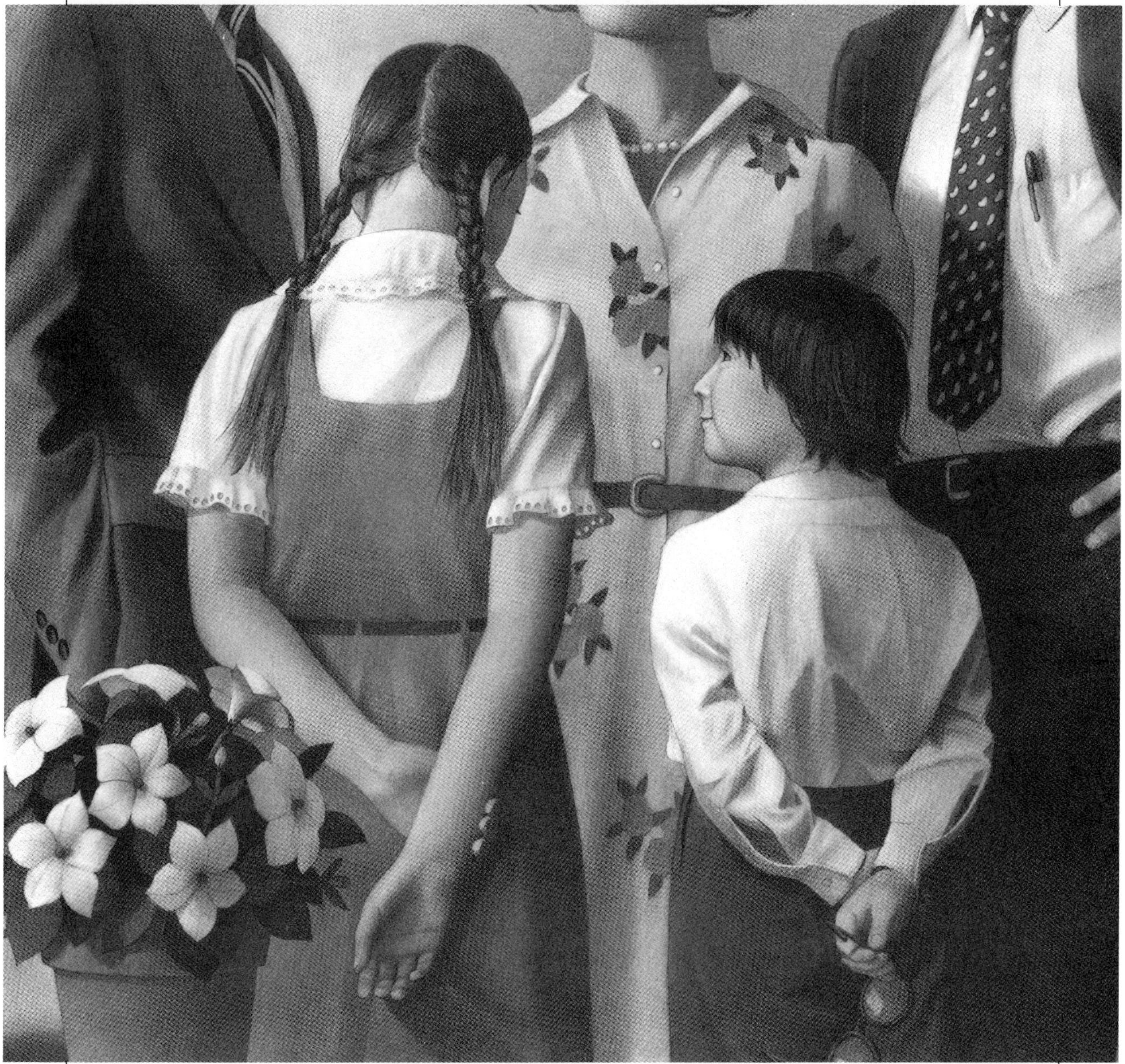

pajamas on? Then you can finish your puzzle and have some dinner."

When Peter and Judy came back downstairs they found that Father had moved the puzzle into the den. While the children were working on it, one of the guests, Mrs. Budwing, brought them a tray of food.

"Such a hard puzzle," she said to the children. "Daniel and Walter are always starting puzzles and never finishing them." Daniel and Walter were Mrs. Budwing's sons. "They never read instructions either. Oh well," said Mrs. Budwing, turning to rejoin the guests, "I guess they'll learn."

Both children answered, "I hope so," but they weren't looking at Mrs. Budwing. They were looking out the window. Two boys were running through the park. It was Danny and Walter Budwing, and Danny had a long thin box under his arm.

Warning! This Is No Ordinary Game!

Design your own board game, complete with strange happenings. On a sheet of paper draw a picture of your game and all its pieces. Under the picture, write the name of the game and a paragraph that tells how the game is played. Make your game one *you* would like to play to spice up a boring day.

Assignment: Imagination

If Chris Van Allsburg were your art teacher, *he might ask you to draw some very unusual things.*

In his classes at the Rhode Island School of Design, Van Allsburg asked his students to make up their own country. They had to name their imaginary country, draw postage stamps and travel posters, and even write a national anthem, *or song, for it.*

Chris Van Allsburg

When Chris Van Allsburg was a boy, playing ordinary board games bored him. They never seemed real enough to him. It was this memory that inspired Van Allsburg to write *Jumanji*.

Van Allsburg has written and illustrated many other books. All of them include a strange mix of mystery and fantasy, and most of them have a surprise twist at the end. You never know what's going to happen next if you're reading a book by Chris Van Allsburg.

Other Van Allsburg books you may enjoy are *The Mysteries of Harris Burdick, The Stranger,* and *The Wreck of the* Zephyr.

Dog Watch

Did you notice the little white dog with the black patch over his eye on page 19 of *Jumanji*? That's Fritz. He first appeared in *The Garden of Abdul Gasazi,* Chris Van Allsburg's first book. Since then, Van Allsburg has included Fritz in each of his books. As you read other books by Van Allsburg, keep an eye out for Fritz. But look carefully — sometimes he's hiding in odd places.

From *The Garden of Abdul Gasazi*

The Mysterious Girl in the Garden

from the book by Judith St. George

illustrated by Alexander Farquarson

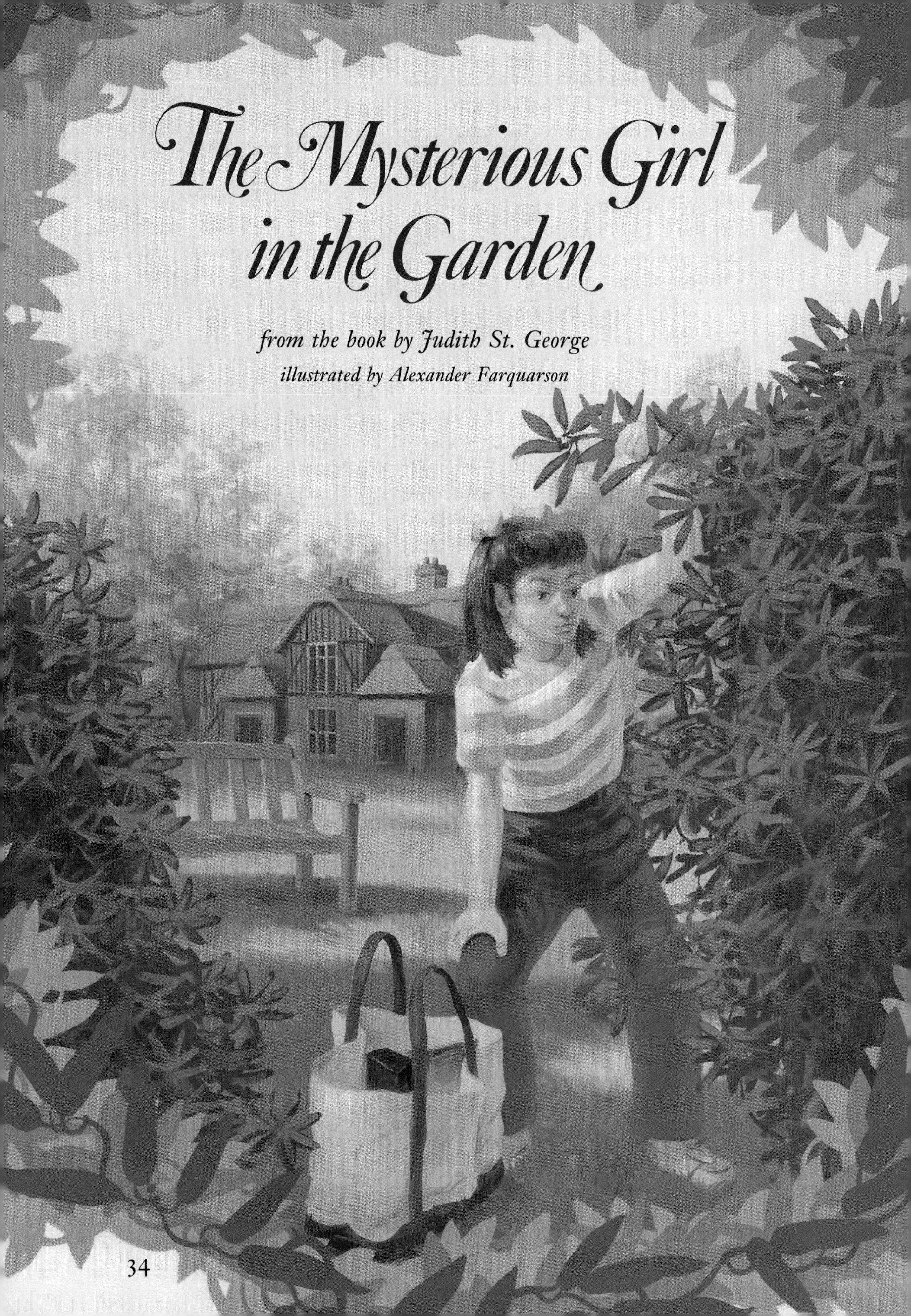

CHAPTER 1

Mom, we're not going to Kew Gardens again today, are we?" Terrie poured more milk on her cereal than she needed and it splashed on the table.

"Please don't start that again, Terrie. You know I'll be working at Kew Gardens all summer," her mother answered. She seemed annoyed about the milk, but she mopped it up without a word.

Terrie Wright and her parents were spending the summer in Chiswick, England, just outside of London. Mr. Wright had to be in England on business and Mrs. Wright had decided to take courses at the Kew Botanic Gardens nearby. That meant Terrie had to hang around the Gardens every day with nothing to do. The worst part was she could have spent the summer with her grandmother on Cape Cod. Granny had a house right on the beach and she had invited not only Terrie but her dog, Wags, too. Terrie had begged and nagged and pleaded with her parents to let her go. But they had said no, she had to come to England with them. So here she was, having the most boring, awful summer an almost-eleven-year-old American girl ever had.

"I'll tell you what, Terrie. On Saturday we'll go to the London Zoo and have a Chinese dinner afterwards. How does that sound?" Dad reached across the table and squeezed Terrie's hand.

"Okay, I guess," Terrie mumbled. That still left almost the whole week to get through.

"When we're in London, let's get your hair cut, Terrie," Mom suggested. "It's much too long."

"I like it long."

Mrs. Wright didn't answer. Terrie figured she probably didn't want to argue. Mom must know what a terrible summer she was having, when she could have been swimming and sailing every day on Cape Cod.

Tuesday was Mrs. Wright's day to work in the Bamboo Garden out by the Queen's Cottage. Kew Botanic Gardens covered three hundred acres and it was a long walk. Neither Terrie nor her mother said much the whole way. Mrs. Wright was glancing through her notes and Terrie was wondering what she would do all day. When they arrived at the Queen's Cottage, Terrie flopped down on a park bench. She had already been through the Cottage and it was a big nothing, just a house with a thatched roof that some queen had built two hundred years ago.

"I've packed us a nice picnic lunch," Mrs. Wright said. "I'll come back at noon and we can eat in the rose garden."

"Mmm."

Mrs. Wright had already started to leave, but now she turned back. "Really, Terrie, I wish you weren't so negative. I know this summer isn't very exciting for you, but you've closed your mind to enjoying yourself in any way. I saw a whole group of children sailing boats on the pond yesterday. Your father and I would be happy to buy you a boat so you can join them."

"Babies sail boats, Mom. I'm not a baby."

"Well, sometimes you act like one." Mom handed Terrie her tote bag. "There's plenty in here to keep you busy. Good-bye, dear." She gave Terrie a worried kind of kiss and left.

Terrie didn't even open her tote bag. She already knew what was in it — books to read, her flute to

practice, playing cards and writing paper. Boring, boring, boring. Terrie watched two old ladies feeding pigeons. They looked bored too. Finally, clucking and cooing like pigeons themselves, they got up and walked away.

Terrie was still slumped on the bench doing nothing when she saw the dog. He was a small, white dog with long hair that covered his eyes. He was chasing a red ball that rolled over the grass. A little bell around his neck tinkled. He picked up the ball in his mouth, then trotted into an enormous stand of rhododendron bushes. Because Terrie knew dogs weren't allowed in Kew Gardens, she tried to watch where he went. But she couldn't see into the dense rhododendrons, which were at least twice as high as a tall man. The ball flew out again. It bounced over the grass and stopped by her foot. A moment later, the little dog ran out after it.

Terrie had never liked long-haired dogs much, but she missed Wags terribly. And this dog was cute. He had a prancing kind of walk as if he were on the most important errand in the world. Without even looking at Terrie, he picked up the ball and strutted back into the bushes with it.

Terrie stood up, walked over to the rhododendrons, and peered in. But she couldn't see anything more than twisted roots, thick branches and big shiny leaves.

Swish, out came the ball again, followed by the white dog with his jingling bell. He brushed so close Terrie could have touched him. This time she went after him. She stooped under a low hanging branch and entered the shadowy thicket. Two steps farther in and the leaves became a dark roof. Even the air seemed cooler and damper. Ahead of her, Terrie saw the flash of a white tail. She stumbled after it in the dim light.

"For pity's sake, can't I be left alone for five minutes? Truly, I shall expire of impatience."

Terrie was so surprised she jumped back, cracking her shoulder on a branch. She rubbed her shoulder where it hurt and looked in the direction of the voice. A girl about her age sat on a dusty root, her feet tucked up under her long skirts. The little dog played with his ball nearby.

The girl seemed furious as she glared at Terrie. "What do they want of me this time?" she demanded. "I promised I wouldn't stray. Still, they send their spies to snoop on me. Give me your message, girl, and begone."

Terrie cleared her throat to answer, but nothing came out. She could only stare.

CHAPTER 2

Must I repeat myself? What do they want of me now?" the girl asked even more crossly than before.

Terrie was getting cross herself. "No one wants you for anything. I saw your dog and followed him in here, that's all."

The girl reached down and rubbed her dog's ears. "Lioni is my dog. He does anything I tell him. He will even attack you if I give the order." The girl stuck her chin up in the air.

Lioni didn't look like he would attack anyone. Besides, Terrie had always gotten along well with dogs. She crouched down and whistled. "Here, Lioni, here, boy."

The dog got up and padded right over. Terrie scratched his throat as he wagged his tail with pleasure.

The girl jammed her hands on her hips. "I don't believe it. Lioni is my dog and mine alone. He hates everyone else."

Terrie had to laugh as Lioni nuzzled into her lap. "He doesn't hate me." Never in her life had she met such an impossible girl. And her outfit was unbelievable. She wore earrings, a necklace, bracelets, and a long dress that looked like a nightgown. Maybe it *was* a nightgown and she was sleepwalking.

"Humph." The girl scowled, her hands still on her hips. "This is my private place. You have no right to be here. I order you to leave."

Terrie smiled, hoping it would annoy her. "I have as much right to be here as you do."

"You certainly do not. My grandfather owns all this land. I shall call for my guards if you don't leave."

"Will they attack me like your dog did?"

The girl sputtered. "How dare you be flippant with me, Princess Charlotte Augusta of Windsor Castle, Carlton House and Kew Palace, future queen of England?"

Terrie stood up and curtsied. "Pardon me for not introducing myself, Your Majesty. I am Princess Terrie Ann Wright of Stilton, Massachusetts, future president of the United States."

"United States!" the girl cried. "I should have guessed from your horrid accent that you were American. Who would expect anything more from an American female than to have a man's name and to appear before me in trousers?"

"Now just a minute . . ."

The girl Charlotte made a big show of looking at the watch pinned to her dress as if the conversation bored her. "Personally I never believed that losing the American colonies was the tragedy that Grandpapa thought it was. A country full of ragtag failures never was worth fighting a war over."

That was too much. Terrie leaped up, ready to take Charlotte on. But a yelp of pain stopped her. She had jumped on Lioni's foot. He whimpered and hobbled back to his mistress.

The girl hugged her injured dog. "Did that dreadful person harm you, my precious?"

Terrie patted him too. "I'm sorry. I didn't mean to hurt him."

"Princess Charlotte, where are you? Are you sulking in those bushes again?"

It was a woman's shrill voice right outside the rhododendron bushes. Charlotte put her finger to her lips for Terrie to be still. "I'm here, Miss Hayman," she called back, all nicey-nice. She shook Lioni's bell so it jingled.

"Hear? Lioni's with me. He hurt his paw and I am comforting him."

"You mustn't frighten me. I feared something had happened to you."

"Who . . . ?" Terrie started to ask, but Charlotte shook her head for silence.

"That was Miss Hayman, my great goose of a governess," Charlotte whispered after a few minutes. "She never lets me be. If she doesn't see Lioni or hear his bell, she pursues me."

Terrie stared at Charlotte. What was going on? Charlotte had said she was a princess and that woman had called her princess too. They must both be crazy. Terrie jumped up and brushed off her jeans. "I'd better go," she announced.

"No, please don't." All of a sudden, Charlotte didn't sound so uppity. "I mean, I have nothing to entertain me. I haven't seen anyone my own age since I arrived here at Kew Palace in June to spend the summer with my grandparents."

Terrie could understand that. She hadn't had anything to do since she arrived in June either. Besides, Charlotte didn't really seem dangerous and her dog Lioni was adorable. He had dropped his ball in Terrie's lap for her to play with him. "I'll stay only if you stop ordering me around," Terrie agreed.

"I order anyone around I please." Charlotte's chin went up in the air again. Then she seemed to wilt. "At least I order my guards around. Otherwise, everyone orders me about, Papa and Grandmama and Grandpapa and all my aunts and uncles. I'm like a piece of taffy pulled first in one direction, then in another."

For some reason, Terrie felt sorry for her. "I get ordered around too," she said. "I wanted to stay with my grandmother this summer, but my mother and father ordered me to come here to England with them. It's been the worst summer I ever had." Terrie picked up the ball and threw it out of the bushes. Lioni took off after it. His injured paw seemed all better.

"If my parents did anything together, I would be pleased beyond measure." Charlotte scratched lines in the hard dirt with the toe of her black slipper. "Mama and Papa have been separated since seventeen ninety-six. They have hardly spoken to each other since the year I was born."

Seventeen ninety-six! Charlotte *was* crazy. "Are your parents divorced?" Maybe that was why Charlotte was so weird.

"Naturally not. My father is the Prince of Wales and royalty never divorce. But Mama and Papa detest each other and it has caused great gossip and scandal."

Lioni had already returned, and without thinking, Terrie took the ball from his mouth and tossed it out of the bushes again.

"Because Papa won't let me live with Mama, I had nowhere to go this summer," Charlotte went on. "That's why I'm here at Kew Palace with my grandparents, King George III and Queen Charlotte. It's been

horrid. My parents have always fought over me, but now my grandparents have joined in the bickering. And Grandpapa's court is dull beyond words. Even his subjects call him 'Farmer George.' When I become queen, my court will sparkle with wit and gay music and interesting people."

Wow, it was time to get off the subject of parents, Terrie decided. She pointed to a big hatbox half-hidden behind a root. "What's that?" she asked.

"It's my playbox." Charlotte pulled out the box. It was covered with colored, varnished paper with "Royal Playthings" stenciled on the top. She lifted the cover. Inside were two packs of playing cards, a tiny chess set, a backgammon board and a set of dominoes.

"I always win at dominoes," Charlotte declared. "Are you willing to risk a game with me?"

Royal Playthings

Terrie had never met anyone in her life who could be pathetic one minute and completely obnoxious the next. "You bet I am," Terrie answered, "and you'd better watch out. I'm the best domino player in Stilton, Massachusetts."

CHAPTER 3

Terrie had a surprisingly good time with Charlotte. They each won two games of dominoes and Terrie was all set for a rematch the next day. But when she woke up, she saw it was raining. It wasn't just raining, it was pouring. There would be no finding Charlotte in the park today. And rainy days in Kew Gardens were deadly. Mrs. Wright always worked in the greenhouse, which Terrie hated because it was so hot and steamy.

But as Terrie and her mother hurried through the rain from the main gate to the greenhouse, Terrie noticed the Kew Palace building set back a way from the path. She remembered that was where Charlotte had said she was spending her summer. Terrie knew that was impossible because Kew Palace was a museum, but all of a sudden, taking a tour through the palace seemed like a good idea. Mrs. Wright, delighted at Terrie's new interest in history, was happy to buy her a ticket.

Terrie took her time walking through the building. It wasn't big, more of a house than a palace, but every room had a fireplace and great high windows that let in lots of light. Deep window seats in the King's Breakfast Room were perfect for snuggling up with a book. Terrie looked out one of the rear windows. A lovely formal garden bloomed out back, all soft heathery blues and silvers and purples in the rain. The highest point in the garden was a gazebo that overlooked the River Thames as it slowly flowed toward London.

The museum display was in the last room of the palace. Terrie and a guard sitting on a stool reading his newspaper were the only ones in the room. Terrie strolled around looking at everything and reading her booklet. King George III and Queen Charlotte had first stayed at Kew Palace in 1760 and lived here on and off for fifty years. There were portraits of them both, as well as pictures of their fifteen children. Fifteen children. It seemed like an awful lot. As Terrie studied the portraits, the words "Farmer George" caught her eye. Wasn't that what Charlotte had called her grandfather?

From then on, Terrie paid closer attention to the displays and the descriptions that went with them. Then unexpectedly, she found herself reading about Princess Charlotte Augusta. As the only child of King George III's oldest son, she was the future queen of England. Princess Charlotte's parents separated soon after her birth and for years Charlotte was shuttled back and forth between her parents and grandparents.

It was just the way Charlotte had described herself. But that was ridiculous. That girl in the rhododendron bushes couldn't be Princess Charlotte Augusta. Then Terrie almost laughed out loud. Charlotte must have toured Kew Palace too, read all this history and made up a big fat story. And it had been a pretty good story, Terrie had to admit.

The glass case of toys was the last display in the room. Terrie glanced at it in passing, then stopped short. A colored, varnished hatbox with "Royal Playthings" lettered across the top sat in the middle of the case. Surrounding it were two packs of faded playing cards, a tiny chess set, a backgammon game and a yellowed set of ivory dominoes.

As Terrie raised her eyes to a picture above the case, little mice feet scampered up her back. She was looking at a portrait of a young girl about her own age with short blonde hair. The girl wore a necklace, bracelets, earrings and a dress that looked like a nightgown with a tiny watch pinned to it. And in her lap was a little dog with long white hair. Terrie stared at the girl's bright blue eyes set in a mischievous face, and the bright blue eyes seemed to stare back at her. "Princess Charlotte Augusta and her Maltese terrier, Lioni. 1805," stated the label.

Terrie jumped as a loud harrumph sounded behind her. It was only the guard clearing his throat and rattling his newspaper. Before Terrie's heart had been ready to burst through her shirt, now it didn't seem to be beating at all. Terrie turned back to the portrait. Princess Charlotte Augusta was the same in every way as the girl Terrie had met, and there was the toybox . . . and Lioni . . . and Charlotte's story about her parents . . .

Stop it, Terrie told herself, it can't be. It's just an English girl playing dress-up to fool a dumb American. Yes, it was only a joke. Nevertheless, Terrie stood looking at Princess Charlotte's portrait for a long, long time.

Is Charlotte playing a trick on Terrie, or is she really a princess from long ago? You can find out if you read the rest of *The Mysterious Girl in the Garden* by Judith St. George.

Will the Real Princess Please Stand Up?

Form two teams. Each team should meet and decide who they think the girl Terrie met in the garden really is. A ghost? An actress? Then the two teams should come back together and share their ideas. Each team should try to convince the other team that their explanation is the correct one.

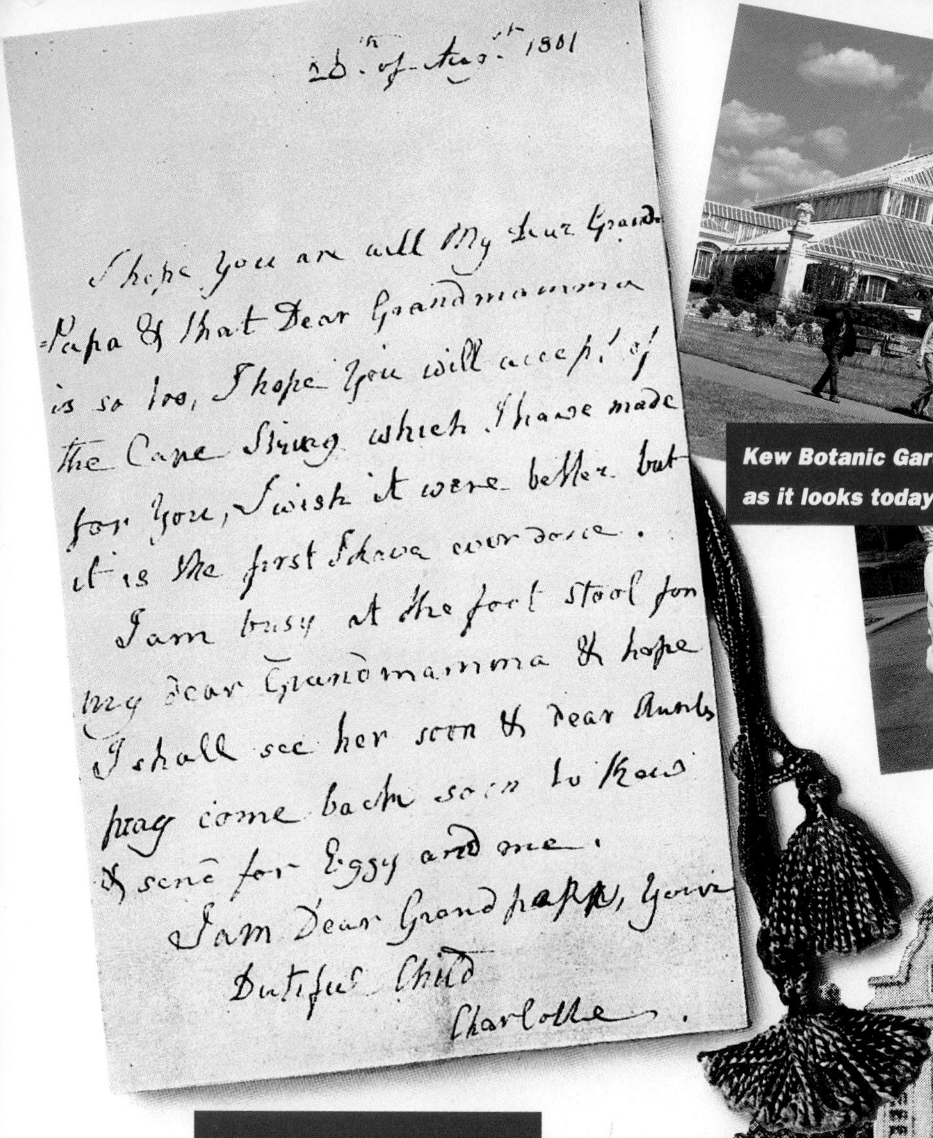

26th of Augst 1801

I hope you are well My dear Grand-Papa & that Dear Grandmamma is so too, I hope You will accept of the Cape String which I have made for You, I wish it were better but it is the first I have ever done.

I am busy at the foot stool for my dear Grandmamma & hope I shall see her soon & dear Aunts may come back soon to Kew & send for Eggy and me.

I am Dear Grandpapa, Your Dutiful Child

Charlotte.

Kew Botanic Gardens as it looks today

Who Is That Girl?

Princess Charlotte Augusta, the mysterious girl in the garden, was a *real* princess who lived from 1796 to 1817. She spent many summers at Kew Palace, just like the character did in the story.

The photo above shows a letter Charlotte wrote to her "grandpapa," King George III of England. The tassel on the letter is a cape string she made for him. She sent the letter from Kew Palace.

Princess Charlotte Augusta, age nine

Judith St. George

One Sunday afternoon, while living in London for the summer, Judith St. George and her family visited Kew Botanic Gardens. It was there, in Kew Palace, that St. George first saw a portrait of Princess Charlotte Augusta. Back home in New Jersey, St. George began to do research to learn more about the mysterious princess. She decided Princess Charlotte would make an interesting character in a book, and that is how *The Mysterious Girl in the Garden* came to be.

St. George has written a number of books with historical settings, including *The Shad Are Running* and *The Amazing Voyage of the* New Orleans.

Judith St. George, age nine . . . and today

THE SHRINKING

Florence Parry Heide

OF TREEHORN
Drawings by Edward Gorey

Something very strange was happening to Treehorn.

The first thing he noticed was that he couldn't reach the shelf in his closet that he had always been able to reach before, the one where he hid his candy bars and bubble gum.

Then he noticed that his clothes were getting too big.

"My trousers are all stretching or something," said Treehorn to his mother. "I'm tripping on them all the time."

"That's too bad, dear," said his mother, looking into the oven. "I do hope this cake isn't going to fall," she said.

"And my sleeves come down way below my hands," said Treehorn. "So my shirts must be stretching, too."

"Think of that," said Treehorn's mother. "I just don't know why this cake isn't rising the way it should. Mrs. Abernale's cakes are *always* nice. They *always* rise."

Treehorn started out of the kitchen. He tripped on his trousers, which indeed did seem to be getting longer and longer.

At dinner that night Treehorn's father said, "Do sit up, Treehorn. I can hardly see your head."

"I *am* sitting up," said Treehorn. "This is as far up as I come. I think I must be shrinking or something."

"I'm sorry my cake didn't turn out very well," said Treehorn's mother.

"It's very nice, dear," said Treehorn's father politely.

By this time Treehorn could hardly see over the top of the table.

"Sit up, dear," said Treehorn's mother.

"I *am* sitting up," said Treehorn. "It's just that I'm shrinking."

"What, dear?" asked his mother.

"I'm shrinking. Getting smaller," said Treehorn.

“If you want to pretend you’re shrinking, that’s all right,” said Treehorn’s mother, “as long as you don’t do it at the table.”

“But I *am* shrinking,” said Treehorn.

“Don’t argue with your mother, Treehorn,” said Treehorn’s father.

“He does look a little smaller,” said Treehorn’s mother, looking at Treehorn. “Maybe he *is* shrinking.”

“Nobody shrinks,” said Treehorn’s father.

“Well, I’m shrinking,” said Treehorn. “Look at me.”

Treehorn’s father looked at Treehorn.

“Why, you’re shrinking,” said Treehorn’s father. “Look, Emily, Treehorn is shrinking. He’s much smaller than he used to be.”

“Oh, dear,” said Treehorn’s mother. “First it was the cake, and now it’s this. Everything happens at once.”

"I *thought* I was shrinking," said Treehorn, and he went into the den to turn on the television set.

Treehorn liked to watch television. Now he lay on his stomach in front of the television set and watched one of his favorite programs. He had fifty-six favorite programs.

During the commercials, Treehorn always listened to his mother and father talking together, unless they were having a boring conversation. If they were having a boring conversation, he listened to the commercials.

Now he listened to his mother and father.

"He really is getting smaller," said Treehorn's mother. "What will we do? What will people say?"

"Why, they'll say he's getting smaller," said Treehorn's father. He thought for a moment. "I wonder if he's doing it on purpose. Just to be different."

"Why would he want to be different?" asked Treehorn's mother.

Treehorn started listening to the commercial.

The next morning Treehorn was still smaller. His regular clothes were much too big to wear. He rummaged around in his closet until he found some of his last year's clothes. They were much too big, too, but he put them on and rolled up the pants and rolled up the sleeves and went down to breakfast.

Treehorn liked cereal for breakfast. But mostly he liked cereal boxes. He always read every single thing on the cereal box while he was eating breakfast. And he always sent in for the things the cereal box said he could send for.

In a box in his closet Treehorn saved all of the things he had sent in for from cereal box tops. He had puzzles and special rings and flashlights and pictures of all of the presidents and pictures of all of the baseball players and he had pictures of scenes suitable for framing, which he had never framed because he didn't like them very much, and he had all kinds of games and pens and models.

Today on the cereal box was a very special offer of a very special whistle that only dogs could hear. Treehorn did not have a dog, but he thought it would be nice to have a whistle that dogs could hear, even if *he* couldn't hear it. Even if *dogs* couldn't hear it, it would be nice to have a whistle, just to have it.

He decided to eat all of the cereal in the box so he could send in this morning for the whistle. His mother never let him send in for anything until he had eaten all of the cereal in the box.

Treehorn filled in all of the blank spaces for his name and address and then he went to get his money out of the piggy bank on the kitchen counter, but he couldn't reach it.

"I certainly *am* getting smaller," thought Treehorn. He climbed up on a chair and got the piggy bank and shook out a dime.

His mother was cleaning the refrigerator. "You know how I hate to have you climb up on the chairs, dear," she said. She went into the living room to dust.

Treehorn put the piggy bank in the bottom kitchen drawer. "That way I can get it no matter *how* little I get," he thought.

He found an envelope and put a stamp on it and put the dime and the box top in so he could mail the letter on the way to school. The mailbox was right next to the bus stop.

It was hard to walk to the bus stop because his shoes kept slipping off, but he got there in plenty of time, shuffling. He couldn't reach the mailbox slot to put the letter in, so he handed the letter to one of his friends, Moshie, and asked him to put it in. Moshie put it in. "How come you can't mail it yourself, stupid?" asked Moshie.

"Because I'm shrinking," explained Treehorn. "I'm shrinking and I'm too little to reach the mailbox."

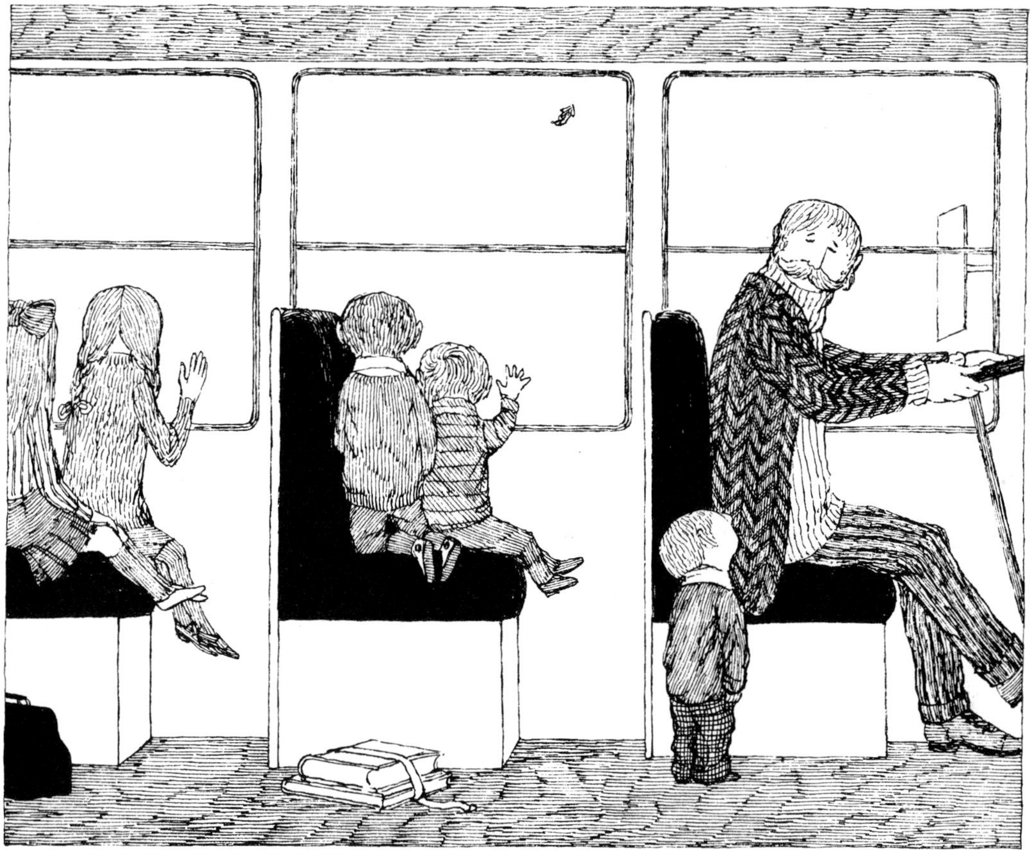

"That's a stupid thing to do," said Moshie. "You're *always* doing stupid things, but that's the *stupidest.*"

When Treehorn tried to get on the school bus, everyone was pushing and shoving. The bus driver said, "All the way back in the bus, step all the way back." Then he saw Treehorn trying to climb onto the bus.

"Let that little kid on," said the bus driver.

Treehorn was helped onto the bus. The bus driver said, "You can stay right up here next to me if you want to, because you're so little."

"It's me, Treehorn," said Treehorn to his friend the bus driver.

The bus driver looked down at Treehorn. "You do look like Treehorn, at that," he said. "Only smaller. Treehorn isn't that little."

"I am Treehorn. I'm just getting smaller," said Treehorn.

"Nobody gets smaller," said the bus driver. "You must be Treehorn's kid brother. What's your name?"

"Treehorn," said Treehorn.

"First time I ever heard of a family naming two boys the same name," said the bus driver. "Guess they couldn't think of any other name, once they thought of Treehorn."

Treehorn said nothing.

When he went into class, his teacher said, "Nursery school is down at the end of the hall, honey."

"I'm Treehorn," said Treehorn.

"If you're Treehorn, why are you so small?" asked the teacher.

"Because I'm shrinking," said Treehorn. "I'm getting smaller."

"Well, I'll let it go for today," said his teacher. "But see that it's taken care of before tomorrow. We don't shrink in this class."

After recess, Treehorn was thirsty, so he went down the hall to the water bubbler. He couldn't reach it, and he tried to jump up high enough. He still couldn't get a drink, but he kept jumping up and down, trying.

His teacher walked by. "Why, Treehorn," she said. "That isn't like you, jumping up and down in the hall. Just because you're shrinking, it does not mean you have special privileges. What if all the children in the *school* started jumping up and down in the halls? I'm afraid you'll have to go to the Principal's office, Treehorn."

So Treehorn went to the Principal's office.

"I'm supposed to see the Principal," said Treehorn to the lady in the Principal's outer office.

"It's a very busy day," said the lady. "Please check here on this form the reason you have to see him. That will save time. Be sure to put your name down, too. That will save time. And write clearly. That will save time."

Treehorn looked at the form:

CHECK REASON YOU HAVE TO SEE PRINCIPAL (that will save time)

☐ 1. *Talking in class*
☐ 2. *Chewing gum in class*
☐ 3. *Talking back to teacher*
☐ 4. *Unexcused absence*
☐ 5. *Unexcused illness*
☐ 6. *Unexcused behavior*

P.T.O.

There were many things to check, but Treehorn couldn't find one that said "Being Too Small to Reach the Water Bubbler." He finally wrote in "SHRINKING."

When the lady said he could see the Principal, Treehorn went into the Principal's office with his form.

The Principal looked at the form, and then he looked at Treehorn. Then he looked at the form again.

"I can't read this," said the Principal. "It looks like SHIRKING. You're not SHIRKING, are you, Treehorn? We can't have any shirkers here, you know. We're a team, and we all have to do our very best."

"It says SHRINKING," said Treehorn. "I'm shrinking."

"Shrinking, eh?" said the Principal. "Well, now, I'm very sorry to hear that, Treehorn. You were right to come to me. That's what I'm here for. To guide. Not to punish, but to guide. To guide all the members of my team. To solve all their problems."

"But I don't have any problems," said Treehorn. "I'm just shrinking."

"Well, I want you to know I'm right here when you need me, Treehorn," said the Principal, "and I'm glad I was here to help you. A team is only as good as its coach, eh?"

The Principal stood up. "Goodbye, Treehorn. If you have any more problems, come straight to me, and I'll help you again. A problem isn't a problem once it's solved, right?"

By the end of the day Treehorn was still smaller.

At the dinner table that night he sat on several cushions so he could be high enough to see over the top of the table.

"He's still shrinking," sniffed Treehorn's mother. "Heaven knows I've *tried* to be a good mother."

"Maybe we should call a doctor," said Treehorn's father.

"I did," said Treehorn's mother. "I called every doctor in the Yellow Pages. But no one knew anything about shrinking problems."

She sniffed again. "Maybe he'll just keep getting smaller and smaller until he disappears."

"No one disappears," said Treehorn's father positively.

"That's right, they don't," said Treehorn's mother more cheerfully. "But no one shrinks, either," she said after a moment. "Finish your carrots, Treehorn."

The next morning Treehorn was so small he had to jump out of bed. On the floor under the bed was a game he'd pushed under there and forgotten about. He walked under the bed to look at it.

It was one of the games he'd sent in for from a cereal box. He had started playing it a couple of days ago, but he hadn't had a chance to finish it because his mother had called him to come right downstairs that minute and have his breakfast or he'd be late for school.

Treehorn looked at the cover of the box:

The game was called The *Big* Game for Kids to Grow On.

Treehorn sat under the bed to finish playing the game.

He always liked to finish things, even if they were boring. Even if he was watching a boring program on TV, he always watched it right to the end. Games were the same way. He'd finish this one now. Where had he left off? He remembered he'd just had to move his piece back seven spaces on the board when his mother had called him.

He was so small now that the only way he could move the spinner was by kicking it, so he kicked it. It stopped at number 4. That meant he could move his piece ahead four spaces on the board.

The only way he could move the piece forward now was by carrying it, so he carried it. It was pretty heavy. He walked along the board to the fourth space. It said Congratulations, and Up You Go: Advance Thirteen Spaces.

Treehorn started to carry his piece forward the thirteen spaces, but the piece seemed to be getting smaller. Or else *he* was getting *bigger.* That was it, he *was* getting bigger, because the bottom of the bed was getting close to his head. He pulled the game out from under the bed to finish playing it.

He kept moving the piece forward, but he didn't have to carry it any longer. In fact, he seemed to be getting bigger and bigger with each space he landed in.

"Well, I don't want to get *too* big," thought Treehorn. So he moved the piece ahead slowly from one space to the next, getting bigger with each space, until he was his own regular size again. Then he put the spinner and the pieces and the instructions and the board back in the box for THE *BIG* GAME FOR KIDS TO GROW ON and put it in his closet. If he ever wanted to get bigger or smaller he could play it again, even if it *was* a pretty boring game.

Treehorn went down for breakfast and started to read the new cereal box. It said you could send for a hundred balloons. His mother was cleaning the living room. She came into the kitchen to get a dust rag.

"Don't put your elbows on the table while you're eating, dear," she said.

"Look," said Treehorn. "I'm my own size now. My own regular size."

"That's nice, dear," said Treehorn's mother. "It's a very nice size, I'm sure, and if I were you I wouldn't shrink anymore. Be sure to tell your father when he comes home tonight. He'll be so pleased." She went back to the living room and started to dust and vacuum.

That night Treehorn was watching TV. As he reached over to change the channels, he noticed that his hand was bright green.

He looked in the mirror that was hanging over the television set. His face was green. His ears were green. His hair was green. He was green all over.

Treehorn sighed. "I don't think I'll tell anyone," he thought to himself. "If I don't say anything, they won't notice."

Treehorn's mother came in. "Do turn the volume down a little, dear," she said. "Your father and I are having the Smedleys over to play bridge. Do comb your hair before they come, won't you, dear," said his mother as she walked back to the kitchen.

You've got a lot of explaining to do, young man.

As he grew smaller, Treehorn had lots of explaining to do — at home, on the bus, and at school. With others in your group, make a list of all the people Treehorn tried to convince that he was shrinking. Then take turns acting out scenes in which Treehorn tries to convince the same people that now he's turning green.

Florence Parry Heide

Florence Parry Heide grew up with the sound of a typewriter. Her mother wrote a daily newspaper column and encouraged Heide to write too. It was not, however, until after she was married and had children of her own that Heide began to write. Today, Heide's grown daughter Roxanne is a writer too. Mother and daughter have teamed up to write *Mystery of the Melting Snowman*, *Mystery at Southport Cinema*, and other mysteries. "Writing for young people is the most exciting and rewarding thing I've done," Heide says, "and I hope to continue happily ever after."

Heide has also written three other books about Treehorn: *Treehorn's Treasure*, *The Adventures of Treehorn*, and *Treehorn's Wish*.

Edward Gorey

Did you enjoy the pictures of Treehorn? Edward Gorey is the illustrator of this story, as well as the other stories of Treehorn's adventures.

Since 1959, Gorey has illustrated more than one hundred and thirty books. He has designed sets and costumes for ballets and plays, such as *Dracula*. If you ever watched the opening credits of the television series *Mystery!* you saw more of Gorey's work. The credits are animations of some of his drawings.

SCAPE

M THE LAND OF
ORED OM

anley

Brown

ey Lambchop is a perfectly ary boy — until the night a tin board falls on him and ens him like a pancake.

zard of Oz

ank Baum

a cyclone strikes her 's Kansas farm, Dorothy herself magically trans- d to the Land of Oz.

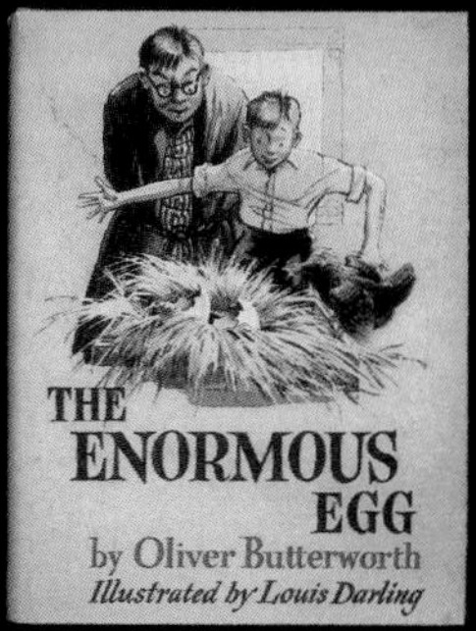

ormous Egg

er Butterworth

Twitchell is quite surprised his hen lays the biggest n the world. He's even surprised at what hatches f the egg.

The Pigs Are Flying!

by Emily Rodda

Being sick in bed with a cold is no fun, Rachel complains. But when she wakes up the next morning, she seems to be in another world.

Mail-Order Wings

by Beatrice Gormley

When Andrea orders a pair of Wonda-Wings from an ad in a comic book, she never dreams they will actually work.

The Hoboken Chicken Emergency

by Daniel M. Pinkwater

When young Arthur Bobowicz is sent to buy a Thanksgiving turkey, he returns with a 266-pound, talking chicken named Henrietta.

FLAT
STANLEY
by Jeff Brown
pictures by Tomi Ungerer

NONFICTION

BOOK 2

THEY WALKED THE EARTH

GASP...
AT
PREHISTORIC
ANIMALS
SO
ENORMOUS
you won't believe your
EYES
MARVEL...
at some of the
FIERCEST
MEANEST
STRANGEST
CREATURES
that ever lived!
SEE...
AMAZING
CREATURES
that actually
LIVED
millions of years ago!

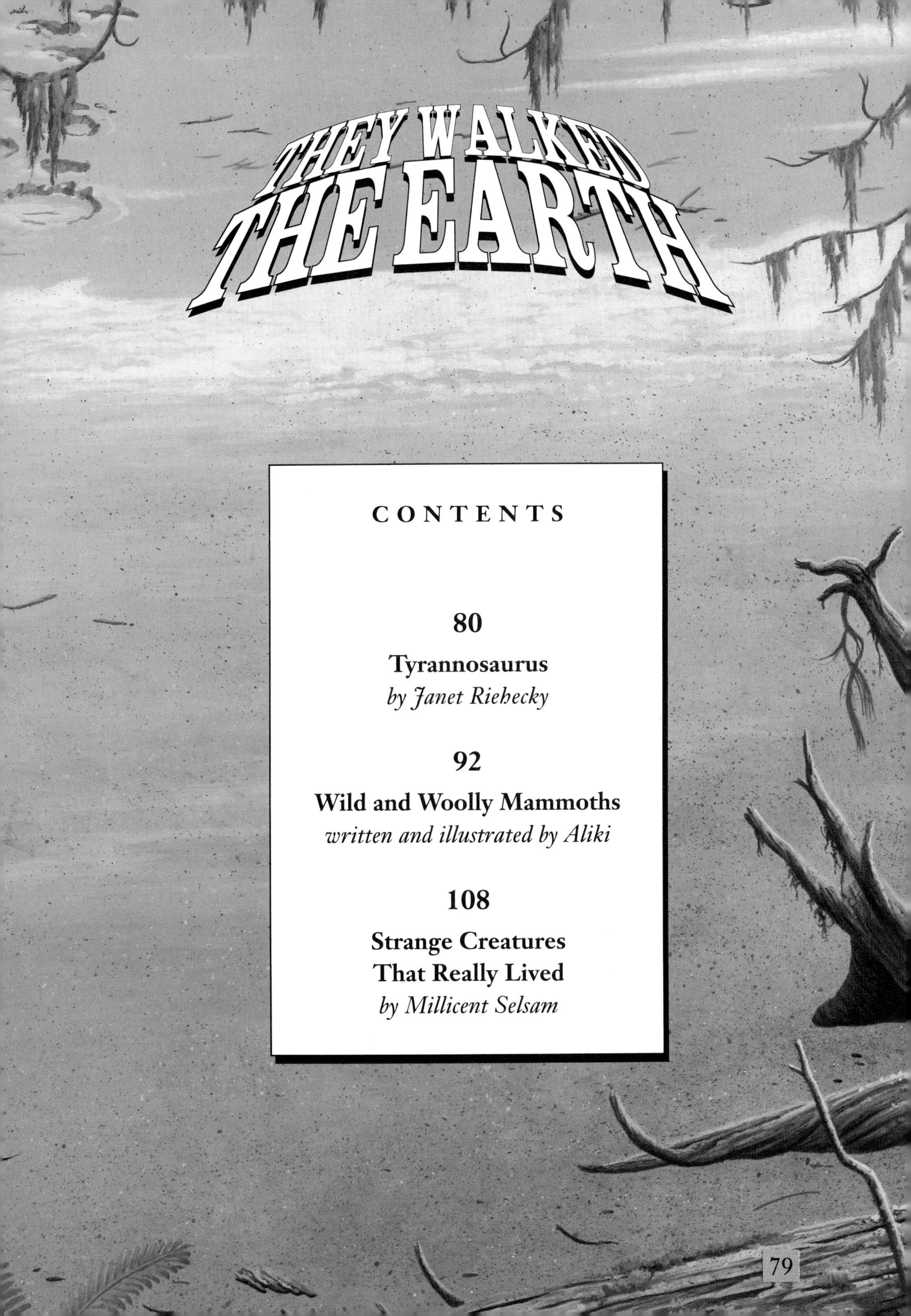

THEY WALKED THE EARTH

CONTENTS

TYRANNOSAURUS

BY JANET RIEHECKY

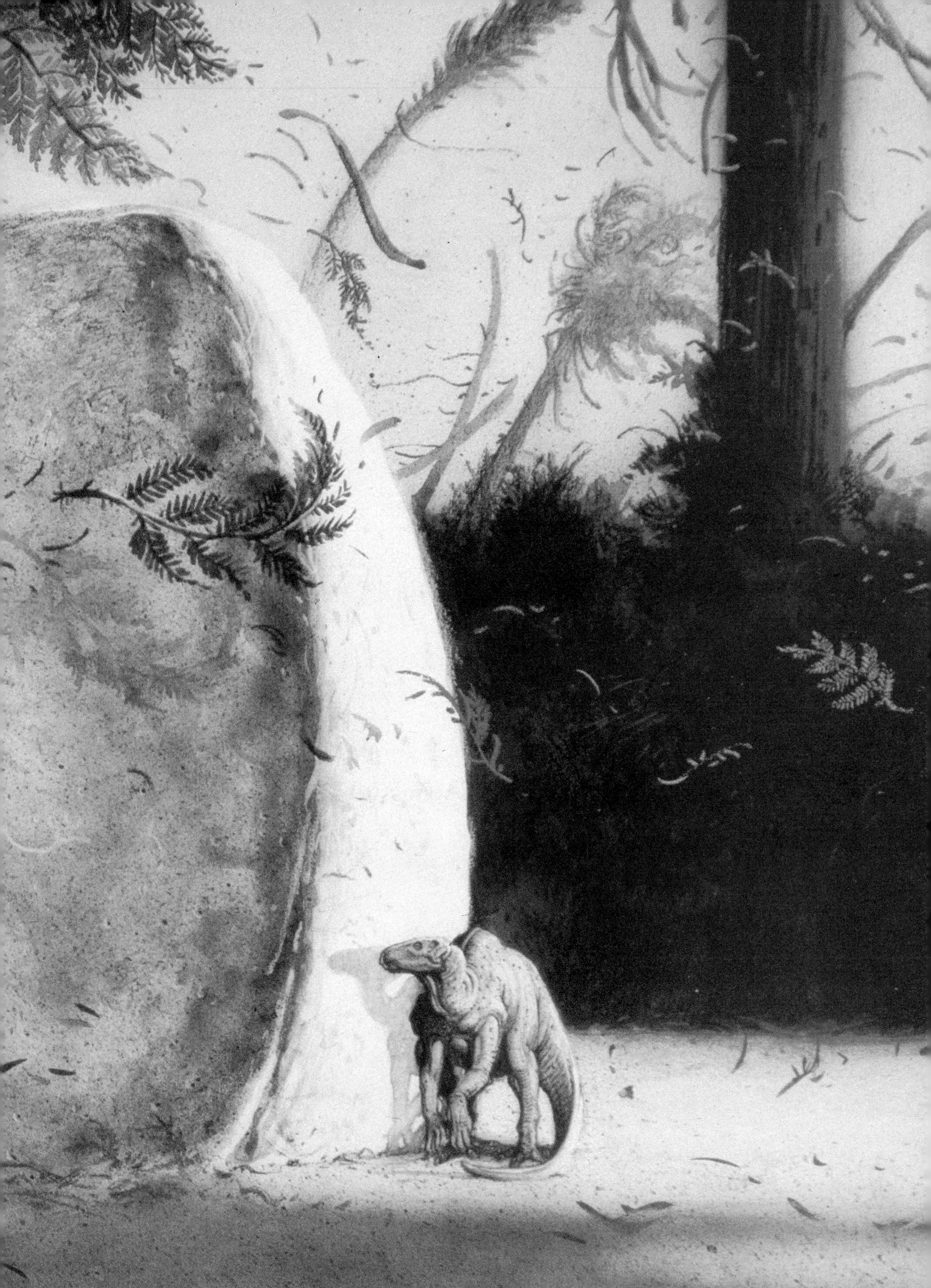

Before people lived on the earth, dinosaurs roamed the world.

It was a dangerous world then. But dinosaurs had many ways to protect themselves.

Some were small and fleet-footed. When trouble came, they just ran away.

Some were too big to be able to move quickly. When trouble came near them, they just moved together and formed a wall.

Others were protected by armor on their bodies. Animals that tried to bite an armored body might end up breaking their teeth.

Still others used parts of their bodies as weapons. They used the horns on their heads or clubs on their tails against enemies.

But there was one kind of dinosaur that didn't care what the other dinosaurs did to protect themselves — it would get them anyway! That dinosaur was the Tyrannosaurus!

The Tyrannosaurus (ti-ran-o-SAWR-us), whose name means "tyrant lizard," was the biggest meat eater ever to live on the earth. There were dinosaurs that grew bigger than the Tyrannosaurus, but they were gentle plant eaters. There was nothing gentle about Tyrannosaurus!

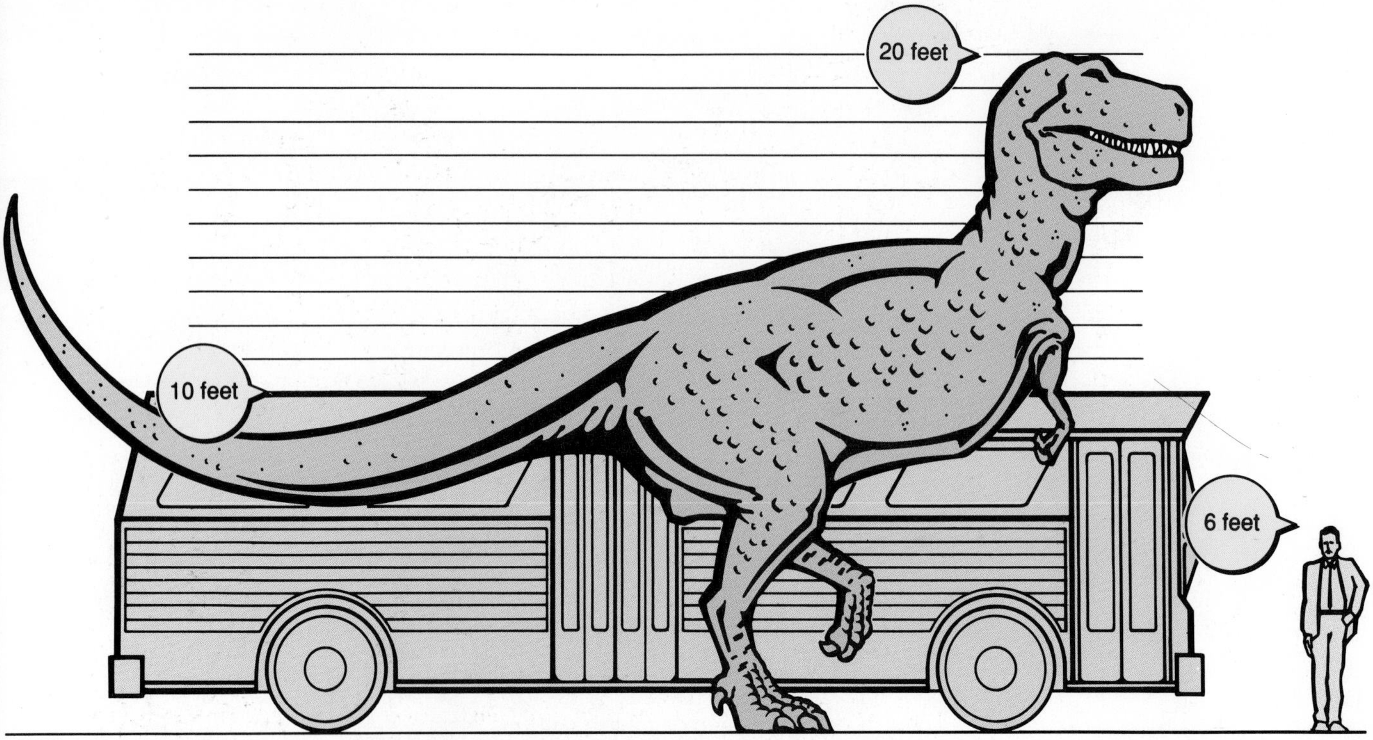

The Tyrannosaurus could grow twenty feet tall (that's more than three times as tall as your father), fifty feet long (that's longer than a city bus), and weighed more than seven tons (that's 14,000 pounds!). And every bit of the Tyrannosaurus was designed for hunting.

The Tyrannosaurus walked on its two back legs, towering over the countryside. Those legs were very strong. Some scientists think they were strong enough to let the Tyrannosaurus chase its prey at speeds as fast as 30 miles per hour — at least for a short distance. And then when Tyrannosaurus caught its prey, the three sharp claws on each foot became fearsome weapons!

Even more frightening, though, were the teeth of the Tyrannosaurus. They were more than six inches long with very sharp edges. Some scientists think the Tyrannosaurus killed its prey by just running at it with its mouth open and those awful teeth sticking out. This would save time. When the two would collide, the Tyrannosaurus would already have its first mouthful!

The Tyrannosaurus' big head also contained a fairly big brain — bigger than a human brain. But that didn't mean that the Tyrannosaurus was as smart as a person. Only a small part of that brain was for thinking (probably about its next meal). Most of the brain controlled how the Tyrannosaurus could see and smell (the better to track down its next meal!).

It would seem that a dinosaur like the Tyrannosaurus couldn't have a problem at all. But it did — a very strange problem. Scientists think that if the Tyrannosaurus lay down, it had trouble getting back up. And this was a dinosaur who couldn't wait to get up in the morning — for breakfast!

The Tyrannosaurus' arms were much too small and weak to push itself up. In fact, scientists wondered for years why the Tyrannosaurus even had those little-bitty arms — they weren't even long enough to reach the Tyrannosaurus' mouth.

Then one scientist suggested what those arms might have been used for. Each hand had two fingers with long claws. If the Tyrannosaurus dug those claws into the ground, they would keep it from slipping. Then it could use its strong back legs to lift its body.

We don't know if this is true or not, but it might be that those tiny arms were all that kept the mighty Tyrannosaurus from falling on its nose.

Not much is known about the family life of the Tyrannosaurus. The tracks that have been found suggest that most Tyrannosaurs traveled alone or in pairs. Apparently, they didn't like each other any more than the other dinosaurs liked them.

They probably laid eggs, but scientists don't know if the mothers took care of the babies when they hatched or just left the babies to take care of themselves.

Scientists continue to study the Tyrannosaurus, hoping to find the answers to these and other questions.

The Tyrannosaurus was one of the last of the dinosaurs to die, but it died out just as all the other dinosaurs did 65 million years ago.

Scientists don't know whether a sudden catastrophe killed all the dinosaurs, or whether they just gradually died off.

It could be that a terrible disease spread through the world. Or that the food supply disappeared. Or that the earth became too hot or too cold for dinosaurs to live. We may never know for sure.

But perhaps it's just as well the Tyrannosaurus isn't around today. It would make today's world a dangerous place for people.

A Day in the Life of Tyrannosaurus

Pretend you could go back in time to observe a Tyrannosaurus "in the wild" for one day. Write notes on everything you might observe. Use what you have learned from reading this selection to describe the creature's day.

In the distance, I see a large reptile.

TYRANNOSAURUS

Tyrannosaurus was a beast
that had no friends, to say the least.
It ruled the ancient out-of-doors,
and slaughtered other dinosaurs.

Jack Prelutsky

DINOSAURS LIVE *again*

If you ever visit the Smithsonian in Washington, D.C., be sure to go to the dinosaur hall in the National Museum of Natural History.

The hall has more than twenty dinosaur skeletons, as well as skeletons of other prehistoric reptiles. Most of the skeletons are built from real fossils, but some are made of plaster. You will see a giant pterosaur overhead, perhaps the largest animal that ever flew.

The skeletons look so real that one young visitor said, "I wonder if the dinosaurs come to life at night?"

skeleton of a Tyrannosaurus Rex

Wild and Woolly Mammoths

written and illustrated by Aliki

Thousands of years ago, a wild and woolly beast roamed the northern part of the earth. It had two great, curved tusks and a long, hairy trunk. Its big bones were covered with tough skin and soft fur. The long hair on its humped back reached almost to the ground. It looked like an elephant, but it was not quite as big. It was a woolly mammoth.

Hundreds of woolly mammoths lived during the last Ice Age. Long before then, the earth was hot and swampy. That was when the dinosaurs lived.

Slowly, the earth grew cold. Some places in the north were so cold the snow never melted. It formed into great rivers of ice called glaciers.

Many animals died out because of the cold. That is probably what happened to the dinosaurs. Other animals did not die out, but went south, where it was warmer. Still others stayed in the cold north.

Some of the animals which lived during the Ice Age.

Many animals of the Ice Age grew heavy coats of hair. The hair protected them from the cold. The woolly mammoth was one of these. It lived in what is now Europe, and in China, Siberia, and Alaska.

The Colombian mammoth lived in a warmer climate, too. It traveled from Asia to Europe, and to parts of America.

Sometimes it is called the Jeffersonian mammoth. It was named after Thomas Jefferson, who was president when one was discovered in the United States. President Jefferson was interested in the past. He encouraged scientists to find out more about it.

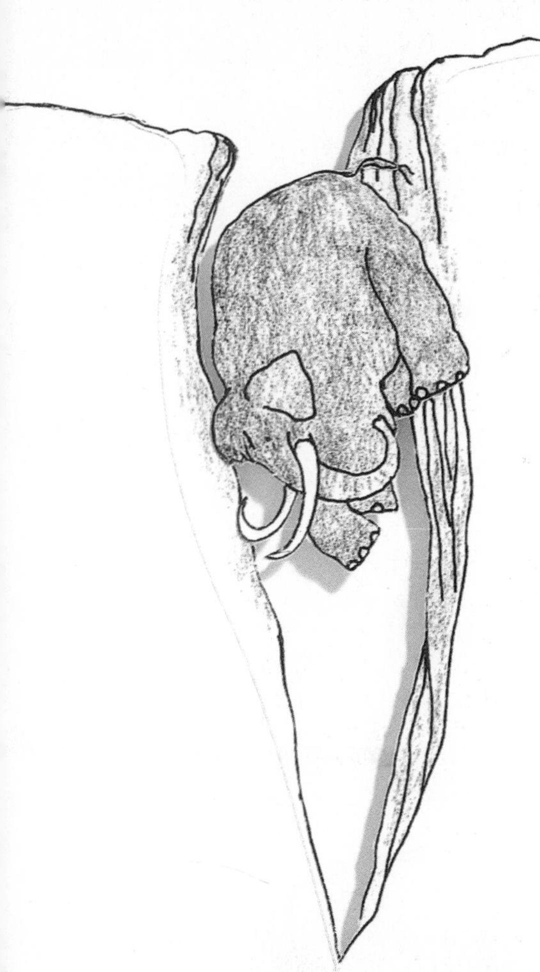

One day, a woolly mammoth fell into a deep crack in a glacier. It broke some bones and died. Snow and ice covered its body.

Thousands of years passed. Slowly the weather grew warmer again. The Ice Age ended. Ice began to melt.

In 1901, the mammoth's body was discovered in Siberia. Part of it was showing above the ice. Men passing by noticed their dogs sniffing the rotting flesh.

Scientists uncovered the body. Most of it was still frozen. That part was perfectly fresh. Dogs ate some of the meat, and liked it, even though it was more than 10,000 years old.

The food the mammoth had eaten before it died was still in its stomach. And what food! There were about thirty pounds of flowers, pine needles, moss, and pine cones.

Later, scientists tasted mammoth flesh, too, and lived to brag about it.

Now scientists know a great deal about this ancient animal, even though the last one died thousands of years ago. Scientists found more frozen woolly mammoths. They found other kinds of mammoths, too.

The imperial mammoths lived 3 million years before the woolly mammoths. At first the imperial mammoths were about the size of a pony. But by the time of the woolly mammoths they had become the biggest mammoths of all.

Imperial mammoths were not hairy. They didn't need to be. They lived in the warmest parts of the world. They lived in giant forests. Their teeth were flat, like those of the woolly mammoth — perfect to grind and crush leaves and twigs.

Mammoths were mammals. All mammals are warm-blooded. They usually have hair. They have milk to nurse their young. Mice, bats, monkeys, bears, and whales are mammals. So are human beings.

Mammoths were the giant land mammals of their time. They roamed quietly in groups. Mammoths were peaceful plant eaters. They did not have to hunt other animals for food. But they had enemies. One was the fierce saber-toothed tiger.

There were other enemies, too. Man was the mammoth's greatest enemy. Inside dark, damp caves scientists found out how important the mammoth was to early man. They discovered paintings of mammoths on cave walls.

These are some of the things found in caves in France.

Bone knife carved with bison and plants.

Woolly mammoth carved in stone

They found clay figures and bone carvings of mammoths and other animals. They knew no animal made them. They were made by early people who lived in the caves. They were made in the days of the mammoth hunters, more than 25,000 years ago. These hunters used tools made of stone, so we call their time the Stone Age.

A whole Stone Age village was found in Czechoslovakia and dug up. Archaeologists, who are scientists who study ancient ruins, learned a lot from this village and others like it. They learned more about mammoth hunters and how they lived.

This is what they found out. Mammoth hunters left the caves where they lived in the winter. In the spring they moved to river valleys where herds of mammoths roamed. They made tents in the valleys to be near the mammoths.

The mammoth hunters made knives and other tools of stone. They used wooden spears with sharp stone points to kill the mammoths. But first they had to trap them. Sometimes the hunters made fires around the herds. Then they forced the frightened mammoths down steep cliffs.

Other hunters waited at the bottom to kill the mammoths with their spears.

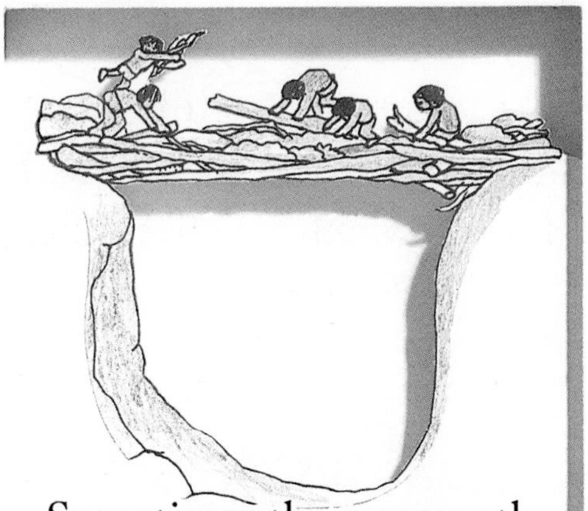

Sometimes the mammoth hunters dug deep pits. They covered the pits with branches and earth.

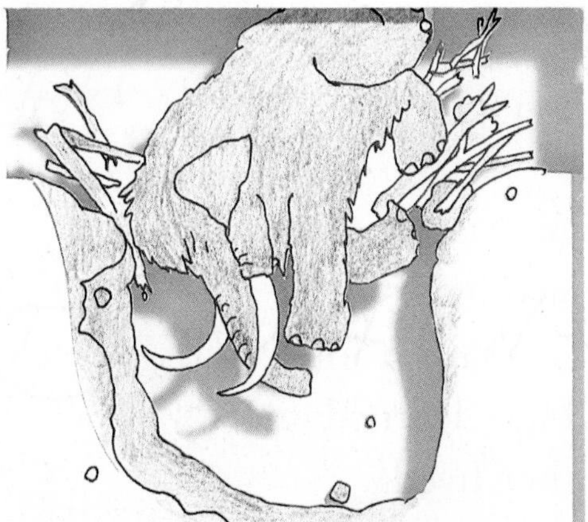

When a mammoth walked over the pit, the branches broke, and the mammoth fell in. It could not escape.

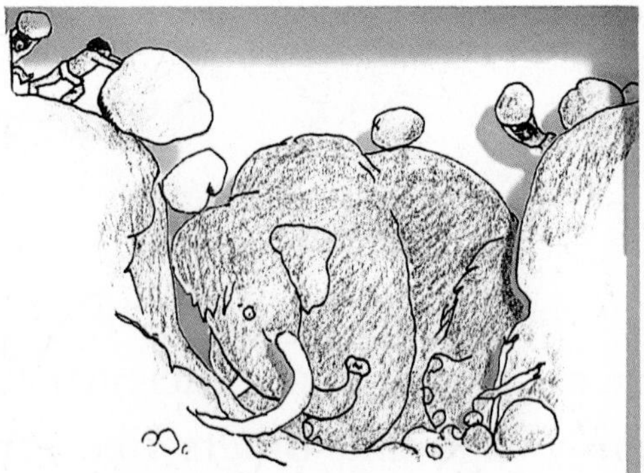

Hunters rolled heavy stones down on it and killed the trapped mammoth.

The hunters and their families ate the mammoth meat. They crushed the skulls and ate the brains. They used the bones to make tent frames. They used bones and tusks to make jewelry. They burned bones for fuel, too. The earliest musical instruments we know about were made of mammoths' bones and tusks. But their skin was too tough for anything.

These people hunted other animals, too. The woolly rhinoceros and the giant sloth lived then. Today they are extinct. But bison, reindeer, horses, and foxes, which also lived then, have not died out.

Mammoths were hunted for a long time. There were plenty of them, and one mammoth was enough to feed many families.

Today there are no mammoths. Some people think it was the mammoth hunters who killed them all. Perhaps they died out when the climate grew too warm. No one knows. But not one live woolly mammoth has been seen for 11,000 years.

More Than One Way to Catch a Mammoth

There are more ways to catch a woolly mammoth than those in the story. See if you can think of another way. Then draw a diagram that shows how your way works.

Weather:
High: -25
Low: Very low

PALEO PRESS

Make no bones about it!

Mammoth Discoveries:
How We Know What We Know

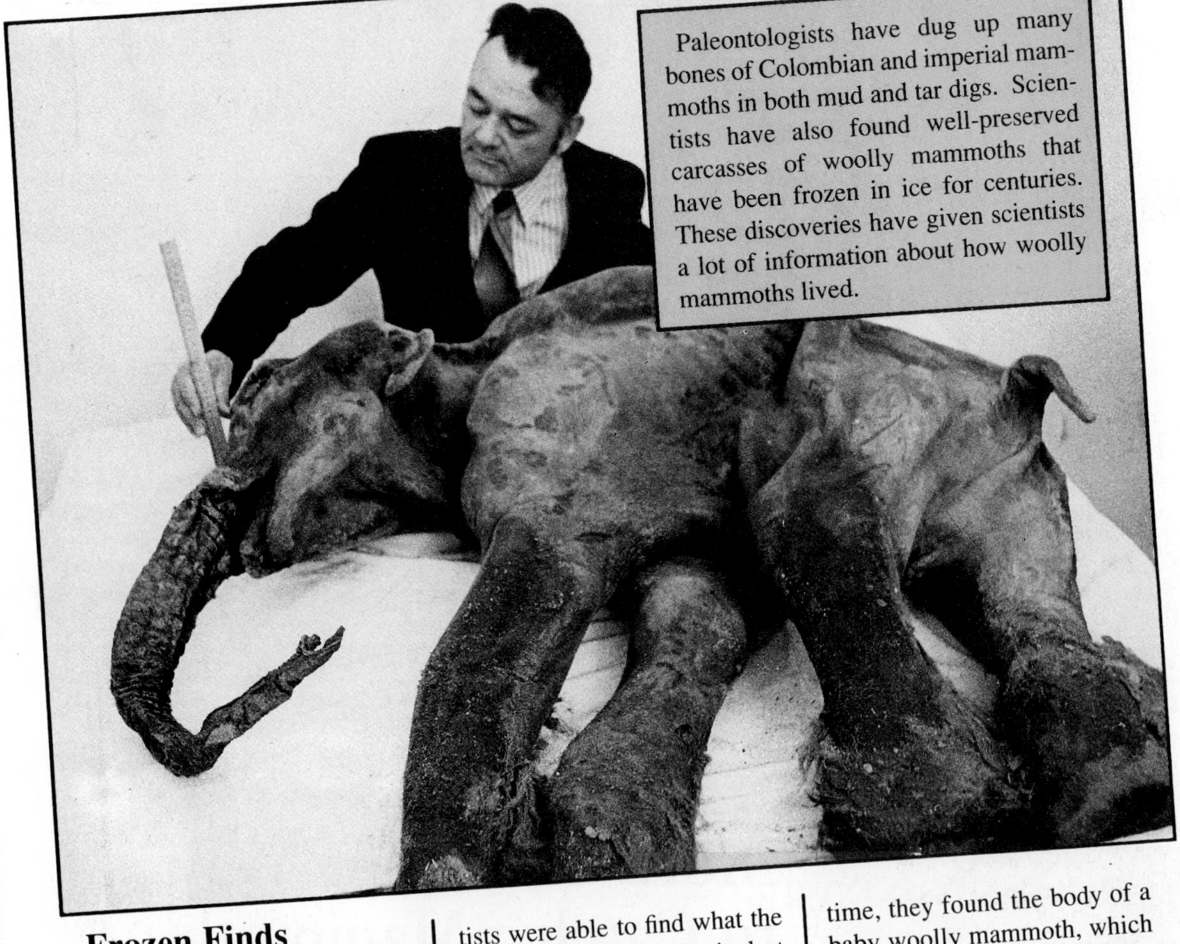

Paleontologists have dug up many bones of Colombian and imperial mammoths in both mud and tar digs. Scientists have also found well-preserved carcasses of woolly mammoths that have been frozen in ice for centuries. These discoveries have given scientists a lot of information about how woolly mammoths lived.

Frozen Finds

In 1906 Russian scientists found the carcass of a woolly mammoth in the frozen ground of Siberia. When they opened the mammoth's stomach, scientists were able to find what the mammoth had eaten for its last meal, over 20,000 years ago!

In 1977, Russian scientists made another frozen mammoth discovery in Siberia. This time, they found the body of a baby woolly mammoth, which the scientists named "Baby Dima" (above). It had fallen into an icy pit over 27,000 years ago.

Muddy Finds

The skull of a mammoth was discovered in 1902 after the ground thawed out near the Berezovka River in Russia.

Tar Pits

Prehistoric bones were first discovered in the tar pits of Rancho La Brea, California, in 1906. Since then, scientists have found bones of over 420 different prehistoric animals, including woolly mammoths and saber-toothed tigers. These animals fell into the tar pits centuries ago. Their bones are clues to the prehistoric past. Rancho La Brea is Spanish for "the tar ranch."

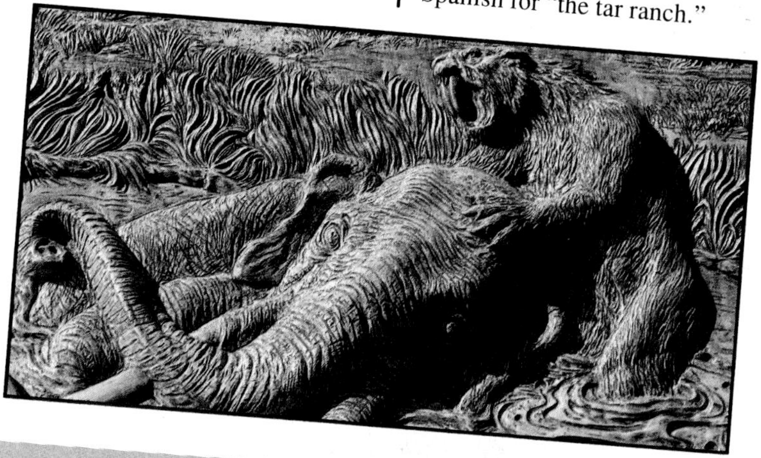

Drawings

Stone Age cave drawings of woolly mammoths and other prehistoric animals were discovered in caves in France and Siberia. They help us know how important these animals were to prehistoric humans.

Visitors to Pech Merle Cave in France can see prehistoric paintings of many woolly mammoths, horses, and bison. These paintings were discovered in 1922.

A large painting of twenty-seven mammoths was found in Rouffignac (RUE fee nyak) Cave in France in 1956.

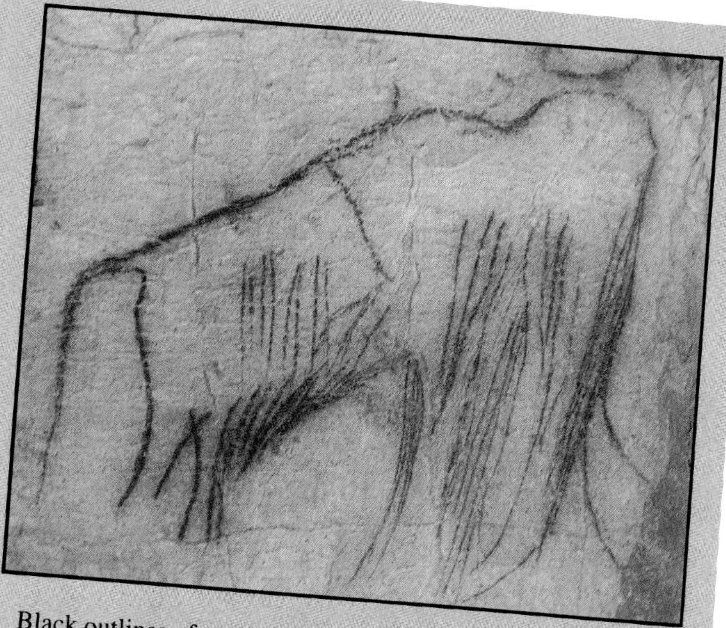

Black outlines of mammoths, deer, elk, and elephants were discovered in France in 1953. Cave drawings of woolly mammoths have also been discovered in the Soviet Union.

STRANGE CREATURES THAT REALLY LIVED

BY MILLICENT SELSAM

Strange animals have always lived on Earth. Some, like the dinosaurs, lived on land. Other queer animals lived in the sea. Some looked like fish, and some looked like lizards. Others looked like turtles with very long necks.

pteranodon

Strange-looking animals flew through the air, too. One of the largest of the flying animals was the *pteranodon* (ter-an-o-don). It looked like a huge bat with leathery wings. It could glide down from the sky and with its long bill snatch fish from the sea waves. It lived seventy million years ago.

Many other strange animals lived long ago. *Archelon* (ar-ka-lon) was the largest turtle that ever lived. It was twelve feet long — about the size of a car. It weighed six thousand pounds! It had a hooked beak and huge flippers. Its bones were found in South Dakota. Twenty-five million years ago, South Dakota was covered by water. Archelon lived in that inland sea.

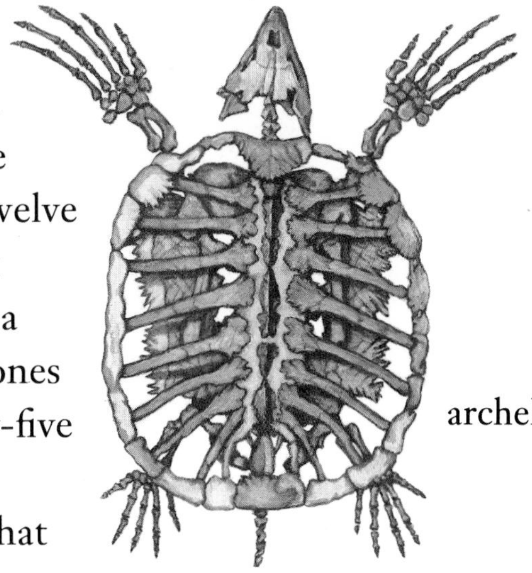

archelon

Here is another strange animal — a colossal crocodile (crok-o-dile) longer than a school bus! Two hundred million years ago, it roamed swamps and riverbanks all over the world. It snapped up any animal that came close to shore. The largest crocodiles today are dwarfs compared to the fifty-foot body of this animal.

crocodile

fossil of an
archaeopteryx

archaeopteryx

The *archaeopteryx* (ar-kay-op-ter-icks) looked like a small dinosaur with feathers. Scientists think it might have been the first bird ever to exist. It lived one hundred forty million years ago. It had a tail and rounded wings. It also had teeth in its jaws. No bird today has teeth. Did it fly? Did it glide from tree to tree? Scientists are not sure. Archaeopteryx may be the missing link between scaly reptiles and feathered birds.

Six horns on its head! Here is an animal as strange as any dinosaur. Its name was *uintatherium* (yoo-in-ta-ther-ee-um). It was about the size of an elephant. Its sharp teeth made it look scary, but scientists have discovered that it ate only plants. Sixty million years ago, it thundered over the plains of the American West.

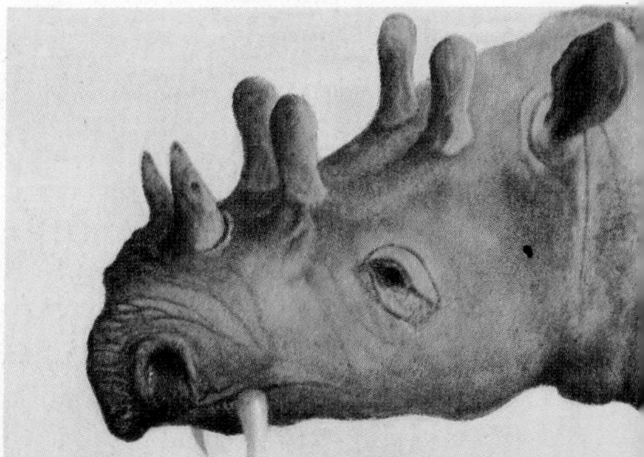

uintatherium

Huge animals once lived in South America. About one hundred years ago, a scientist named Charles Darwin found their bones. Other scientists put the bones together so they could see what these animals looked like.

One of these animals was a giant land *sloth* (slawth). It looked like a great hairy bear. It was as tall as a telephone pole. From its flat teeth, you can see that it ate plants. Scientists think it pushed over trees to get at the leaves in the upper branches. There are no such sloths alive in the world today. The last giant sloths died one million years ago. But we can find their relatives in Central and South America — the slow-moving sloths that hang upside down in the treetops there.

skeleton of a sloth

skeleton of a stabbing cat

This animal was called the "stabbing cat" because it had enormous teeth shaped like daggers. It used its teeth to stab and kill its prey. Fifty thousand years ago, many cats of this kind walked into tar pits and were trapped there. Their flesh decayed, but their bones remained. The bones of stabbing cats can still be seen in tar pits around the city of Los Angeles, California.

skull of a stabbing cat

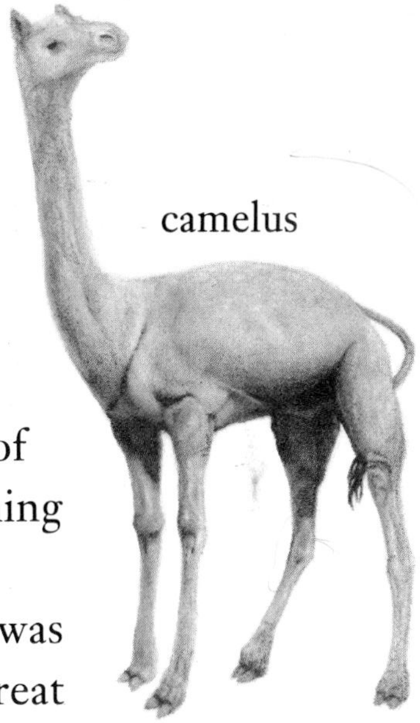
camelus

About twenty million years ago, there lived an animal called the *camelus* (ca-me-lus). It looked like a camel with a very long neck. No wonder it was called the "giraffe camel." Like the giraffe we know today, this camel fed on the leaves of trees. Did it have a hump? We don't know. Nothing is left that can give us an answer.

Three hundred million years ago, the land was covered with millions of insects. They lived in great swampy forests all over the earth. Some of them were no bigger than ants. But others were bigger than any insect that lives today. Huge roaches the size of a pencil ran on the forest floor. Giant-sized dragonflies flew overhead like kites.

In later times — forty to fifty million years ago — there were great pine forests. Sticky resin oozed from the cracks in the trees, and many small insects got caught in it. When the resin hardened, it turned into clear amber. When we look inside that amber today, the insects seem as though they might still be alive. But of course they are not.

gnat *preserved in clear amber*

In 1922, scientists went on an expedition to the Gobi Desert in Asia. There they found the bones of a giant animal that lived twenty to thirty million years ago. It looked like a rhinoceros without horns. Today all rhinoceroses have horns. It was called the *baluchitherium* (ba-loo-ki-ther-ee-um), or the "Beast of Baluchistan" (Ba-loo-ki-stan), because its bones were first found in Baluchistan, Mongolia.

It was the size of a small house. It measured thirty-four feet from nose to tail, and eighteen feet from the ground up. It traveled in herds across the plains of Asia. It was taller than a giraffe, but much heavier. Like a giraffe, it could reach the highest branches. It had only to stretch out its neck to eat twigs, leaves, and flowers twenty feet off the ground.

Just over three hundred years ago, there lived a funny-looking bird called the *dodo* (doh-doh). It was as big as a turkey. It waddled as it walked on short, stubby legs. Its curved beak was nine inches long. Its wings were so short that it could not fly. It lived on islands in the Indian Ocean. When ships stopped there, sailors killed the dodo for food. They left pigs and rats that ate up the dodos' eggs and their young. Now there are no dodos anywhere in the world.

dodo

All the animals in this book lived a long time ago. You cannot see them anywhere in the world today because they have died out. They are *extinct.* Right now, many kinds of animals are disappearing. Some of these animals may never be found again. They may also become extinct.

People spread over the land. They cut down forests. They build roads where only animals lived before. Soon there may be a time when we won't be able to see the animals we are looking at today. Only their skeletons will remain in museums. "What? No more elephants?" It may be, if we don't give them space to live alongside us.

Models of several extinct animals surround Iain Bishop at England's Tring Zoological Museum. He holds the one species still living — an endangered aye-aye from Madagascar.

1. Giant ground sloth 2. Aye–aye
3. Quagga 4. Moa 5. Passenger pigeon
6. Carolina parakeet 7. Tasmanian wolf
8. Toolach wallaby 9. Dodo
10. Great auk 11. Male heath hen
12. Female heath hen 13. Labrador duck

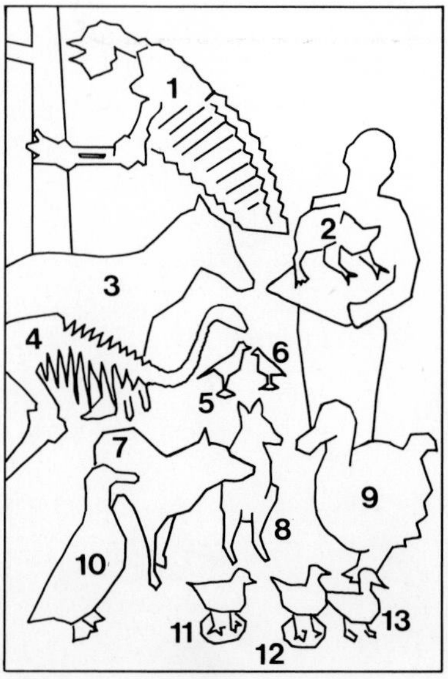

Save 'em, Trade 'em

The selection told you about strange animals. Choose five of them. With a partner, make up a set of Information Cards — one for each animal. Draw a picture of the animal on the front of the card and then write information about it on the back. Use the cards to test your knowledge.

Name pteranodon

Can you describe the creature?
Well... he looked like a huge leathery bat...

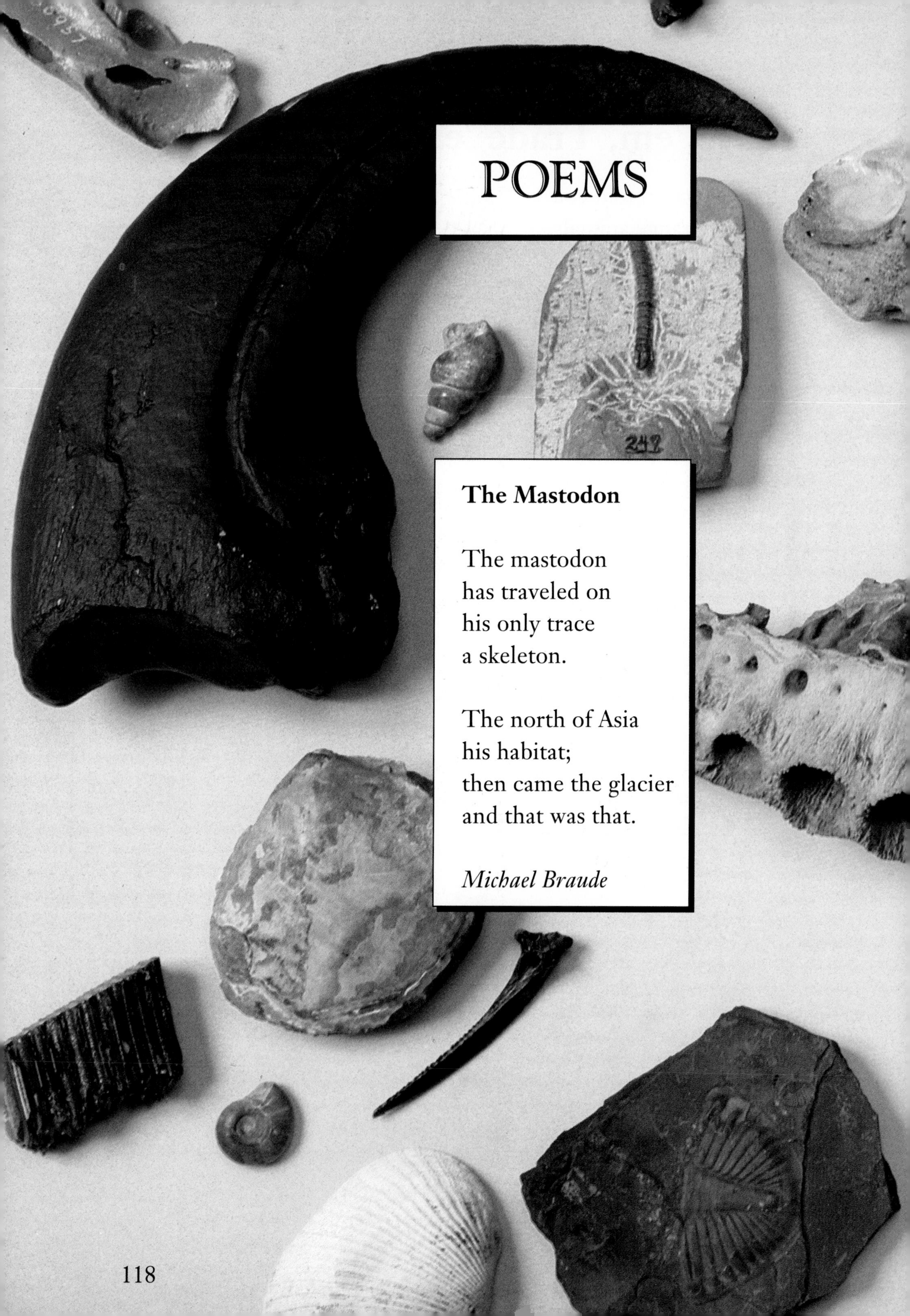

POEMS

The Mastodon

The mastodon
has traveled on
his only trace
a skeleton.

The north of Asia
his habitat;
then came the glacier
and that was that.

Michael Braude

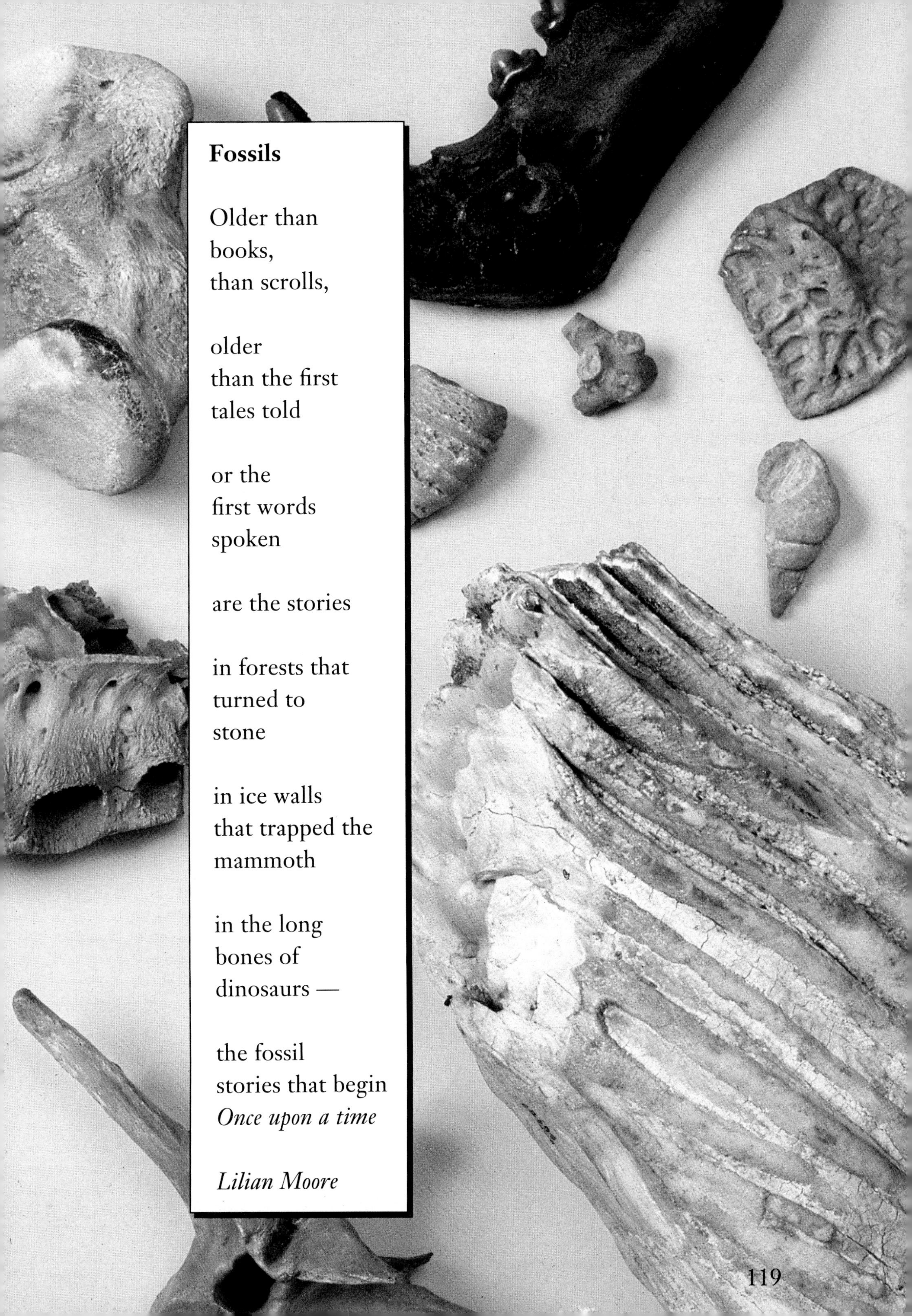

Fossils

Older than
books,
than scrolls,

older
than the first
tales told

or the
first words
spoken

are the stories

in forests that
turned to
stone

in ice walls
that trapped the
mammoth

in the long
bones of
dinosaurs —

the fossil
stories that begin
Once upon a time

Lilian Moore

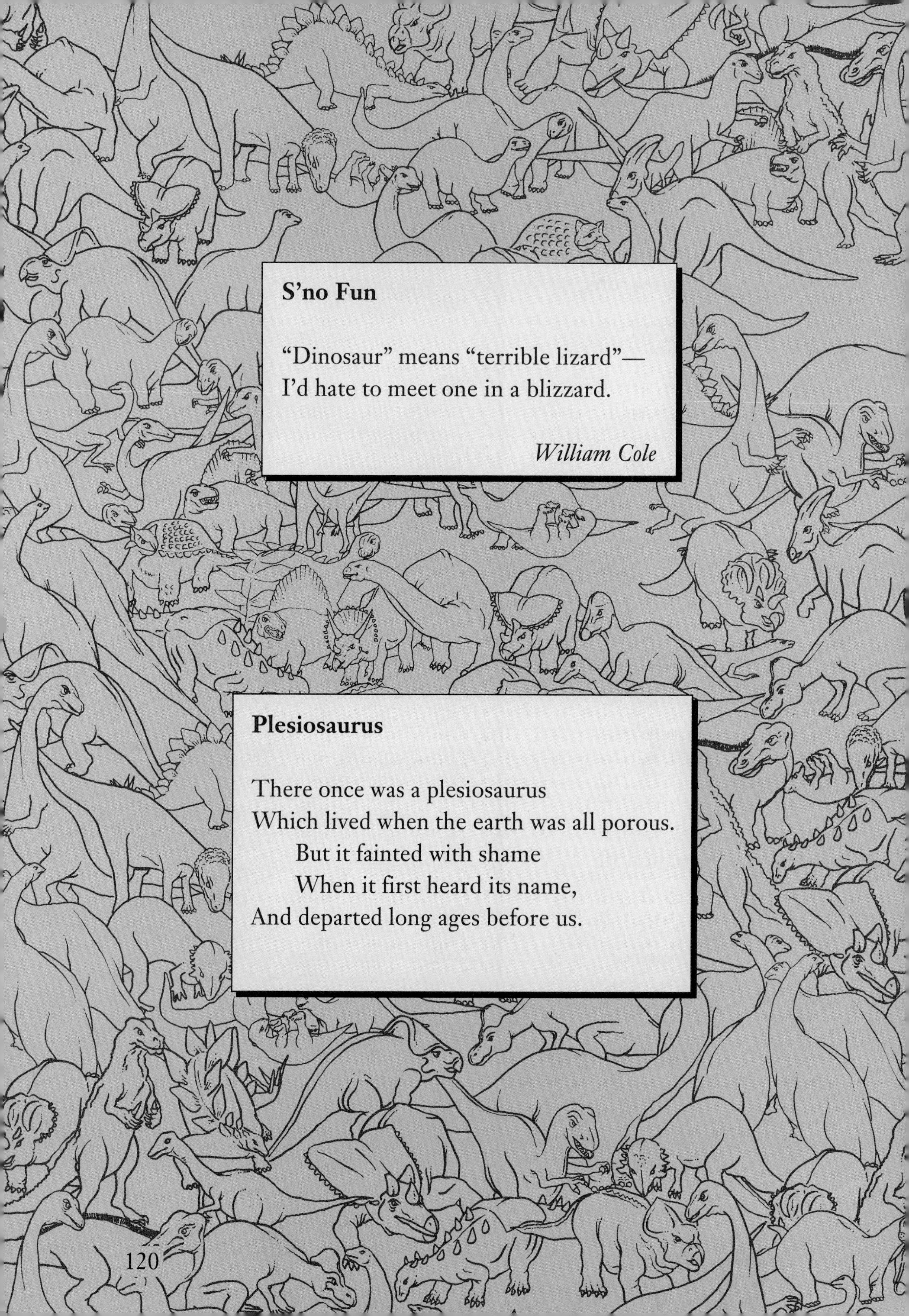

S'no Fun

"Dinosaur" means "terrible lizard"—
I'd hate to meet one in a blizzard.

William Cole

Plesiosaurus

There once was a plesiosaurus
Which lived when the earth was all porous.
    But it fainted with shame
    When it first heard its name,
And departed long ages before us.

What If . . .

What if . . .
You opened a book
About dinosaurs
And one stumbled out
And another and another
And more and more pour
Until the whole place
Is bumbling and rumbling
And groaning and moaning
And snoring and roaring
And dinosauring?

What if . . .
You tried to push them
Back inside
But they kept tromping
Off the pages instead?
Would you close the covers?

Isabel Joshlin Glaser

AUTHORS

Janet Riehecky

By age ten, Janet Riehecky had read all the children's books in her local library.

But reading is not her only interest. She has loved prehistoric animals since she saw museum exhibits of these giant, long-vanished animals when she was still a child. Riehecky decided then that someday she would write books about these creatures. Four of her books that you might enjoy reading are *Allosaurus*, *Apatosaurus*, *Stegosaurus*, and *Triceratops*.

Aliki

When Aliki was five years old, one of her teachers predicted that she would become an artist. She did. She also became a writer. Aliki's full name is Aliki Brandenberg, but she uses only her first name when writing. Aliki's books are all about subjects that interest her very much. And, like many people, she is interested in dinosaurs. You might enjoy reading her books *Digging Up Dinosaurs* and *Dinosaur Bones*.

Millicent Selsam

Millicent Selsam's interest in biology and botany led her to begin writing science books for children. Her books encourage young readers to make their own observations and to trust those observations. "Children are excellent observers," she says. Millicent Selsam has written many science books for children. Two of her other books on prehistoric animals are *A First Look at Dinosaurs* and *Tyrannosaurus Rex*.

THEY LIVE in books

Dinosaur Hunters
by Kate McMullan

Go on a dig with "Dinosaur" Jim Jensen and other dinosaur hunters, as they search for fossils and clues to the past.

The Monsters Who Died: A Mystery About Dinosaurs
by Vicki Cobb

What really happened to the giant creatures that roamed the earth millions of years ago? This book sorts out possible explanations.

The News About Dinosaurs
by Patricia Lauber

Believe it or not, different kinds of dinosaurs are still being discovered today. This book will bring you up to date with what's new in dinosaurs.

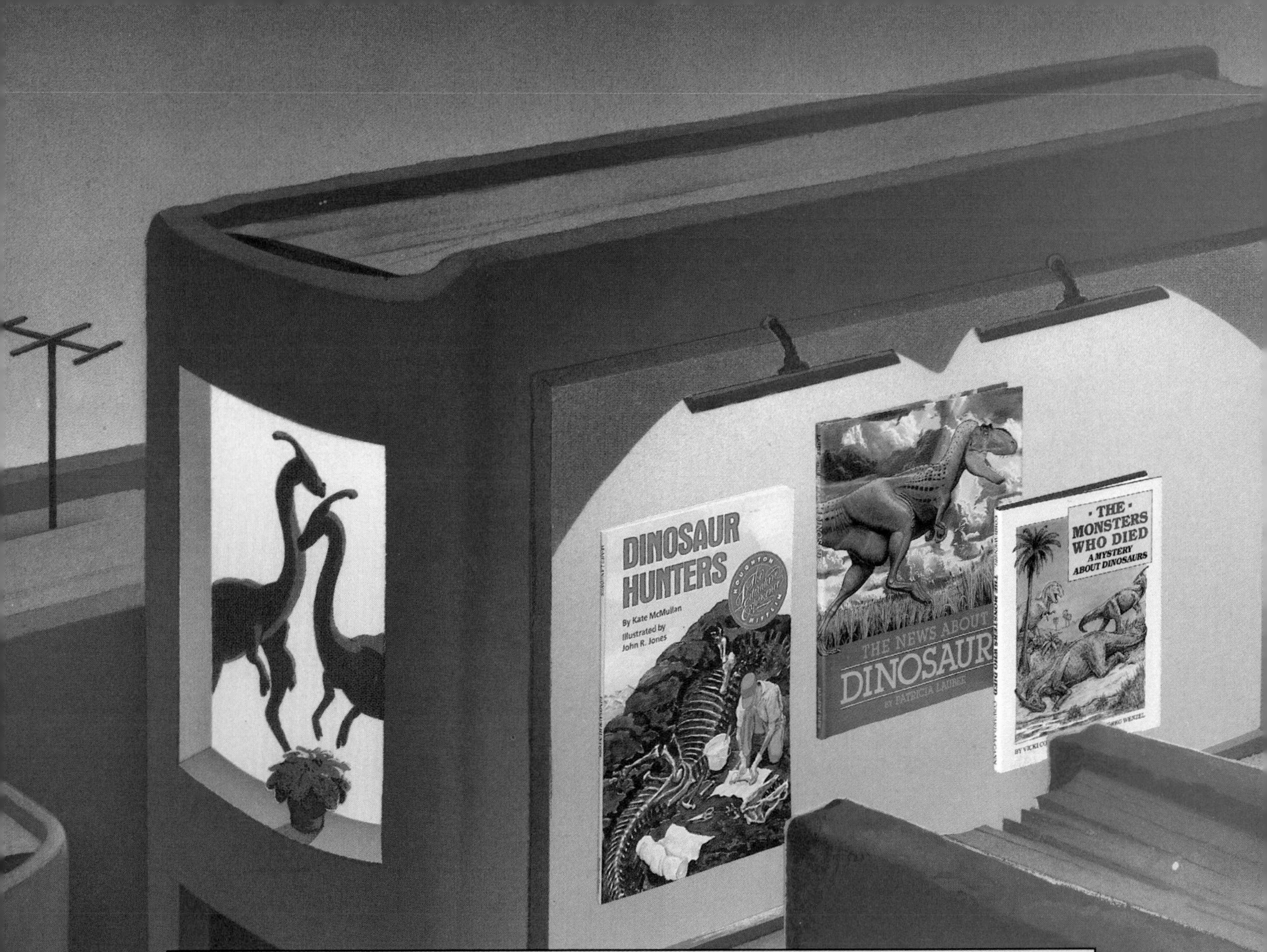

Dinosaur Babies
by Maida Silverman

You have learned about grown-up dinosaurs, but have you ever wondered what life was like for dinosaur babies? This book tells how dinosaurs may have cared for their babies.

The Big Beast Book
by Jerry Booth

Learning about dinosaurs can be more fun than a barrel full of brontosauri. This book has games, poems, riddles, puzzles, and fun projects to keep you busy until the next Ice Age.

Dinosaur Cousins?
by Bernard Most

Could the rhinoceros and triceratops be cousins? Is the ankylosaurus an armadillo ancestor? Were the giraffe and brachiosaurus from the same family?

FICTION

BOOK 3
Battle
of
Wits

Watch as these characters attempt to outwit their opponents and solve tricky problems, using only their brains!

Contents

The Boy of the Three-Year Nap

by Dianne Snyder ♦ illustrated by Allen Say

On the banks of the river Nagara, where the long-necked cormorants fish at night, there once lived a poor widow and her son.

All day long the widow sewed silk kimonos for the rich ladies in town. As she worked, her head bobbed up and down, up and down, like the heads of the birds hunting for fish.

"What next? What next?" she seemed to say, as if the work would never end. Her only son, Taro, was, oh, such a clever lad and as healthy as a mother could wish. But, alas! He was as lazy as a rich man's cat. All he did was eat and sleep, sleep and eat.

If he was asked to do any work, he would yawn and say, "After my nap."

It was said that if no one woke him, Taro would sleep three years at a stretch. And so he was called "The Boy of the Three-Year Nap."

When Taro was nearly grown, a rice merchant moved to town and built a mansion. It had twenty rooms with sliding doors that opened onto the most exquisite garden. In the center was a pond filled with golden carp. And at the end of the garden was a teahouse where one could sit in the cool of the evening and gaze at the moon.

The merchant's wife and daughter wore elegant kimonos with obis of gold brocade. The merchant himself carried a cane made of ivory and smoked a pipe with a bowl of solid gold.

Taro was impressed with his fine new neighbors and began to sneak into the garden between his naps. Everything he saw enchanted him — the magnificent house, the elegant daughter, the fat carp in the pond.

When the merchant counted out his sacks of rice with a tap of his cane, Taro would sigh. "Ah, what a life!"

As the months passed, Taro grew even more lazy. His mother began to pester him, first in one ear, then the other.

"I hear the merchant is looking for a boy to work for him," she told Taro.

"What does he need a boy for?" Taro asked.

"To haul rice sacks, what else?" said the mother.

"Hauling rice sacks!" Taro laughed. "I pity the fool who takes the job. His back will get bent like an old man's."

"How can you sit here and do nothing?" she cried. "The roof leaks like a basket, the walls are crumbling, the rice sack is empty. I don't know how we shall live. I don't know how!"

"Cheer up, Mother. I have a plan."

"How you talk! What you need is a job, not a plan!"

"Don't worry, but you must make me a black kimono and hat like a priest wears."

"What will you do with them?"

"Oh, they are part of my plan." That was all he would say.

"Maybe he is planning to become a priest," Taro's mother thought. But the priests she knew got up before dawn, ate only one meal a day, and never took naps. Try as she might, she could not imagine her son doing that. Still, she decided to make the kimono and hat, for she did not know what else to do.

The next evening, Taro put on the new clothes. Then, with a piece of charcoal, he blackened his brows and drew scowl lines on his forehead and on each side of his nose. When he was done he looked as fierce as a samurai warrior.

"Taro, is it really you?" his mother cried out.

"Don't be alarmed, Mother," said Taro. "It's all part of my plan. Now, don't say a word of this to anyone."

Before she could say more, he ran out of the house.

At sundown, the merchant came out of his house for his evening walk.

"Good evening, madam," he called to Taro's mother. "I suppose that lazy son of yours is still in bed."

"He's a little tired tonight, sir," said the widow.

"Ha! You are a soft one. What he needs is a good smack on his back and a kick on his bottom. Napping at dusk, indeed!"

The merchant went on his stroll until he came to a shrine by the roadside. It was the shrine of the ujigami, the patron god of the town. As he stopped to make an offering, a black figure appeared before him, scowling like a goblin.

"Wh— who are you?" asked the startled merchant.

"I am the ujigami," a fierce voice bellowed.

"What do you want of me? What did I do?" cowered the merchant.

"It is time for your daughter to take a husband," said the ujigami. "You must wed her at once to that fine lad who lives on your street."

"What fine lad, my lord?"

"That fine young man called Taro."

"Taro!" The merchant rubbed his ears. "You mean 'The Boy of the Three-Year Nap,' *that* Taro?"

"The same!"

"Oh, no! There must be some mistake!"

"Gods do not make mistakes!"

The merchant began to tremble. "Surely there must be someone else my daughter can marry. Anyone but Taro — "

"Not a one," growled the ujigami. "It has been decreed, ordained, and sanctified!"

"Oh, my lord, grant me time to think about this. Couldn't we wait a year or two?"

"Impudent mortal!" the ujigami thundered. "How dare you bargain with me! If you delay my command, I shall turn your daughter into a cold clay pot! See if she can find a husband then!"

"No, no!" wailed the merchant. "My child, a pot? Have mercy!"

Falling on his knees, the merchant beat his fists against the ground and sobbed until he was quite worn out.

By then, however, the god had disappeared.

Quite early the next morning, the merchant came knocking on the widow's door. His eyes were red and his face was drawn, as though he had cried all night.

"Madam, I come on the most urgent business," he said grimly. "It seems that my daughter must marry your . . . ah . . . son."

The poor woman's mouth fell open.

"Yes, your son," the merchant repeated. "The ujigami appeared to me last night, and that is his command."

"But the ujigami has never appeared to anyone before," the widow exclaimed.

"That was so, until last night. I am ruined."

"Tell me, honorable sir, what did the god look like?"

The merchant shivered. "In dress, he is like a priest. But in manner, he is more like a goblin. His face is as black as coal and as fierce as a warrior's."

The widow saw at once what her son was up to. Her head began to bob up and down, up and down — like a cormorant about to dive after a fish. Still, she did not want to seem too eager.

So she said to the merchant, "We are humble folk, my good sir. My Taro could never marry a lady as fine as your daughter."

"Agreed," the merchant cried. "But unfortunately what we think matters not. We must do as the god commands or he will turn my daughter into a clay pot."

"How terrible!" The widow widened her eyes. "But, sir, even if they are to marry, your daughter could never live in this wretched house. Why, the roof leaks in a hundred places, and the walls have so many cracks the wind blows right through."

The merchant frowned. He had not thought of that.

"Very well then, I will send a man to mend the cracks and leaks," he said.

First thing the next morning, a plasterer came to repair the house.

"Fine work, fine work," Taro mumbled from his bed.

In the evening the merchant said to the widow, "Now will you consent to the marriage?"

"Alas, how can I, sir?" The widow bowed. "As you can see, our house has but one room. Your daughter would be ashamed to live in a place as small as this."

"True," muttered the merchant. "All right, I will send carpenters to build you many rooms."

After the merchant left, Taro chuckled. "Splendid. My plan is working!"

When the widow's house was finished, the merchant asked, "Now will you consent to the marriage?"

"I fear, sir, that your daughter will still not find happiness here."

"What is it now?" cried the merchant. "Speak your mind or my daughter will turn into a clay pot!"

"My Taro has no job," said the widow. "How can he keep your daughter in luxury and comfort?"

"Surely this is the end of me," groaned the merchant. "All right, your son shall manage my storehouse. But I warn you, madam, he will have no time for naps at my place. Now do you consent to the marriage?"

Taro's mother tossed her head like a cormorant that has caught a large fish. "You have my consent," she said.

No sooner had the merchant left than the widow hurried to tell Taro the news. "The merchant has made a most wonderful offer," she cried.

Taro sat up in bed, ho-hum, stretching and yawning like a satisfied cat.

"It was all part of my plan, Mother. I hope you accepted the offer."

"Indeed I have," said his mother. "You start work first thing tomorrow morning."

"Work!" Taro leaped out of bed. "What do you mean? That was not part of my plan!"

"Ha! Do you think you are the only one who makes plans?" his mother answered.

The wedding ceremony was the finest the townfolk had ever seen. And as it turned out, the marriage is a happy one.

The ujigami must be pleased, for he has never shown himself again. And the merchant's daughter has shown no signs of turning into a pot.

As for Taro, he does a good job keeping count of the rice for his father-in-law, which is no easy task. If he is not the busiest man in town, neither is he the laziest.

It has been a long time since anyone has called Taro "The Boy of the Three-Year Nap." Perhaps everyone has forgotten by now.

ZZZzzzzzz

What if this story had ended another way? Suppose this had happened: It's the morning of Taro's wedding to the merchant's daughter — but Taro has overslept! Write another ending to this story, telling how Taro tries to talk his way out of this one. Read your new ending to your classmates.

Author

Dianne Snyder

Above: Snyder (kneeling) with friends in Niigata, Japan, 1953

Snyder doing homework, with her mother and sister in Japan in 1954

Dianne Snyder, the author of *The Boy of the Three-Year Nap*, had some practice playing the part of the *ujigami*, the same part Taro played in the story. One Halloween while growing up in Japan, Snyder, like Taro, painted her face with *sumi*, the black paint used in traditional Japanese art. As a child Snyder also heard many folktales and trickster stories told by Japanese storytellers who traveled from village to village. *The Boy of the Three-Year Nap*, her first book, is one of those stories.

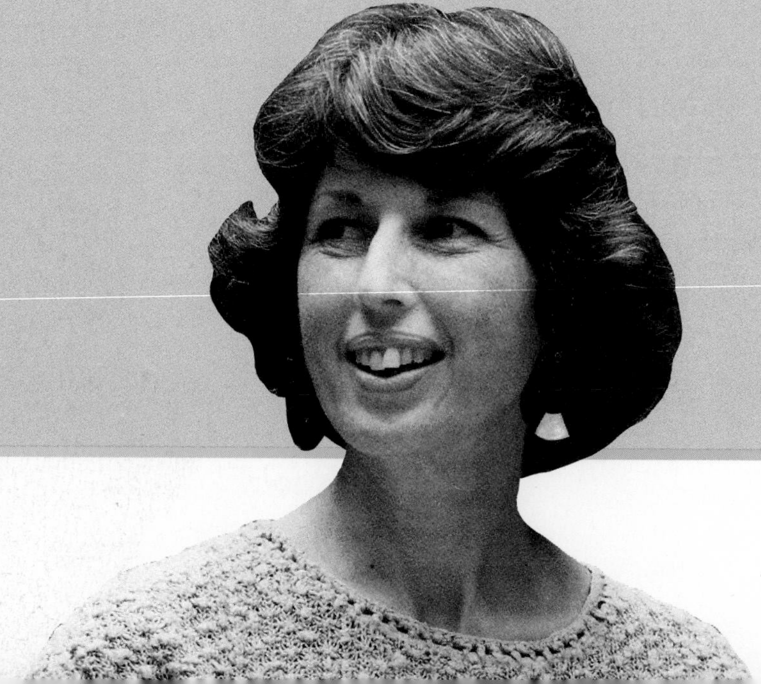

Allen Say

Above: A scene from The Bicycle Man, *a true story about Say and his family*

When Allen Say was first asked to illustrate *The Boy of the Three-Year Nap*, he replied "No!" He didn't want to illustrate any more picture books.

But Say finally agreed to do the book — and something amazing happened. "I locked myself in my room, I took out my old paint box, and I began working," he says. "It gave me an intense joy."

The Boy of the Three-Year Nap was named a Caldecott Honor Book in 1988. Working on this book reminded Say of his childhood in Yokohama, Japan. Many of his books, such as *The Bicycle Man*, are set in his homeland.

FARMER SCHULZ'S DUCKS

by Colin Thiele ❖ with illustrations by Mary Milton

In the hills of South Australia there is a little river with a big name — the Onkaparinga.[1] It flowed through a valley full of apple trees and cabbage patches, pastures and gardens, red gum trees and poplars.

In springtime blossoms fell like confetti, as if the hills were having a wedding, and there was celery on the breath of the wind.

In autumn the willows bowed down by the river, their branches like arches of gold.

And in winter the tall trees whipped the air in the wind and the rain, and the high water in the river went fussing and gurgling on its crooked way.

A narrow road wound down the valley. Sometimes it ran by the side of the river and sometimes it veered away. And it ran right past the front gate of Farmer Schulz's farm, between his house and the Onkaparinga River.

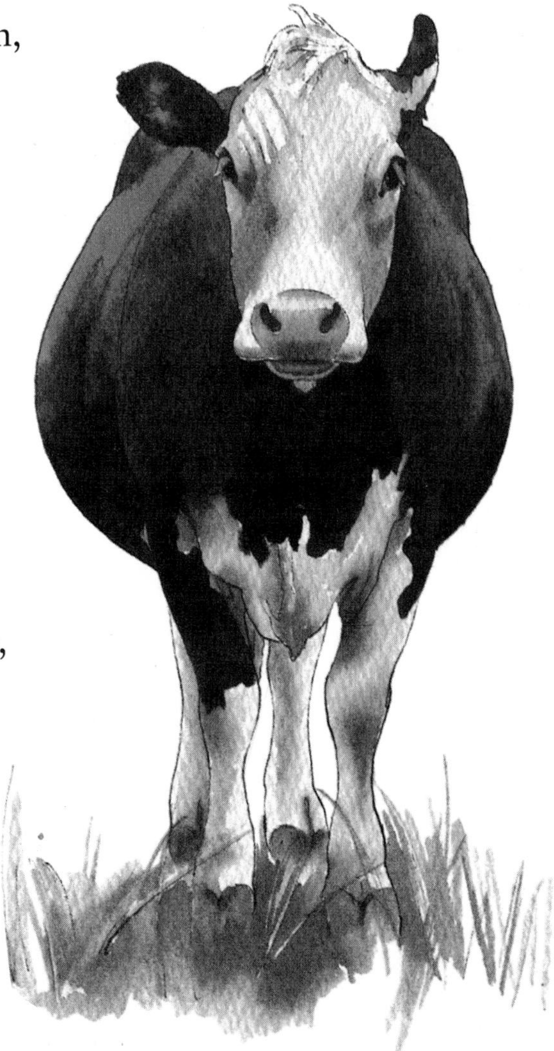

Farmer Schulz was a busy man, and his farm was a busy place. There were cows in the paddocks. There were geese on the pastures and goats on the hillsides. There were pear trees and apple, carrots and cucumbers, berries and bacon. There were furrows combed out for potatoes, and trellises like wigwams for beans.

The beams of the cellar were loaded with German sausage, and the shelves held dishes of scalded cream. And in the yard at the back of the house there were more than fifty ducks.

---

[1]**Onkaparinga** (ahn•kuh•puh•RIHNG•uh)

Farmer Schulz's ducks were the most beautiful in the world. There were brown ducks and gray ducks and speckled ducks. There were ducks with necks of opal and wings of amethyst; their colors gleamed in the sunlight, their feathers shone like jewels. There were ducks with the sheen of emerald, of sapphire and turquoise and jasper, like the glint of Aladdin's treasure. There were ducks like burnished gold.

There were drakes as well — brown drakes, mottled drakes, muddy drakes. Drakes with eyes like night and bills like scoops. There were great white drakes with noses redder than roses. And ducklings as tiny as tennis balls and as soft as clusters of golden wattle when it bloomed on the hills by the Onkaparinga River.

Every morning after breakfast Farmer Schulz opened the backyard gate so that the ducks could go down to the river. They took their time, even when they were in a hurry to reach the water. They held their heads high and waddled with dignity, even though they had to jostle each other when they went through the gate. The ducklings hurried to line up behind their mothers.

They went quickly down the drive by the side of the house and poured out across the road on their way to the Onkaparinga River. Sometimes a car would go by, or a trailer loaded high with meadow hay, or a tractor coughing in the frosty morning air. The drivers always stopped, because everyone knew that the ducks had the right of way.

All day long the ducks swam in the pools of the peaceful and weedy river. They explored the reeds and tugged at the waterweeds and dug at the muddy banks. They floated like petals and sailed like boats with their webbed feet paddling hard. They waddled onto shore and blinked their eyes and used their bills like spades.

But at sunset they all went home.

For when the shadows deepened and the valley was blue with haze, there were nasty things by the side of the Onkaparinga River. There were wild cats with eyes like ice and claws like steel; there were slinking foxes as crafty as serpents and as silent as falling dew; and there were hunters with shotguns. So the drakes led the way back home, and the ducks and the ducklings hurried along in a line.

Farmer Schulz was proud of their wisdom. "Good boys," he said to the drakes. "Good girls, good little children," he said to the ducks and ducklings. "Now safe from the fox you will be. Now we all in peace can sleep."

As the years went by the number of people grew. The city beyond the hills became as fat as a big balloon. More houses were built in the valley by the side of the gentle river, and lines of cars like strings of beads went racing down the road. They raced away in the morning and they all raced back in the evening. The drivers were always late. They blew their horns, and shouted loudly and rudely, and accelerated much too quickly.

Sometimes they didn't even stop for the ducks!

One Christmas Eve a drake was run over and had to be added to the Christmas dinner.

Farmer Schulz was red with rage. "We must this nonsense stop!" he cried. "We must put up a big notice for the ducks." And he called his family together to think of the right words.

DUCKS COMMING HERE he wrote. But Farmer Schulz's son Hans laughed and said it wasn't even English.

"Crossing ducks," suggested Gretchen. Some liked that, but others did not.

"Ducks cross here," ventured Adolf, but his mother said that people would think it was a place for angry ducks.

"Stop for ducks," suggested Helga, but Hans said it would make everyone think there were ducks for sale.

Four-year-old Anna, who was rolling breadcrumbs into a ball, looked up suddenly. "Why don't you say 'ducks crossing'?" she asked. "Because that's what they're always doing."

"Wonderful!" said her father. "You are smarter than Einstein, Anna."

"Great!" said Gretchen.

"Brilliant!" said Hans.

And so Anna's sign was painted and nailed to a post by the side of the road.

The sign was not a success. Some cars stopped, but others did not. This made the crossing more dangerous than ever. And then one morning there was a terrible accident.

A truck slowed down when the ducks were coming from Farmer Schulz's drive. But not the driver who came racing along behind it. He swerved out of his lane without even seeing if the way was clear. He accelerated to pass the truck. He drove headlong into the waddling ducks.

CRASH!

There were shouts and cries and squealing tires. There were gabbles and quacks and flying feathers. Four ducks had concussions and had to be nursed in a box beside the kitchen fire. Two drakes had broken legs and had to wear splints for months. And three little ducklings were dead. Anna buried them beside the lettuce.

Farmer Schulz's face was the color of one of his favorite ducks — mottled and blue and purple with anger. "Lunatic!" he shouted.

"Give up," said Hans. "Sell the ducks before all of them are killed."

"Never!" answered Farmer Schulz furiously. "Never, never."

"Then build a house on the other side of the road. Build a house by the river."

"Never. Why for should I move my house when it is not my fault?"

"Then we'd better teach them to fly," said Anna. "They can't cross the road anymore unless they go over the top."

Farmer Schulz opened his eyes wide. "Over the top? Of course!" He slapped his hand on his thigh. "You are smarter than Einstein, Anna. From now on the ducks will go over the top."

Hans was flabbergasted. "How are you going to manage that?" he asked.

His father's mind was running at a feverish pitch. "With a bridge, of course. Then the people can drive like lunatics if they want. My ducks will be safe. They will go over the top."

He brought two tall poles and put them up beside his drive about three feet apart. Then he put another two by the fence

on the river side. And between them he slung the trunks of two long pine trees, like beams, more than twelve feet above the road — an overpass with safety fences of wire mesh at the sides, and two long ramps at the ends for the ducks to walk up and down.

Before long the ducks knew the way. When they came out of their yard they went straight to the ramp. Then, with waddling feet and quacking, they hurried up — and across — and down. It was a wonderful sight: a procession of ducks against the sky.

Before long the cars were all stopping to watch them. Even the drivers who had no time for the ducks on the ground now stopped to watch them pass overhead.

Soon the Bridge of Ducks was famous. People came in carloads. They came with cameras, and they posed for pictures with a line of ducks behind them. They trampled the grass like buffaloes. Poor Farmer Schulz was beside himself!

Then disaster struck on the first of March. The ducks were coming out of the Onkaparinga River and waddling toward the ramp. Farmer Schulz had just stopped his tractor and was stretching his weary arms. At that very moment a monstrous semitrailer came roaring around the bends of the narrow road. The driver was new to the valley, and he was late with his goods for the city. He was driving too fast. He was tired and sleepy.

And his load was too high for the bridge!

The ducks were waddling across the overpass, hurrying and quacking as they went.

The semitrailer came roaring around the corner like a cyclone. It struck the bridge at the center, shattering the beams like matchsticks. The ducks were flung like flotsam — backward, forward, upward, sideways — trumpeting and shrieking. Some landed back in the river. Some flew, some fell, some leaped. Some were hurled along the side of the road, some even into their own backyard. Some were unharmed. Some were hurt. And some were dead.

It took a long time for Farmer Schulz to recover from the shock. He had to clear away the wreckage of the bridge. He had to breed more ducks. And he was in trouble with the government for building an overpass without permission. "You can't build bridges wherever you like," the government said. "There could have been a terrible accident."

"There *was* a terrible accident," Farmer Schulz said angrily.

Once more there was a family meeting.

"Give up," said Hans. "Get rid of the ducks while you can."

"Never!" answered his father. "The ducks are part of the family. They are like brothers and sisters, nearly."

"But how in the world are they going to cross the road? They have to go down to the water."

"We must all think," his father said. "We must all think hard."

"There's no point in building another bridge," Hans said. "It will simply be smashed again."

Little Anna had come home from kindergarten and was busy rolling breadcrumbs, as usual. "Why

don't you have a pipe," she said, "so the ducks can cross under the road?"

There was silence for a while, and then the others raised their eyebrows in amazement.

"Wonderful!" exclaimed her mother.

"Brilliant!" cried Hans.

"By golly, Anna, you are smarter than Einstein, even!" shouted her father, with eyes as wide as an owl's.

This time Farmer Schulz was going to do it right. He wrote an official letter to the government. He drew up a plan for everyone to see. He went from one building to another building, from one floor to another floor, from one person to another person. He had to fill in one form and another form, and wait in one room and another room. It was almost more than Farmer Schulz could bear — just to put a duck pipe underneath the road. For nobody had ever heard of such a thing before.

There were water pipes and sewer pipes and drain pipes and fuel pipes; there were cable pipes and steam pipes and oil pipes and gas pipes. There were copper pipes and steel pipes, plastic pipes and concrete pipes, and a hundred other pipes besides. But nowhere had there ever been a duck pipe before.

"A duck pipe?" They laughed. "You must be joking."

Farmer Schulz was red with anger and blue with impatience and purple with frustration. "It is no joke," he roared. "My ducks are never joking."

But the government told him to go home quietly and wait.

Farmer Schulz waited. He milked his cows and planted potatoes and picked apples — and he bred more ducks. And at last, after waiting for twelve months and twenty-three days, Farmer Schulz was allowed to build his pipe. It was a beautiful pipe, three feet in diameter and one hundred and eighty feet long. It went under the ground at the side of the house and it came out near the bank of the gently flowing Onkaparinga River.

Farmer Schulz built flaps of wire mesh at each end to guide the ducks in. They hustled and quacked at first, trying to learn the way. Farmer Schulz shooed and Mrs. Schulz shushed. Hans and Gretchen and Helga and Adolf held out their arms and flapped. And little Anna clapped her hands when at last the ducks went through. Everyone kissed her and said she was smarter than Einstein to think of a plan like that.

After that there was peace at last. All day long the ducks lazed by the riverside, listening to the secrets of the earth and the words of the running water. They could hear the grass growing and the small seeds stretching and the earthworms moving under the ground. They snoozed in the sunshine with their heads tucked under, or floated on the river as softly as blossoms.

Shortly afterward one of Farmer Schulz's friends carved a life-sized duck from a piece of marble and placed it on a pillar of stone by the side of the road. Then he carved two words in the stone for all to see: DUCK DORF, the village of ducks. Farmer Schulz looked at it and grinned. He was as happy and contented as he had ever been.

That year Farmer Schulz won three blue ribbons at the Show, and a Grand Champion Medal for a flinty-eyed drake. He was as proud as a peacock and as boastful as a fisherman.

"My ducks," he said loudly, "are the best and the smartest in the whole wide world."

The ducks were contented too. It was wonderful to see them streaming out of the pipe in the morning, like ants coming out of the ground, and to watch them hurrying back in the evening, like beetles bound for their burrows.

In the summer the pipe gave them shelter from the heat. In winter, when the rain poured down and the water swept out of the pipe in a torrent, they came skidding and skiing, swimming and splashing, in a wild, rollicking rush — a waterfall of ducks. In the spring they came out into a magic land that was white with blossom, and in autumn they waddled out onto a carpet of golden leaves.

They are still there now, dawdling and dabbling happily where the willows arch and sway by the banks of the beautiful Onkaparinga River.

Now It's Farmer Schulz's *Goat!*

Imagine that Farmer Schulz's favorite goat has wandered into the duck pipe and gotten stuck! Can you think of a way to free the goat? With a group of classmates, come up with a plan. If you can figure out how to do this, you are smarter than Einstein.

Author

Colin Thiele

Thiele and his wife, Rhonnie, with a pelican made for them by a young admirer

Colin Thiele (whose last name is pronounced **TEE-LEE**) grew up on a farm in South Australia. There he churned butter, milked the cows, fed the pigs and practiced his writing.

When Thiele was only eleven, he wrote his first book — a pirate novel — working at night by candlelight. Today Thiele still lives in Australia and he still writes books, but now he prefers working by daylight.

Illustrator

Mary Milton

Illustrator Mary Milton specializes in ducks!

She draws and paints people and wildlife, and has a special affection for ducks. The ducks you see in *Farmer Schulz's Ducks* are drawn from the ones found in Mary Milton's yard.

POOR OLD LION

Poor old lion,
Lyin' in his den.
Never goin' huntin'
In the jungle again.
Poor old lion,
Lyin' there sick.
If you want to see him,
Better see him quick.

Here come the animals,
Payin' a call.
How does he thank 'em?
By eatin' 'em all!

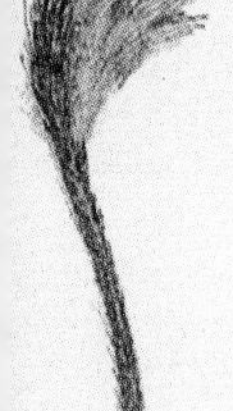

When he's finished,
What's he done?
Eaten his callers,
One by one.

Poor old lion,
Lyin' on some rocks.
Out in the sunlight
Stands Mister Fox.
"Hey, Mister Lion,
You're lookin' mighty thin."
"Yes, Mister Fox.
Won't you step right in?"

"No thanks, Mister Lion.
I'm stayin' right here.
You might feel ill,
But the message is clear.
That you're still a danger,
I have no doubt.
I see tracks goin' in,
But none comin' out!"

from Aesop's Fables
retold by Tom Paxton
illustrated by Robert Rayevsky

DONKEY

Oh, he likes us, he's our friend
that's why he lets us pretend
we're going for a donkey ride
but all the time he knows inside
that he's not going anywhere
he's just going to stand right there
he says as much in donkey talk,
"Hee-haw, when you get down, I'll walk.
I don't take passengers or freight,
I only carry my own weight."
Still we like to play this game
and we love him just the same
even though he'll stand right there
and never take us anywhere

written by Eloise Greenfield
illustrated by Amos Ferguson

PAINT BY MR AMOS 1969
FERGUSON

THE SIGN IN MENDEL'S WINDOW

by Mildred Phillips

illustrated by Margot Zemach

They called Kosnov a town. It was like calling a puddle a pond, a leaf a bush, a branch a tree. The whole town of Kosnov was no more than a dozen old wooden buildings huddled close, each leaning on its neighbor for support, just as the people who lived and worked in them did.

So when Mendel the butcher put the sign in the front window of his shop, the whole town came out to ask: Had Mendel and Molly struck it rich? Had fortune come knocking on their door? Why was the butcher shop FOR RENT? Goodness, could Mendel or Molly be sick?

"So many questions," Mendel said. "If only questions were zloty! Then we wouldn't have to rent out *half* the butcher shop!"

It wasn't a sudden gust of wind from the north that swept Mendel's hat off his head. It was the sigh of relief from his dear friends in Kosnov. Mendel and Molly were not leaving, and only half the shop would be rented.

Roshana the wigmaker kissed Tempkin the candlemaker, who hugged Simka the shoemaker, who hugged Mendel's wife, Molly, who, brushing away a joyful tear from her cheek, whispered to Mendel, "If only kisses and hugs could fatten the calf and buy feed for the chickens."

Mendel smiled. "Then, again, there'd be no need to rent, and we wouldn't be getting these kisses and hugs."

The new wall dividing the butcher shop was made by Molly from two old bed sheets sewn down the middle, bleached white until they dazzled and starched so stiff they stood straight up like a board. Tacked to the ceiling and tacked to the floor, the wall was better than perfect, Mendel said. It didn't even have to be painted.

For many weeks, the sign sat in the window. Then one day, late in the afternoon, a gentleman came into town and stopped in front of the butcher shop window. He was wearing a wide-brimmed black felt hat trimmed with fur and a fine cloth coat. Mendel went to the door.

"Mr. Butcher," said the stranger, tipping his hat, "you are looking at a very lucky man. After traveling so far, I was worried indeed that upon arriving I would find your shop already rented."

Not often, thought Mendel, did such an eloquent and prosperous-looking gentleman come to Kosnov. Mendel was impressed. "And who is to say which of us is the luckier, Mr. . . . ?"

"Tinker. Tinker is my name."

"Come in, Mr. Tinker. Put down your bag and rest your feet."

Tinker entered and sat down on a wooden stool. Stroking his thick, black beard, he spoke. "I heard by word of mouth from an old acquaintance of a distant cousin's uncle in the city — may

he rest in peace — that in this charming town there was a place for rent, a quiet room just right for my kind of work."

"Which is?" asked Mendel.

"I'm a thinker, Mr. Butcher. Tinker the thinker, a simple man with simple needs. For a humble meal and a place where I can think, I will gladly pay a week's rent in advance."

"Come take a look," Mendel said, leading the way out to a side door that opened directly into the new space. He stepped aside, saying, "Judge for yourself."

Moments later, Tinker returned. "It's a deal," he said as he paid the rent. Delighted, Mendel shook the gentleman's hand and wished him good night.

Soon it would be dark, for the sun was about to set. If only Molly weren't spending the night in Glitnik with her cousin. Mendel felt that if he didn't share the news, he would burst. He decided to drop in on Simka.

"Come in, landlord," Simka said jokingly.

"Already you know?" asked Mendel.

"Why else would a stranger stop right in front of the sign in your window? And why else would you be looking so pleased? So sit, Mendel, and tell me all about your new tenant."

While Simka worked on a pair of boots, Mendel gave an exact account of the meeting. "Imagine, Simka, so splendidly dressed and yet so humble, asking for nothing more than a place to work. Surely some divine providence has sent this great man to Molly and me."

Simka looked up. "Be careful," he warned. "Though it has only five letters, 'great' is a very big word. . . . You'll stay for supper? Don't worry, there's plenty."

Mendel felt very good.

What a busy week it was for Molly and Mendel in the shop. And with so many neighbors coming to welcome him, Tinker had little time in the day to do his work. But not once did he complain.

"A better tenant we couldn't have asked for," said Molly that Friday.

Late that day, as every Friday before the Sabbath began, Mendel was in his shop doing the books. It was his habit to count his weekly earnings aloud, dropping the coins one by one into a small wooden box that he kept on the shelf. So as not to disturb Tinker, he began in a whisper: "Five groszy, ten groszy, fifty groszy, one zloty, one zloty twenty, one zloty forty, two zloty — "

"Mendel, my friend," called Tinker, "you don't have to whisper. I enjoy the sound of your voice."

So Mendel counted louder: "Forty zloty seventy-one, forty zloty seventy-two, forty zloty and seventy-three groszy. That does it!"

"Your voice is like music to my ears," said Tinker. "Just once more!"

Flattered, Mendel counted again, this time chanting in his finest tenor voice. Still humming, he closed the box and put it on the shelf.

"I am thinking," called Tinker, "that I will go to the city for the weekend. May I borrow your horse?"

"Go in good health," said Mendel. "I will see you on Monday."

"First thing," answered Tinker. "First thing."

Just after sunrise on Monday morning, as Mendel was taking a few deep knee-bends in front of the window, he saw that his horse was back from the city, tied to the front post. But what were two other horses doing beside it?

Mendel dressed and went downstairs to his shop. Waiting for him there were not only Tinker but two uniformed policemen from the city, as well.

"Arrest that man!" shouted Tinker. "He is the man who stole my money, and the proof lies in that wooden box on the shelf. And in that wooden box are exactly forty zloty and seventy-three groszy. Count it, gentlemen. If it be so, then without a doubt the money is mine!"

Stunned and speechless, Mendel stared at a small hole in the partition, two inches from the floor. Not big enough for a mouse to get through, the hole was ample for a rat to get an eyeful.

Molly, awakened by all the commotion, rushed downstairs still in her nightgown. "Am I dreaming a nightmare?" she cried out. "What are you up to?"

"Forty zloty and seventy-three groszy," answered a policeman as he counted the last coin. "This proves without a doubt that your husband is a thief."

Molly laughed. "Mendel a thief? My Mendel is so honest that he wouldn't steal another man's joke. Mendel, darling, what happened?"

Mendel told her. "It hurts in my heart to know that I was fooled by fancy manners."

Just then, Simka's face appeared at the window. Molly rushed to open the door.

"I was worried that Mendel should go barefoot," said Simka, peering inside, "so I brought him his shoes, as good as new."

"In jail it doesn't matter," cried Molly. "Come in, Simka, and say good-bye."

"Are you going somewhere?"

"Not me, Simka. Him!"

Poor Mendel. A pair of handcuffs had been slapped on his wrists. "Mr. Policemen," cried Simka, "I am a senior citizen of Kosnov, and I demand to know what is going on!"

As the story unfolded, Simka nodded. "I'm a little deaf in my left ear," he said. "but from what I just heard it is perfectly clear that *Tinker* is the scoundrel."

"And where is your proof?" shouted Tinker.

Simka smiled. He whispered to the policemen, and one of them quickly left the shop.

Outside a crowd had gathered, as had dark clouds overhead. Simka paced the floor.

It felt like an hour, but it was only a matter of minutes before the policeman returned with his report. "How you knew about the money is a mystery," he said to Simka. "And, just as you said, everyone I questioned up and down the street also knew, exactly to the groszy, how much was in the wooden box. How is this possible?"

"I have the answer," said Tinker abruptly. "If a man is a thief, then why not a braggart, too?"

"I am not a judge," said the policeman. "We will have to take this case to the city!"

"Hold it!" Molly yelled. She flung open the door and called to her neighbors, "Get me a potful of scalding hot water!"

When this was done, Molly dumped all the coins from the wooden box into the water. Had Molly gone mad? What was she making?

Molly chuckled. "Groszy soup. And while it is cooking, I have three questions for Mr. Tinker.

"First," she began, "if you were a painter, what would be on your hands?"

"Paint, of course," answered Tinker.

"Second question. If you were a potter, would there be paint on your hands?"

"The answer to your foolish question is no! There'd be clay on my hands."

"Now let's say that you were a butcher. A customer just paid for his chicken. You took the coins and maybe put them in your pocket. My question is, would the coins be covered with clay?"

Tinker snickered. "If I were a butcher, the coins would be covered with — "

He looked into the pot. Skimming the surface, coating the water was a pale thin layer of fat. It had risen from the coins that lay on the bottom.

"A little fat?" Molly asked.

"A little fat," muttered Tinker.

As the handcuffs closed around his wrists, Tinker turned to Simka. "How *did* everyone know how much money was in the box?"

"Simple," said Simka. "Only a stranger like you wouldn't know that when our Mendel sings in his finest tenor voice, not only can everyone hear him, but we all stop to listen."

Tinker shrugged, and with a deep sigh he said, "I think I made a few mistakes. The biggest was coming to a little town like Kosnov."

At that, the whole town cheered. Yes, the whole town. Did you know that the town of Kosnov was so small that when Roshana the wigmaker sneezed, Mishkin the tailor said "God bless you" — though he lived a dozen doors away?

WELCOME TO KOSNOV

Where's the best place to spend your groszy in Kosnov? Kosnov may be a small town, but there's a lot to see and do there. Make a guidebook for people who want to visit Kosnov. Include places to shop, eat, and visit. Start with what you know from the story. You may want to draw a few pictures for your guidebook.

Author

Mildred Phillips

Phillips feeding lambs on her farm

Author Mildred Phillips is a busy woman. Writer, painter, sculptor, and even farmer, she has written a number of books for children, including *Maxie*, *I Wonder if Herbie's Home Yet*, and *Goodbye, Kitchen*. In college, she studied painting and sculpture. For a time she even put her artistic training to work at Macy's Department Store doing window displays.

Phillips lives in an 1820's farmhouse with "a big red barn and twenty-five acres, and lots of animals!"

Margot Zemach

Margot Zemach once thought she would be a "serious" artist. Maybe people would walk through museums where her paintings were hanging and say, "Hmmmmmmm" under their breath.

Yet no matter how hard Zemach tried to be serious, her work always made people smile. So she gave up trying to be serious.

"Humor is the most important thing to me — it's what I'm thinking about," she once said. "If I can make it beautiful too — so much the better."

Zemach earned many awards for her work, including the Caldecott Medal for *Duffy and the Devil* and Caldecott Honors for *The Judge* and *It Could Always Be Worse*.

An illustration from
Self Portrait: Margot Zemach

Match Wits

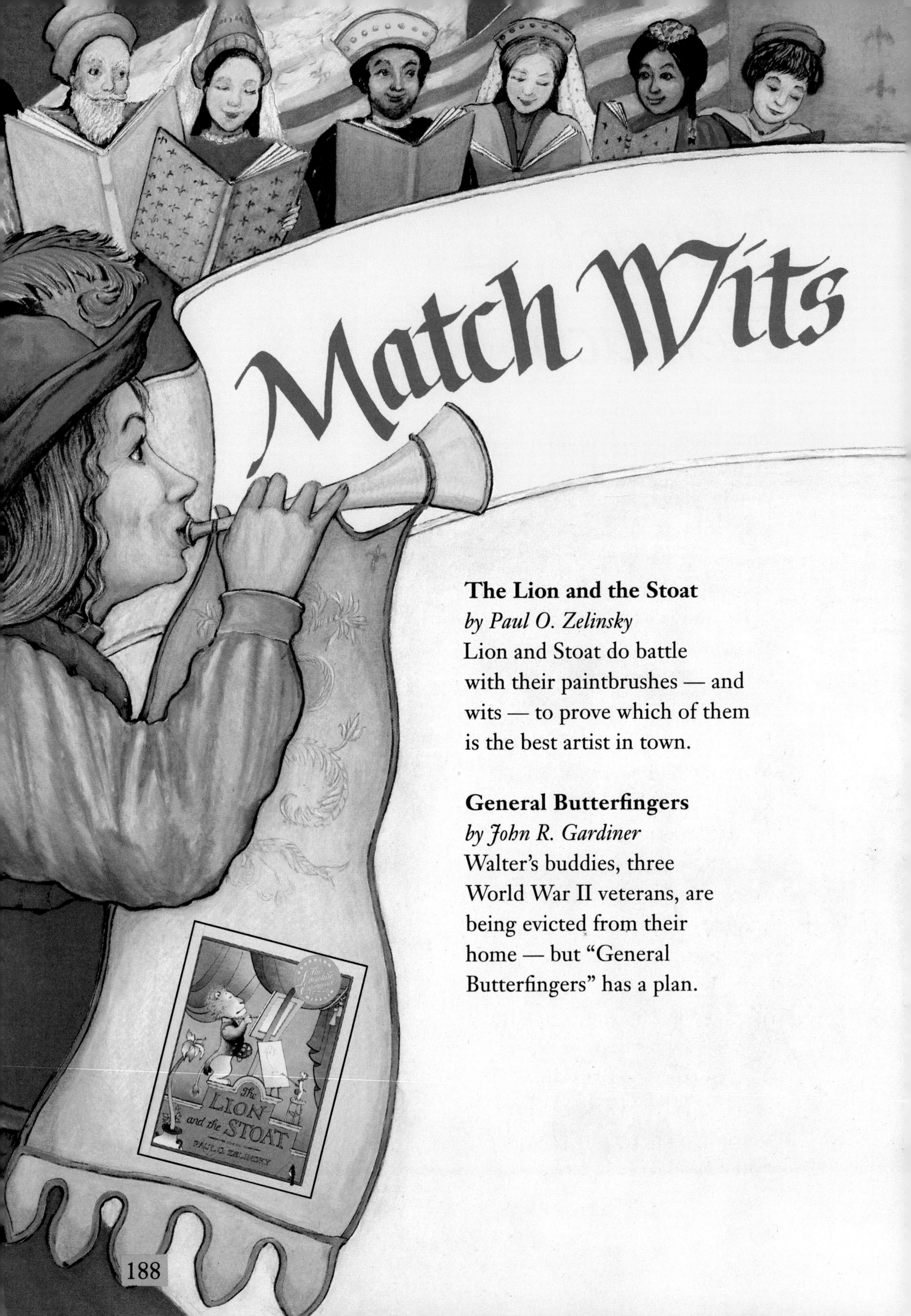

The Lion and the Stoat
by Paul O. Zelinsky
Lion and Stoat do battle with their paintbrushes — and wits — to prove which of them is the best artist in town.

General Butterfingers
by John R. Gardiner
Walter's buddies, three World War II veterans, are being evicted from their home — but "General Butterfingers" has a plan.

with these Books

A Grain of Rice
by Helena C. Pittman
It's the powerful emperor versus a poor farmer's son. Who will be victorious?

Wonder Kid Meets the Evil Lunch Snatcher
by Lois Duncan
Brian must prevent the school bully from taking the other students' lunches. "Wonder Kid" may be the answer.

The Great Cheese Conspiracy
by Jean Van Leeuwen
Marvin (a mouse) lives in a movie theater. When he tires of eating popcorn, he plots to raid The Cheese Barrel.

AUTHOR

BOOK 4

Laura Ingalls Wilder

1867-1957

I lived everything that happened in my books.
It is a long story, filled with sunshine and shadow.
— Laura Ingalls Wilder, 1937

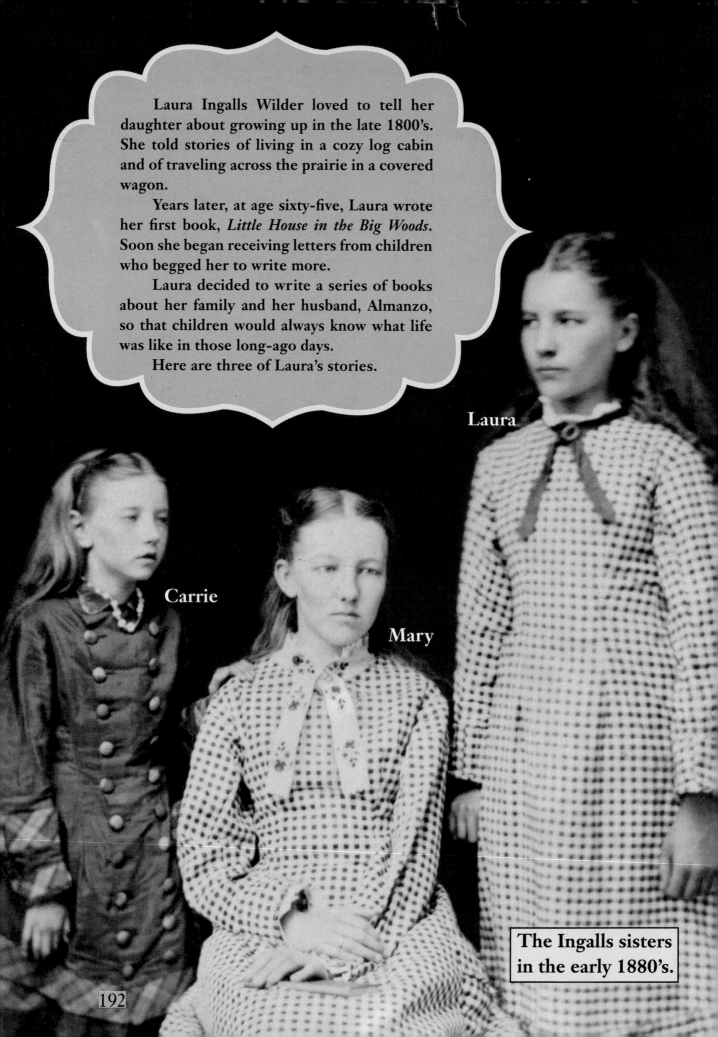

Laura Ingalls Wilder loved to tell her daughter about growing up in the late 1800's. She told stories of living in a cozy log cabin and of traveling across the prairie in a covered wagon.

Years later, at age sixty-five, Laura wrote her first book, *Little House in the Big Woods*. Soon she began receiving letters from children who begged her to write more.

Laura decided to write a series of books about her family and her husband, Almanzo, so that children would always know what life was like in those long-ago days.

Here are three of Laura's stories.

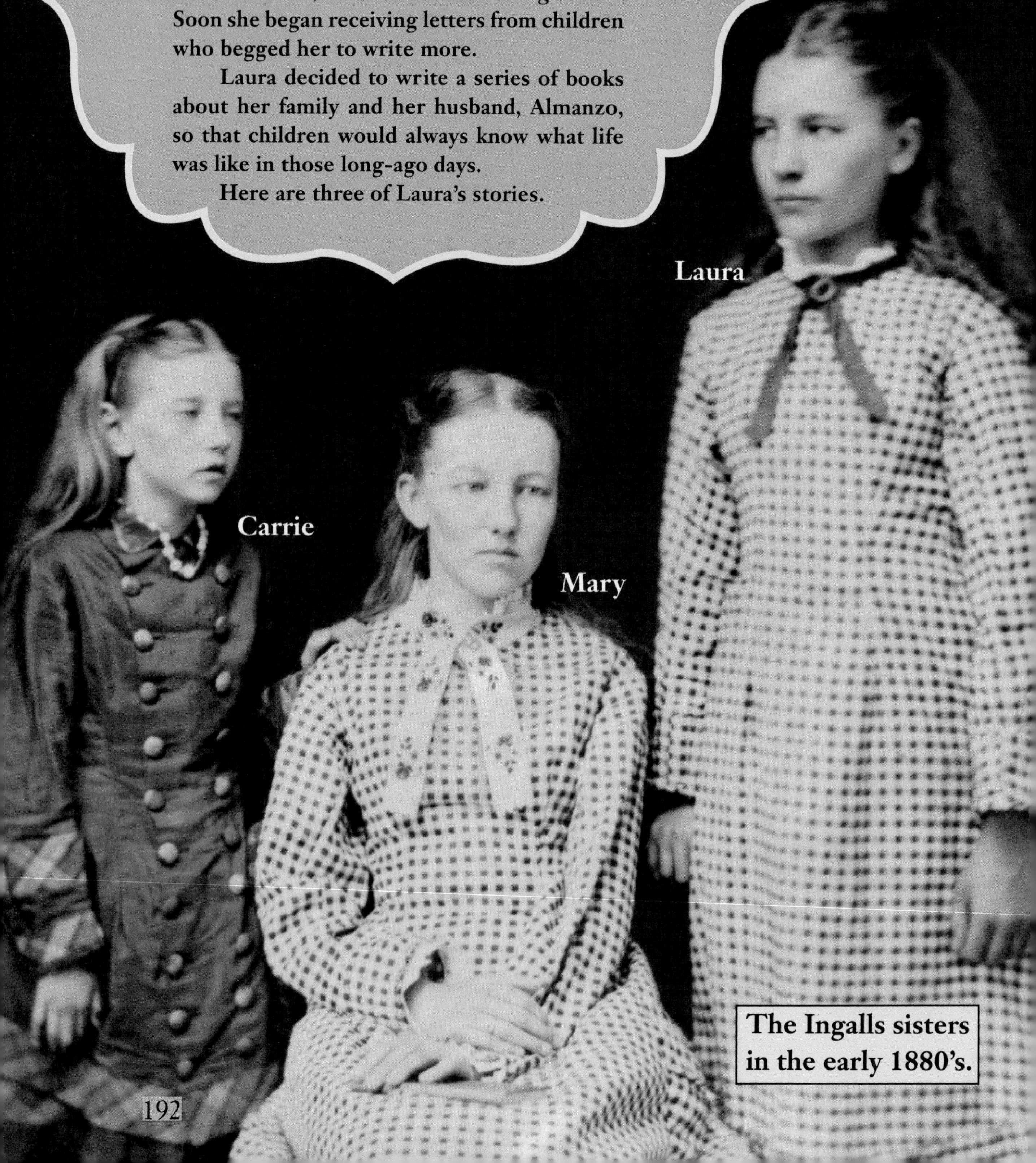

The Ingalls sisters in the early 1880's.

CONTENTS

Laura Ingalls Wilder

From the book

LITTLE HOUSE ON THE PRAIRIE

by Laura Ingalls Wilder • Illustrated by Garth Williams

Laura Ingalls has always lived in the Big Woods of Wisconsin with her parents and sisters, Mary and Carrie. Now the Ingalls family and their dog, Jack, are moving far away to Kansas.

Crossing the Creek

They had come in the covered wagon all the long way from the Big Woods of Wisconsin, across Minnesota and Iowa and Missouri. All that long way, Jack had trotted under the wagon. Now they set out to go across Kansas.

Kansas was an endless flat land covered with tall grass blowing in the wind. Day after day they traveled in Kansas, and saw nothing but the rippling grass and the enormous sky. In a perfect circle the sky curved down to the level land, and the wagon was in the circle's exact middle.

All day long Pet and Patty went forward, trotting and walking and trotting again, but they couldn't get out of the middle of that circle. When the sun went down, the circle was still around them and the edge of the sky was pink. Then slowly the land became black. The wind made a lonely sound in the grass. The camp fire was small and lost in so much space. But large stars hung from the sky, glittering so near that Laura felt she could almost touch them.

Next day the land was the same, the sky was the same, the circle did not change. Laura and Mary were tired of them all. There was nothing new to do and nothing new to look at. The bed was made in the back of the wagon and neatly covered with a gray blanket; Laura and Mary sat on it. The canvas sides of the wagon-top were rolled up and tied, so the prairie wind blew in. It whipped Laura's straight brown hair and Mary's golden curls every-which-way, and the strong light screwed up their eyelids.

Sometimes a big jack rabbit bounded in big bounds away over the blowing grass. Jack paid no attention. Poor Jack was tired, too, and his paws were sore from traveling so far. The wagon kept on jolting, the canvas top snapped in the wind. Two faint wheel tracks kept going away behind the wagon, always the same.

Pa's back was hunched. The reins were loose in his hands, the wind blew his long brown beard. Ma sat straight and quiet, her hands folded in her lap. Baby Carrie slept in a nest among the soft bundles.

"Ah-wow!" Mary yawned, and Laura said: "Ma, can't we get out and run behind the wagon? My legs are so tired."

"No, Laura," Ma said.

"Aren't we going to camp pretty soon?" Laura asked. It seemed such a long time since noon, when they had eaten their lunch sitting on the clean grass in the shade of the wagon.

Pa answered: "Not yet. It's too early to camp now."

"I want to camp, now! I'm so tired," Laura said.

Then Ma said, "Laura." That was all, but it meant that Laura must not complain. So she did not complain any more out loud, but she was still naughty, inside. She sat and thought complaints to herself.

Her legs ached and the wind wouldn't stop blowing her hair. The grass waved and the wagon jolted and nothing else happened for a long time.

"We're coming to a creek or a river," Pa said. "Girls, can you see those trees ahead?"

Laura stood up and held to one of the wagon bows. Far ahead she saw a low dark smudge. "That's trees," Pa said. "You can tell by the shape of the shadows. In this country, trees mean water. That's where we'll camp tonight."

Pet and Patty began to trot briskly, as if they were glad, too. Laura held tight to the wagon bow and stood up in the jolting wagon. Beyond Pa's shoulder and far across the waves of green grass she could see the trees, and they were not like any trees she had seen before. They were no taller than bushes.

"Whoa!" said Pa, suddenly. "Now which way?" he muttered to himself.

The road divided here, and you could not tell which was the more-traveled way. Both of them were faint wheel tracks in the grass. One went toward the west, the other sloped downward a little, toward the south. Both soon vanished in the tall, blowing grass.

"Better go downhill, I guess," Pa decided. "The creek's down in the bottoms. Must be this is the way to the ford." He turned Pet and Patty toward the south.

The road went down and up and down and up again, over gently curving land. The trees were nearer now, but they were no taller. Then Laura gasped and clutched the wagon bow, for almost under Pet's and Patty's noses there was no more blowing grass, there was no land at all. She looked beyond the edge of the land and across the tops of trees.

The road turned there. For a little way it went along the cliff's top, then it went sharply downward. Pa put on the brakes; Pet and Patty braced themselves backward and almost sat down. The wagon wheels slid onward, little by little lowering the wagon farther down the steep slope into the ground. Jagged cliffs of bare red earth rose up on both sides of the wagon. Grass waved along their tops, but nothing grew on their seamed, straight-up-and-down sides. They were hot, and heat came from them against Laura's face. The wind was still blowing overhead, but it did not blow down into this deep crack in the ground. The stillness seemed strange and empty.

Then once more the wagon was level. The narrow crack down which it had come opened into the bottom lands. Here grew the tall trees whose tops Laura had seen from the prairie above. Shady groves were scattered on the rolling meadows, and in the groves deer were lying down, hardly to be seen among the shadows. The deer turned their heads toward the wagon, and curious fawns stood up to see it more clearly.

Laura was surprised because she did not see the creek. But the bottom lands were wide. Down here, below the prairie, there were gentle hills and open sunny places. The air was still and hot. Under the wagon wheels the ground was soft. In the sunny open spaces the grass grew thin, and deer had cropped it short.

For a while the high, bare cliffs of red earth stood up behind the wagon. But they were almost hidden behind hills and trees when Pet and Patty stopped to drink from the creek.

The rushing sound of the water filled the still air. All along the creek banks the trees hung over it and made it dark with shadows. In the middle it ran swiftly, sparkling silver and blue.

"This creek's pretty high," Pa said. "But I guess we can make it all right. You can see this is a ford, by the old wheel ruts. What do you say, Caroline?"

"Whatever you say, Charles," Ma answered.

Pet and Patty lifted their wet noses. They pricked their ears forward, looking at the creek; then they pricked them backward to hear what Pa would say. They sighed and laid their soft

noses together to whisper to each other. A little way upstream, Jack was lapping the water with his red tongue.

"I'll tie down the wagon-cover," Pa said. He climbed down from the seat, unrolled the canvas sides and tied them firmly to the wagon box. Then he pulled the rope at the back, so that the canvas puckered together in the middle, leaving only a tiny round hole, too small to see through.

Mary huddled down on the bed. She did not like fords; she was afraid of the rushing water. But Laura was excited; she liked the splashing. Pa climbed to the seat, saying, "They may have to swim, out there in the middle. But we'll make it all right, Caroline."

Laura thought of Jack and said, "I wish Jack could ride in the wagon, Pa."

Pa did not answer. He gathered the reins tightly in his hands. Ma said, "Jack can swim, Laura. He will be all right."

The wagon went forward softly in mud. Water began to splash against the wheels. The splashing grew louder. The wagon shook as the noisy water struck at it. Then all at once the wagon lifted and balanced and swayed. It was a lovely feeling.

The noise stopped, and Ma said, sharply, "Lie down, girls!"

Quick as a flash, Mary and Laura dropped flat on the bed. When Ma spoke like that, they did as they were told. Ma's arm pulled a smothering blanket over them, heads and all.

"Be still, just as you are. Don't move!" she said.

Mary did not move; she was trembling and still. But Laura could not help wriggling a little bit. She did so want to see what was happening. She could feel the wagon swaying and turning; the splashing was noisy again, and again it died away. Then Pa's voice frightened Laura. It said, "Take them, Caroline!"

The wagon lurched; there was a sudden heavy splash beside it. Laura sat straight up and clawed the blanket from her head.

Pa was gone. Ma sat alone, holding tight to the reins with both hands. Mary hid her face in the blanket again, but Laura rose up farther. She couldn't see the creek bank. She couldn't see anything in front of the wagon but water rushing at it. And in the water, three heads; Pet's head and Patty's head and Pa's small, wet head. Pa's fist in the water was holding tight to Pet's bridle.

Laura could faintly hear Pa's voice through the rushing of the water. It sounded calm and cheerful, but she couldn't hear what he said. He was talking to the horses. Ma's face was white and scared.

"Lie down, Laura," Ma said.

Laura lay down. She felt cold and sick. Her eyes were shut tight, but she could still see the terrible water and Pa's brown beard drowning in it.

For a long, long time the wagon swayed and swung, and Mary cried without making a sound, and Laura's stomach felt sicker and sicker. Then the front wheels struck and grated, and Pa shouted. The whole wagon jerked and jolted and tipped backward, but the wheels were turning on the ground. Laura was up again, holding to the seat; she saw Pet's and Patty's scrambling wet backs climbing a steep bank, and Pa running beside them, shouting, "Hi, Patty! Hi, Pet! Get up! Get up! Whoopsy-daisy! Good girls!"

At the top of the bank they stood still, panting and dripping. And the wagon stood still, safely out of that creek.

Pa stood panting and dripping, too, and Ma said, "Oh, Charles!"

"There, there, Caroline," said Pa. "We're all safe, thanks to a good tight wagon-box well fastened to the running-gear. I never saw a creek rise so fast in my life. Pet and Patty are good swimmers, but I guess they wouldn't have made it if I hadn't helped them."

If Pa had not known what to do, or if Ma had been too frightened to drive, or if Laura

and Mary had been naughty and bothered her, then they would all have been lost. The river would have rolled them over and over and carried them away and drowned them, and nobody would ever have known what became of them. For weeks, perhaps, no other person would come along that road.

"Well," said Pa, "all's well that ends well," and Ma said, "Charles, you're wet to the skin."

Before Pa could answer, Laura cried, "Oh, where's Jack?"

They had forgotten Jack. They had left him on the other side of that dreadful water and now they could not see him anywhere. He must have tried to swim after them, but they could not see him struggling in the water now.

Laura swallowed hard, to keep from crying. She knew it was shameful to cry, but there was crying inside her. All the long way from Wisconsin poor Jack had followed them so patiently and faithfully, and now they had left him to drown. He was so tired, and they might have taken him into the wagon. He had stood on the bank and seen the wagon going away from him, as if they didn't care for him at all. And he would never know how much they wanted him.

Pa said he wouldn't have done such a thing to Jack, not for a million dollars. If he'd known how that creek would rise when they were in midstream, he would never have let Jack try to swim it. "But that can't be helped now," he said.

He went far up and down the creek bank, looking for Jack, calling him and whistling for him.

It was no use. Jack was gone.

At last there was nothing to do but to go on. Pet and Patty were rested. Pa's clothes had dried on him while he searched for Jack. He took the reins again, and drove uphill, out of the river bottoms.

Laura looked back all the way. She knew she wouldn't see Jack again, but she wanted to.

She didn't see anything but low curves of land coming between the wagon and the creek, and beyond the creek those strange cliffs of red earth rose up again.

Then other bluffs just like them stood up in front of the wagon. Faint wheel tracks went into a crack between those earthen walls. Pet and Patty climbed till the crack became a small grassy valley. And the valley widened out to the High Prairie once more.

No road, not even the faintest trace of wheels or of a rider's passing, could be seen anywhere. That prairie looked as if no human eye had ever seen it before. Only the tall wild grass covered the endless empty land and a great empty sky arched over it. Far away the sun's edge touched the rim of the earth. The sun was enormous and it was throbbing and pulsing with light. All around the sky's edge ran a pale

pink glow, and above the pink was yellow, and above that blue. Above the blue the sky was no color at all. Purple shadows were gathering over the land, and the wind was mourning.

Pa stopped the mustangs. He and Ma got out of the wagon to make camp, and Mary and Laura climbed down to the ground, too.

"Oh, Ma," Laura begged, "Jack has gone to heaven, hasn't he? He was such a good dog, can't he go to heaven?"

Ma did not know what to answer, but Pa said: "Yes, Laura, he can. God that doesn't forget the sparrows won't leave a good dog like Jack out in the cold."

Laura felt only a little better. She was not happy. Pa did not whistle about his work as usual, and after a while he said, "And what we'll do in a wild country without a good watchdog I don't know."

Pa made camp as usual. First, he unhitched and unharnessed Pet and Patty, and he put them on their picket-lines. Picket-lines were long ropes fastened to iron pegs driven into the ground. The pegs were called picket-pins. When horses were on picket-lines they could eat all the grass that the long ropes would let them reach. But when Pet and Patty were put on them, the first thing they did was to lie down and roll back and forth and over. They rolled till the feeling of the harness was all gone from their backs.

While Pet and Patty were rolling, Pa pulled all the grass from a large, round space of ground. There was old, dead grass at the roots of the green grass, and Pa would take no chance of setting the prairie on fire. If fire once started in that dry under-grass, it would sweep that whole country bare and black. Pa said, "Best be on the safe side, it saves trouble in the end."

When the space was clear of grass, Pa laid a handful of dry grass in its center. From the creek bottoms he brought an armful of twigs and dead wood. He laid small twigs and larger twigs and then the wood on the handful of dry grass, and he lighted the grass. The fire crackled merrily inside the ring of bare ground that it couldn't get out of.

Then Pa brought water from the creek, while Mary and Laura helped Ma get supper. Ma measured coffee beans into the coffee-mill and Mary ground them. Laura filled the coffee-pot with the water Pa brought, and Ma set the pot in the coals. She set the iron bake-oven in the coals, too.

While it heated, she mixed cornmeal and salt with water and patted it into little cakes. She greased the bake-oven with a pork-rind, laid the cornmeal cakes in it, and put on its iron cover. Then Pa raked more coals over the cover, while Ma sliced fat salt pork. She fried the slices in the iron spider. The spider had short legs to stand on in the coals, and that was why it was called a spider. If it had no legs, it would have been only a frying pan.

The coffee boiled, the cakes baked, the meat fried, and they all smelled so good that Laura grew hungrier and hungrier.

Pa set the wagon-seat near the fire. He and Ma sat on it. Mary and Laura sat on the wagon tongue. Each of them had a tin plate, and a steel knife and a steel fork with white bone handles. Ma had a tin cup and Pa had a tin cup, and Baby Carrie had a little one all her own, but Mary and Laura had to share their tin cup. They drank water. They could not drink coffee until they grew up.

While they were eating supper the purple shadows closed around the camp fire. The vast prairie was dark and still. Only the wind moved stealthily through the grass, and the large, low stars hung glittering from the great sky.

The camp fire was cozy in the big, chill darkness. The slices of pork were crisp and fat,

the corncakes were good. In the dark beyond the wagon, Pet and Patty were eating, too. They bit off bites of grass with sharply crunching sounds.

"We'll camp here a day or two," said Pa. "Maybe we'll stay here. There's good land, timber in the bottoms, plenty of game — everything a man could want. What do you say, Caroline?"

"We might go farther and fare worse," Ma replied.

"Anyway, I'll look around tomorrow," Pa said. "I'll take my gun and get us some good fresh meat."

He lighted his pipe with a hot coal, and stretched out his legs comfortably. The warm, brown smell of tobacco smoke mixed with the warmth of the fire. Mary yawned, and slid off the wagon tongue to sit on the grass. Laura

yawned, too. Ma quickly washed the tin plates, the tin cups, the knives and forks. She washed the bake-oven and the spider, and rinsed the dish-cloth.

For an instant she was still, listening to the long, wailing howl from the dark prairie. They all knew what it was. But that sound always ran cold up Laura's backbone and crinkled over the back of her head.

Ma shook the dish-cloth, and then she walked into the dark and spread the cloth on the tall grass to dry. When she came back Pa said: "Wolves. Half a mile away, I'd judge. Well, where there's deer there will be wolves. I wish — "

He didn't say what he wished, but Laura knew. He wished Jack were there. When wolves howled in the Big Woods, Laura had always known that Jack would not let them hurt her. A lump swelled hard in her throat and her nose smarted. She winked fast and did not cry. That wolf, or perhaps another wolf, howled again.

"Bedtime for little girls!" Ma said, cheerfully. Mary got up and turned around so that Ma could unbutton her. But Laura jumped up and stood still. She saw something. Deep in the dark beyond the firelight, two green lights were shining near the ground. They were eyes.

Cold ran up Laura's backbone, her scalp crinkled, her hair stood up. The green lights moved; one winked out, then the other winked out, then both shone steadily, coming nearer. Very rapidly they were coming nearer.

"Look, Pa, look!" Laura said. "A wolf!"

Pa did not seem to move quickly, but he did. In an instant he took his gun out of the wagon and was ready to fire at those green eyes. The eyes stopped coming. They were still in the dark, looking at him.

"It can't be a wolf. Unless it's a mad wolf," Pa said. Ma lifted Mary into the wagon. "And it's not that," said Pa. "Listen to the horses." Pet and Patty were still biting off bits of grass.

"A lynx?" said Ma.

"Or a coyote?" Pa picked up a stick of wood; he shouted, and threw it. The green eyes went close to the ground, as if the animal crouched to spring. Pa held the gun ready. The creature did not move.

"Don't, Charles," Ma said. But Pa slowly walked toward those eyes. And slowly along the ground the eyes crawled toward him. Laura could see the animal in the edge of the dark. It was a tawny animal and brindled. Then Pa shouted and Laura screamed.

The next thing she knew she was trying to hug a jumping, panting, wriggling Jack, who

lapped her face and hands with his warm wet tongue. She couldn't hold him. He leaped and wriggled from her to Pa to Ma and back to her again.

"Well, I'm beat!" Pa said.

"So am I," said Ma. "But did you have to wake the baby?" She rocked Carrie in her arms, hushing her.

Jack was perfectly well. But soon he lay down close to Laura and sighed a long sigh. His eyes were red with tiredness, and all the under part of him was caked with mud. Ma gave him a cornmeal cake and he licked it and wagged politely, but he could not eat. He was too tired.

"No telling how long he kept swimming," Pa said. "Nor how far he was carried downstream before he landed." And when at last he reached them, Laura called him a wolf, and Pa threatened to shoot him.

But Jack knew they didn't mean it. Laura asked him, "You knew we didn't mean it, didn't you, Jack?" Jack wagged his stump of a tail; he knew.

It was past bedtime. Pa chained Pet and Patty to the feed-box at the back of the wagon and fed them their corn. Carrie slept again, and Ma helped Mary and Laura undress. She put their long nightgowns over their heads while they stuck their arms into the sleeves.

They buttoned the neckbands themselves, and tied the strings of their nightcaps beneath their chins. Under the wagon Jack wearily turned around three times, and lay down to sleep.

In the wagon Laura and Mary said their prayers and crawled into their little bed. Ma kissed them good night.

On the other side of the canvas, Pet and Patty were eating their corn. When Patty whooshed into the feed-box, the whoosh was right at Laura's ear. There were little scurrying sounds in the grass. In the trees by the creek an owl called, "Who-oo? who-oo?" Farther away another owl answered, "Oo-oo, oo-oo." Far away on the prairie the wolves howled, and under the wagon Jack growled low in his chest. In the wagon everything was safe and snug.

Thickly in front of the open wagon-top hung the large, glittering stars. Pa could reach them, Laura thought. She wished he would pick the largest one from the thread on which it hung from the sky, and give it to her. She was wide awake, she was not sleepy at all, but suddenly she was very much surprised. The large star winked at her!

Laura and her family have only just begun their journey to a new home. You can continue *your* journey with the Ingallses by reading the rest of *Little House on the Prairie*.

IT'S A DOG'S LIFE

Jack walked across Minnesota, Iowa, and Missouri. He was carried away by a raging river, mistaken for a wolf, and almost shot! Write a story Jack would tell about one of his adventures if only he could talk.

You can actually visit many of the places Laura Ingalls Wilder lived and see some of the things she owned.

At Home on the Prairie

In Pepin, Wisconsin, a log cabin marks the place where Laura was born in 1867. *Little House in the Big Woods* is about her early years there.

Walnut Grove, Minnesota, is the setting of *On the Banks of Plum Creek.* The Ingallses' dugout home along Plum Creek is still there.

Below: The Ingalls family in the 1890's.
From left are Ma, Carrie, Laura, Pa, Grace, and Mary.

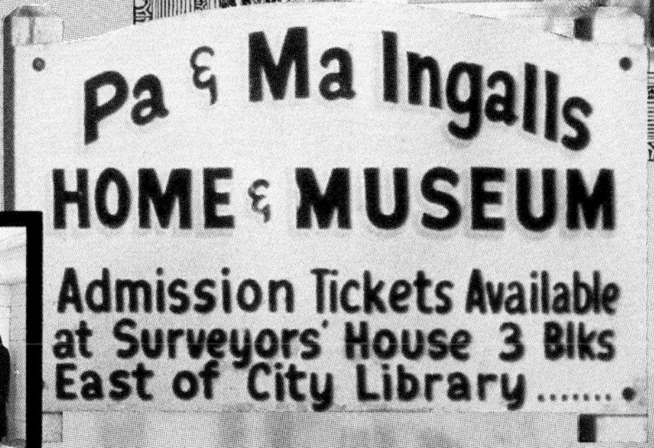

The Long Winter and *Little Town on the Prairie* are books Laura wrote about De Smet, South Dakota. There you can visit the Ingalls family's last home, now a museum furnished with many of their belongings.

In 1894 Laura moved with Almanzo to Rocky Ridge Farm in Mansfield, Missouri. In a museum beside their original house, you can see Pa's fiddle and other family items. Laura and Almanzo are buried in the Mansfield cemetery.

Left: Laura Ingalls Wilder, around the time she wrote the "Little House" books.

From the book

Farmer Boy

by Laura Ingalls Wilder

with illustrations by Garth Williams

Nine-year-old Almanzo Wilder lives with his family on their farm in New York. One evening, Father announces that he and Mother are going to Uncle Andrew's house for a week. "Can you children take care of things and behave yourselves while we're gone?" he asks. Father and Mother decide to leave their older children, Eliza Jane and Royal, in charge of Almanzo, Alice, and the farm.

Keeping House

Uncle Andrew lived ten miles away. For a week Father and Mother were getting ready to go, and all the time they were thinking of things that must be done while they were away.

Even when Mother was climbing into the buggy, she was talking.

"Be sure to gather the eggs every night," she said, "and I depend on you, Eliza Jane, to take care of the churning. Don't salt the butter too much, pack it in the small tub and be sure you cover it. Remember not to pick the beans and peas I'm saving for seed. Now you all be good while we're gone — "

She was tucking her hoops down between the seat and the dashboard. Father spread the lap robe.

" — and mind, Eliza Jane. Be careful of fires; don't you leave the house while there's fire in the cookstove, and don't get to scuffling with lighted candles, whatever you do, and — "

Father tightened the reins and the horses started.

" — don't eat all the sugar!" Mother called back.

The buggy turned into the road. The horses began to trot, rapidly taking Father and Mother away. In a little while the sound of the buggy wheels ceased. Father and Mother were gone.

Nobody said anything. Even Eliza Jane looked a little scared. The house and the barns and the fields seemed very big and empty. For a whole week Father and Mother would be ten miles away.

Suddenly Almanzo threw his hat into the air and yelled. Alice hugged herself and cried:

"What'll we do first?"

They could do anything they liked. There was nobody to stop them.

"We'll do the dishes and make the beds," Eliza Jane said, bossy.

"Let's make ice-cream!" Royal shouted.

Eliza Jane loved ice-cream. She hesitated, and said, "Well — "

Almanzo ran after Royal to the ice-house. They dug a block of ice out of the sawdust and put it in a grain sack. They laid the sack on the back porch and pounded it with hatchets till the ice was crushed. Alice came out to watch them while she whipped egg-whites on a platter. She beat them with a fork, till they were too stiff to slip when she tilted the platter.

Eliza Jane measured milk and cream, and dipped up sugar from the barrel in the pantry. It was not common maple sugar, but white sugar bought from the store. Mother used it only when company came. Eliza Jane dipped six cupfuls, then she smoothed the sugar that was left, and you would hardly have missed any.

She made a big milk-pail full of yellow custard. They set the pail in a tub and packed the snowy crushed ice around it, with salt, and they covered it all with a blanket. Every few minutes they took off the blanket and uncovered the pail, and stirred the freezing ice-cream.

When it was frozen, Alice brought saucers and spoons, and Almanzo brought out a cake and the butcher knife. He cut enormous pieces of cake, while Eliza Jane heaped the saucers. They could eat all the ice-cream and cake they wanted to; no one would stop them.

At noon they had eaten the whole cake, and almost all the ice-cream. Eliza Jane said it was time to get dinner, but the others didn't want any dinner. Almanzo said:

"All I want is a watermelon."

Alice jumped up. "Goody! Let's go get one!"

"Alice!" Eliza Jane cried. "You come right back here and do the breakfast dishes!"

"I will," Alice called out, "when I come back."

Alice and Almanzo went into the hot melon-field, where the melons lay round above their wilting flat leaves. Almanzo snapped his finger against the green rinds, and listened. When a melon sounded ripe, it *was* ripe, and when it sounded green, it *was* green. But when Almanzo said a melon sounded ripe, Alice thought it sounded green. There wasn't really any way to know, though Almanzo was sure he knew more about melons than any girl. So in the end they picked six of the biggest melons, and they lugged them one by one to the ice-house and put them on the damp, cold sawdust.

Then Alice went to the house to do the dishes. Almanzo said he wasn't going to do anything; maybe he'd go swimming. But as soon as Alice was out of sight, he skipped through the barns and stole into the pasture where the colts were.

The pasture was big and the sun was very hot. The air shimmered and wavered with heat, and little insects made a shrill sound. Bess and Beauty were lying down in the shade of a tree, and their little colts stood near them, waggling their small bushy tails and straddling a little on their long, gangling legs. The yearlings and the two-year-olds and the three-year-olds were grazing. All of them lifted their heads and stared at Almanzo.

He went slowly toward them, holding out his hand. There wasn't anything in his hand, but they

didn't know that. He didn't mean to do anything, he only wanted to get near enough to pet them. Starlight and the other little colt ran wabbling to their mothers, and Bess and Beauty lifted up their heads and looked, then laid them down again. The big colts all pricked up their ears.

One big colt stepped toward Almanzo, then another. The six big colts were all coming. Almanzo wished he had brought carrots for them. They were so beautiful and free and big, tossing their manes and showing the whites of their eyes. The sunshine glistened on their strong, arched necks and on the muscles of their chests. Suddenly one of them said:

"Whoosh!"

One of them kicked, one of them squealed, and all at once their heads went up, their tails went up, and their hooves thundered on the ground. All their brown haunches and high black tails were turned to Almanzo. Like a thundering whirlwind those six colts went around the tree, and Almanzo heard them behind him.

He whirled around. He saw their pounding hooves and big chests coming straight at him. They were running too fast to stop. There wasn't time to get out of the way. Almanzo's eyes shut; he yelled:

"Whoa!"

The air and the ground shook. His eyes opened. He saw brown knees rising up in the air, a round belly and hind legs rushed overhead. Brown sides went by him like thunder. His hat flew off. He felt stunned. One of the three-year-olds had jumped over him. The colts were thundering down across the pasture, and Almanzo saw Royal coming.

"Leave those colts be!" Royal shouted. He came up and said that for a cent he'd give Almanzo a licking he'd remember.

"You know better than to fool with those colts," Royal said. He took Almanzo by the ear. Almanzo trotted, but his ear was pulled all the way to the barns. He said he hadn't done anything; Royal wouldn't listen.

"Let me catch you in that pasture again and I'll whale the hide off you," Royal said. "I'll tell Father, too."

Almanzo went away, rubbing his ear. He went down to Trout River and swam in the swimming-hole till he felt better. But he thought it wasn't fair that he was the youngest in the family.

That afternoon the melons were cold, and Almanzo carried them to the grass under the balsam tree in the yard. Royal stuck the butcher knife into the dewy green rinds, and every melon was so ripe that the rinds cracked open.

Almanzo and Alice and Eliza Jane and Royal bit deep into the juicy, cold slices, and they ate till they could eat no more. Almanzo pinched the sleek black seeds, popping them at Eliza Jane until she made him quit. Then he slowly ate the last slice of melon, and he said:

"I'm going to fetch Lucy to eat up the rinds."

"You will not do any such a thing!" Eliza Jane said. "The idea! A dirty old pig in the front yard!"

"She is not, either, a dirty old pig!" said Almanzo. "Lucy's a little, young, clean pig, and pigs are the cleanest animals there are! You just ought to see the way Lucy keeps her bed clean, and turns it and airs it and makes it up every day. Horses won't do that, nor cows, nor sheep, nor anything. Pigs — "

"I guess I know that! I guess I know as much about pigs as you do!" Eliza Jane said.

"Then don't you call Lucy dirty! She's just as clean as you be!"

"Well, Mother told you to obey me," Eliza Jane answered. "And I'm not going to waste melon rinds on any pig! I'm going to make watermelon-rind preserves."

"I guess they're as much my rinds as they are yours," Almanzo began, but Royal got up and said:

"Come along, 'Manzo. It's chore-time."

Almanzo said no more, but when the chores were done he let Lucy out of her pen. The little pig was as white as a lamb, and she liked Almanzo; her little curled tail quirked whenever she saw him. She followed him to the house, grunting happily, and she squealed for him at the door till Eliza Jane said she couldn't hear herself think.

After supper Almanzo took a plate of scraps and fed them to Lucy. He sat on the back steps and scratched her prickly back. Pigs enjoy that. In the kitchen Eliza Jane and Royal were arguing about candy. Royal wanted some, but Eliza Jane said that candy-pulls were only for winter evenings. Royal said he didn't see why candy wouldn't be just as good in the summer. Almanzo thought so, too, and he went in and sided with Royal.

Alice said she knew how to make candy. Eliza Jane wouldn't do it, but Alice mixed sugar and molasses and water, and boiled them; then she poured the candy on buttered platters and set it on the porch to cool. They rolled up their sleeves and buttered their hands, ready to pull it, and Eliza Jane buttered her hands, too.

All the time, Lucy was squealing for Almanzo. He went out to see if the candy was cool enough, and he thought his little pig should have some. The candy was cool. No one was watching, so he took a big wad of the soft, brown candy and dropped it over the edge of the porch into Lucy's wide-open mouth.

Then they all pulled candy. They pulled it into long strands, and doubled the strands, and pulled again. Every time they doubled it, they took a bite.

It was very sticky. It stuck to their teeth and their fingers and their faces, somehow it got in their hair and stuck, and when Almanzo dropped some on the floor, it stuck there. It should have become hard and brittle, but it didn't. They pulled and they pulled; still it was soft and sticky. Long past bedtime, they gave it up and went to bed.

Next morning when Almanzo started to do the chores, Lucy was standing in the yard. Her tail hung limp and her head hung down. She did not squeal when she saw him. She shook her head sadly and wrinkled her nose.

Where her white teeth should have been, there was a smooth, brown streak.

Lucy's teeth were stuck together with candy! She could not eat, she could not drink, she could not even squeal. She could not grunt. But when she saw Almanzo coming, she ran.

Almanzo yelled for Royal. They chased Lucy all around the house, under the snowball bushes and the lilacs. They chased her all over the garden. Lucy whirled and dodged and ducked and ran like anything. All the time she didn't make a sound; she couldn't. Her mouth was full of candy.

She ran between Royal's legs and upset him. Almanzo almost grabbed her, and went sprawling on his nose. She tore through the peas, and squashed the ripe tomatoes, and uprooted the green round cabbages. Eliza Jane kept telling Royal and Almanzo to catch her. Alice ran after her.

At last they cornered her. She dashed around Alice's skirts. Almanzo fell on her and grabbed. She kicked, and tore a long hole down the front of his blouse.

Almanzo held her down. Alice held her kicking hind legs. Royal pried her mouth open and scraped out the candy. Then how Lucy squealed! She squealed all the squeals that had been in her all night and all the squeals she couldn't squeal while they were chasing her, and she ran screaming to her pen.

"Almanzo James Wilder, just look at yourself!" Eliza Jane scolded. He couldn't, and he didn't want to.

Even Alice was horrified because he had wasted candy on a pig. And his blouse was ruined; it could be patched, but the patch would show.

"I don't care," Almanzo said. He was glad it was a whole week before Mother would know.

That day they made ice-cream again, and they ate the last cake. Alice said she knew how to make a pound cake. She said she'd make one, and then she was going to go sit in the parlor.

Almanzo thought that wouldn't be any fun. But Eliza Jane said:

"You'll do no such thing, Alice. You know very well the parlor's just for company."

It was not Eliza Jane's parlor, and Mother hadn't said she couldn't sit in it. Almanzo thought that Alice could sit in the parlor if she wanted to.

That afternoon he came into the kitchen to see if the pound cake was done. Alice was taking it out of the oven. It smelled so good that he broke a little piece off the corner. Then Alice cut a slice to hide the broken place, and then they ate two more slices with the last of the ice-cream.

"I can make more ice-cream," Alice said. Eliza Jane was upstairs, and Almanzo said:

"Let's go into the parlor."

They tiptoed in, without making a sound. The light was dim because the blinds were down, but the parlor was beautiful. The wallpaper was white and gold and the carpet was of Mother's best weaving, almost too fine to step on. The center-table was marble-topped, and it held the tall parlor lamp, all white-and-gold china and pink painted roses. Beside it lay the photograph album, with covers of red velvet and mother-of-pearl.

All around the walls stood solemn horsehair chairs, and George Washington's picture looked sternly from its frame between the windows.

Alice hitched up her hoops behind, and sat on the sofa. The slippery haircloth slid her right off onto the floor. She didn't dare laugh out loud, for fear Eliza Jane would hear. She sat on the sofa again, and slid off again. Then Almanzo slid off a chair.

When company came and they had to sit in the parlor, they kept themselves on the slippery chairs by pushing their toes against the floor. But now they could let go and slide. They slid off the sofa and the chairs till Alice was giggling so hard they didn't dare slide any more.

Then they looked at the shells and the coral and the little china figures on the what-not. They didn't touch anything. They looked till they heard Eliza Jane coming downstairs; then they ran tiptoe out of the parlor and shut the door without a sound. Eliza Jane didn't catch them.

It seemed that a week would last forever, but suddenly it was gone. One morning at breakfast Eliza Jane said:

"Father and Mother will be here tomorrow."

They all stopped eating. The garden had not been weeded. The peas and beans had not been picked, so the vines were ripening too soon. The henhouse had not been whitewashed.

"This house is a sight," Eliza Jane said. "And we must churn today. But what am I going to tell Mother? The sugar is all gone."

Nobody ate any more. They looked into the sugar-barrel, and they could see the bottom of it.

Only Alice tried to be cheerful.

"We must hope for the best," she said, like Mother. "There's *some* sugar left. Mother said, 'Don't eat *all* the sugar,' and we didn't. There's some around the edges."

This was only the beginning of that awful day. They all went to work as hard as they could. Royal and Almanzo hoed the garden, they whitewashed the hen-house, they cleaned the cows' stalls and swept the South-Barn Floor. The girls were sweeping and scrubbing in the house. Eliza Jane made Almanzo churn till the butter came, and her hands flew while she washed and salted it and packed it in the tub. There was only bread and butter and jam for dinner, though Almanzo was starved.

"Now, Almanzo, you polish the heater," Eliza Jane said.

He hated to polish stoves, but he hoped Eliza Jane would not tell that he had wasted candy on his pig. He went to work with the stove-blacking and the brush. Eliza Jane was hurrying and nagging.

"Be careful you don't spill the polish," she said, busily dusting.

Almanzo guessed he knew enough not to spill stove polish. But he didn't say anything.

"Use less water, Almanzo. And, mercy! rub harder than that!" He didn't say anything.

Eliza Jane went into the parlor to dust it. She called: "Almanzo, that stove done now?"

"No," said Almanzo.

"Goodness! don't dawdle so!"

Almanzo muttered, "Whose boss are you?"

Eliza Jane asked, "What's that you say?"

"Nothing," Almanzo said.

Eliza Jane came to the door. "You did so say something."

Almanzo straightened up and shouted,

"I say, *WHOSE BOSS ARE YOU?*"

Eliza Jane gasped. Then she cried out:

"You just wait, Almanzo James Wilder! You just wait till I tell Moth — "

Almanzo didn't mean to throw the blacking-brush. It flew right out of his hand. It sailed past Eliza Jane's head. Smack! it hit the parlor wall.

A great splash and smear of blacking appeared on the white-and-gold wall-paper.

Alice screamed. Almanzo turned around and ran all the way to the barn. He climbed into the haymow and crawled far back into the hay. He did not cry, but he would have cried if he hadn't been almost ten years old.

Mother would come home and find he had ruined her beautiful parlor. Father would take him into the woodshed and whip him with the blacksnake whip. He didn't want ever to come out of the haymow. He wished he could stay there forever.

After a long while Royal came into the haymow and called him. He crawled out of the hay, and he saw that Royal knew.

"Mannie, you'll get an awful whipping," Royal said. Royal was sorry, but he couldn't do anything. They both knew that Almanzo deserved whipping, and there was no way to keep Father from knowing it. So Almanzo said:

"I don't care."

He helped do the chores, and he ate supper. He wasn't hungry, but he ate to show Eliza Jane he didn't care. Then he went to bed. The parlor door was shut, but he knew how the black splotch looked on the white-and-gold wall.

Next day Father and Mother came driving into the yard. Almanzo had to go out to meet them with the others. Alice whispered to him: "Don't feel bad. Maybe they won't care." But she looked anxious, too.

Father said, cheerfully: "Well, here we are. Been getting along all right?"

"Yes, Father," Royal answered. Almanzo didn't go to help unhitch the driving-horses; he stayed in the house.

Mother hurried about, looking at everything while she untied her bonnet strings.

"I declare, Eliza Jane and Alice," she said, "you've kept the house as well as I'd have done myself."

"Mother," Alice said, in a small voice. "Mother — "

"Well, child, what is it?"

"Mother," Alice said, bravely, "you told us not to eat *all* the sugar. Mother, we — we ate almost all of it."

Mother laughed. "You've all been so good," she said, "I won't scold about the sugar."

She did not know that the black splotch was on the parlor wall. The parlor door was shut. She did not know it that day, nor all the next day. Almanzo could hardly choke down his food at mealtimes, and Mother worried. She took him into the pantry and made him swallow a big spoonful of horrible black medicine she had made of roots and herbs.

He did not want her to know about the black splotch, and yet he wished she did know. When the worst was over he could stop dreading it.

That second evening they heard a buggy driving into the yard. Mr. and Mrs. Webb were in it. Father and Mother went out to meet them and in a minute they all came into the dining-room. Almanzo heard Mother saying,

"Come right into the parlor!"

He couldn't move. He could not speak. This was worse than anything he had thought of. Mother was so proud of her beautiful parlor. She was so proud of keeping it always nice. She didn't know he had ruined it, and now she was taking company in. They would see that big black splotch on the wall.

Mother opened the parlor door and went in. Mrs. Webb went in, and Mr. Webb and Father. Almanzo saw only their backs, but he heard the window-shades going up. He saw that the parlor was full of light. It seemed to him a long time before anybody said anything.

Then Mother said:

"Take this big chair, Mr. Webb, and make yourself comfortable. Sit right here on the sofa, Mrs. Webb."

Almanzo couldn't believe his ears. Mrs. Webb said:

"You have such a beautiful parlor, I declare it's almost too fine to sit in."

Now Almanzo could see where the blacking-brush had hit the wall, and he could not believe his eyes. The wall-paper was pure white and gold. There was no black splotch.

Mother caught sight of him and said:

"Come in, Almanzo."

Almanzo went in. He sat up straight on a haircloth chair and pushed his toes against the floor to keep from sliding off. Father and Mother were telling all about the visit to Uncle Andrew's. There was no black splotch anywhere on the wall.

"Didn't you worry, leaving the children alone here and you so far away?" Mrs. Webb asked.

"No," Mother said, proudly. "I knew the children would take care of everything as well as if James and I were to home."

Almanzo minded his manners and did not say a word.

Next day, when no one was looking, he stole into the parlor. He looked carefully at the place where the black splotch had been. The wall-paper was patched. The patch had been cut out carefully all around the

gold scrolls, and the pattern was fitted perfectly and the edges of the patch scraped so thin that he could hardly find them.

He waited until he could speak to Eliza Jane alone, and then he asked:

"Eliza Jane, did you patch the parlor wall-paper for me?"

"Yes," she said. "I got the scraps of wall-paper that were saved in the attic, and cut out the patch and put it on with flour-paste."

Almanzo said, gruffly:

"I'm sorry I threw that brush at you. Honest, I didn't mean to, Eliza Jane."

"I guess I was aggravating," she said. "But I didn't mean to be. You're the only little brother I've got."

Almanzo had never known before how much he liked Eliza Jane.

They never, never told about the black splotch on the parlor wall, and Mother never knew.

How much more trouble can Almanzo get into? You'll find out when you read the rest of *Farmer Boy*.

THAT AWFUL DAY

Eliza Jane, Royal, Almanzo, and Alice had a lot to do the day before their parents returned home! Reread the paragraph on page 236 that starts with "This was only the beginning of that awful day." Then, in groups of four, write a short play based on that paragraph. What do you think the Wilder children said as they did their chores? You decide — you're the playwright. Then perform your play for your class.

Almanzo Wilder spent his childhood in Malone, New York. When he was a young man, he moved to South Dakota with his brother, Royal. It was there that Almanzo met and later married Laura Ingalls.

This announcement of Laura and Almanzo's wedding appeared in the De Smet newspaper.

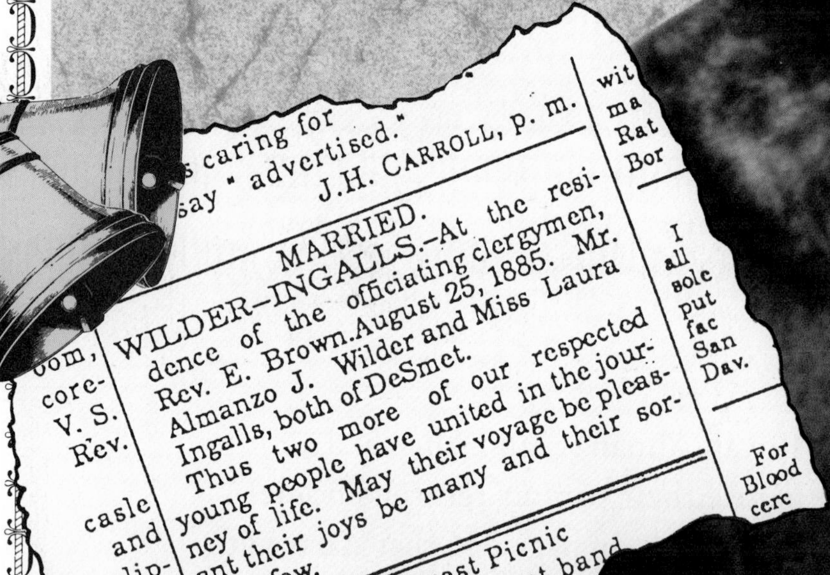
s caring for
say " advertised."
J.H. CARROLL, p. m.

MARRIED.

WILDER–INGALLS.–At the residence of the officiating clergymen, Rev. E. Brown, August 25, 1885. Mr. Almanzo J. Wilder and Miss Laura Ingalls, both of DeSmet.

Thus two more of our respected young people have united in the journey of life. May their voyage be pleasant their joys be many and their sorrows few.

Harvest Picnic
De Smet Cornet band

LAURA & ALMANZO

This photograph of Laura and Almanzo was taken shortly after their marriage in 1885.

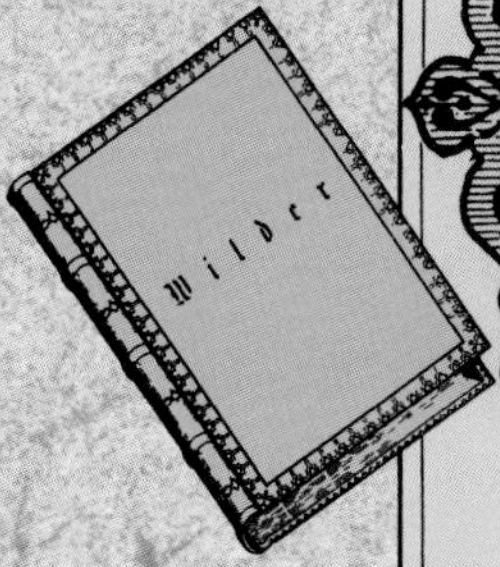

Laura and Almanzo's daughter, Rose, was two when this photo was taken. Rose grew up to become a writer like her famous mother.

From the book

On the Banks of Plum Creek

by Laura Ingalls Wilder with illustrations by Garth Williams

The Ingallses have hitched their horses to their covered wagon and have moved once again. They now live near Walnut Grove, Minnesota, on the banks of Plum Creek.

Now in the daytimes Pa was driving the wagon up and down Plum Creek, and bringing load after load of logs to the pile by the door. He cut down old plum trees and old willows and cotton-woods, leaving the little ones to grow. He hauled them and stacked them, and chopped and split them into stove wood, till he had a big woodpile.

With his short-handled ax in his belt, his traps on his arm, and his gun against his shoulder, he walked far up Plum Creek, setting traps for muskrat and mink and otter and fox.

One evening at supper Pa said he had found a beaver meadow. But he did not set traps there because so few beavers were left. He had seen a fox and shot at it, but missed.

"I am all out of practice hunting," he said. "It's a fine place we have here, but there isn't much game. Makes a fellow think of places out West where — "

"Where there are no schools for the children, Charles," said Ma.

"You're right, Caroline. You usually are," Pa said. "Listen to that wind. We'll have a storm tomorrow."

But the next day was mild as spring. The air was soft and warm and the sun shone brightly. In the middle of the morning Pa came to the house.

"Let's have an early dinner and take a walk to town this afternoon," he said to Ma. "This is too nice a day for you to stay indoors. Time enough for that when winter really comes."

"But the children," said Ma. "We can't take Carrie and walk so far."

"Shucks!" Pa laughed at her. "Mary and Laura are great girls now. They can take care of Carrie for one afternoon."

"Of course we can, Ma," said Mary; and Laura said, "Of course we can!"

They watched Pa and Ma starting gaily away. Ma was so pretty, in her brown-and-red Christmas shawl, with her brown knit hood tied under her chin, and she stepped so quickly and looked up at Pa so merrily that Laura thought she was like a bird.

Then Laura swept the floor while Mary cleared the table. Mary washed the dishes and Laura wiped them and put them in the cupboard. They put the red-checked cloth on the table. Now the whole long afternoon was before them and they could do as they pleased.

First, they decided to play school. Mary said she must be Teacher, because she was older and besides she knew more. Laura knew that was true. So Mary was Teacher and she liked it, but Laura was soon tired of that play.

"I know," Laura said. "Let's both teach Carrie her letters."

They sat Carrie on a bench and held the book before her, and both did their best. But Carrie did not like it. She would not learn the letters, so they had to stop that.

"Well," said Laura, "Let's play keeping house."

"We *are* keeping house," said Mary. "What is the use of playing it?"

The house was empty and still, with Ma gone. Ma was so quiet and gentle that she never made any noise, but now the whole house was listening for her.

Laura went outdoors for a while by herself, but she came back. The afternoon grew longer and longer. There was nothing at all to do. Even Jack walked up and down restlessly.

He asked to go out, but when Laura opened the door he would not go. He lay down and got up, and walked around and around the room. He came to Laura and looked at her earnestly.

"What is it, Jack?" Laura asked him. He stared hard at her, but she could not understand, and he almost howled.

"Don't, Jack!" Laura told him, quickly. "You scare me."

"Is it something outdoors?" Mary wondered. Laura ran out, but on the doorstep Jack took hold of her dress and pulled her back. Outdoors was bitter cold. Laura shut the door.

"Look," she said. "The sunshine's dark. Are the grasshoppers coming back?"

"Not in the winter-time, goosie," said Mary. "Maybe it's rain."

"Goosie yourself!" Laura said back. "It doesn't rain in the winter-time."

"Well, snow, then! What's the difference?" Mary was angry and so was Laura. They would have gone on quarreling, but suddenly there was no sunshine. They ran to look through the bedroom window.

A dark cloud with a fleecy white underside was rolling fast from the north-west.

Mary and Laura looked out the front window. Surely it was time for Pa and Ma to come, but they were nowhere in sight.

"Maybe it's a blizzard," said Mary.

"Like Pa told us about," said Laura.

They looked at each other through the grey air. They were thinking of those children who froze stark stiff.

"The woodbox is empty," said Laura.

Mary grabbed her. "You can't!" said Mary. "Ma told us to stay in the house if it stormed." Laura jerked away and Mary said, "Besides, Jack won't let you."

"We've got to bring in wood before the storm gets here," Laura told her. "Hurry!"

They could hear a strange sound in the wind, like a far-away screaming. They put on their shawls and pinned them under their chins with their large shawl-pins. They put on their mittens.

Laura was ready first. She told Jack, "We've got to bring in wood, Jack." He seemed to understand. He went out with her and stayed close at her heels. The wind was colder than icicles. Laura ran to the woodpile, piled up a big armful of wood, and ran back, with Jack behind her. She could not open the door while she held the wood. Mary opened it for her.

Then they did not know what to do. The cloud was coming swiftly, and they must both bring in wood before the storm got there. They could not open the door when their arms were full of wood. They could not leave the door open and let the cold come in.

"I tan open the door," said Carrie.

"You can't," Mary said.

"I tan, too!" said Carrie, and she reached up both hands and turned the door knob. She could do it! Carrie was big enough to open the door.

Laura and Mary hurried fast, bringing in wood. Carrie opened the door when they came to it, and shut it behind them. Mary could carry larger armfuls, but Laura was quicker.

They filled the woodbox before it began to snow. The snow came suddenly with a whirling blast, and it was small hard grains like sand. It stung Laura's face where it struck. When Carrie opened the door, it swirled into the house in a white cloud.

Laura and Mary forgot that Ma had told them to stay in the house when it stormed. They forgot everything but bringing in wood. They ran frantically back and forth, bringing each time all the wood they could stagger under.

They piled wood around the woodbox and around the stove. They piled it against the wall. They made the piles higher, and bigger.

Bang! they banged the door. They ran to the woodpile. Clop-clop-clop they stacked the wood on their arms. They ran to the door. Bump! it went open, and bang! they back-bumped it shut, and thumpity-thud-thump! they flung down the wood and ran back, outdoors, to the woodpile, and panting back again.

They could hardly see the woodpile in the swirling whiteness. Snow was driven all in among the wood. They could hardly see the house, and Jack was a dark blob hurrying beside them. The hard snow scoured their faces. Laura's arms ached and her chest panted and all the time she thought, "Oh, where is Pa? Where is Ma?" and she felt "Hurry! Hurry!" and she heard the wind screeching.

The woodpile was gone. Mary took a few sticks and Laura took a few sticks and there were no more. They ran to the door together, and Laura opened it and Jack bounded in. Carrie was at the front window, clapping her hands and squealing. Laura dropped her sticks of wood and turned just in time to see Pa and Ma burst, running, out of the whirling whiteness of snow.

Pa was holding Ma's hand and pulling to help her run. They burst into the house and slammed the door and stood panting, covered with snow. No one said anything while Pa and Ma looked at Laura and Mary, who stood all snowy in shawls and mittens.

At last Mary said in a small voice, “We did go out in the storm, Ma. We forgot.”

Laura’s head bowed down and she said, “We didn’t want to burn up the furniture, Pa, and freeze stark stiff.”

“Well, I’ll be darned!” said Pa. “If they didn’t move the whole woodpile in. All the wood I cut to last a couple of weeks.”

There, piled up in the house, was the whole woodpile. Melted snow was leaking out of it and spreading in puddles. A wet path went to the door, where snow lay unmelted.

Then Pa’s great laugh rang out, and Ma’s gentle smile shone warm on Mary and Laura. They knew they were forgiven for disobeying, because they had been wise to bring in wood, though perhaps not quite so much wood.

Sometime soon they would be old enough not to make any mistakes, and then they could always decide what to do. They would not have to obey Pa and Ma any more.

They bustled to take off Ma's shawl and hood and brush the snow from them and hang them up to dry. Pa hurried to the stable to do the chores before the storm grew worse. Then while Ma rested, they stacked the wood neatly as she told them, and they swept and mopped the floor.

The house was neat and cosy again. The teakettle hummed, the fire shone brightly from the draughts above the stove hearth. Snow swished against the windows.

Pa came in. "Here is the little milk I could get here with. The wind blew it up out of the pail. Caroline, this is a terrible storm. I couldn't see an inch, and the wind comes from all directions at once. I thought I was on the path, but I couldn't see the house, and — well, I just barely bumped against the corner. Another foot to the left and I never would have got in."

"*Charles!*" Ma said.

"Nothing to be scared about now," said Pa. "But if we hadn't run all the way from town and beat this storm here — " Then his eyes twinkled, he rumpled Mary's hair and pulled Laura's ear. "I'm glad all this wood is in the house, too," he said.

A sudden blizzard is just one of the many things the Ingallses face on the banks of Plum Creek. If you want to know more of their adventures, read the rest of the book.

But What If . . .

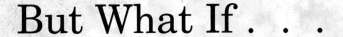

Even though Mary and Laura disobeyed their parents and went outside during the storm, everything turned out for the best.

But what if things had turned out differently?

In small groups, discuss what might have happened

- if the girls had listened to Ma's instructions and stayed in the house instead of getting wood.
- if Ma and Pa hadn't come home that night.

About the Illustrator

Garth Williams

Stuart Little. Wilbur. Charlotte. Tucker Mouse. If you know any of these characters, then you have seen other illustrations by Garth Williams. *Stuart Little* is the first major book that Williams illustrated. He then went on to illustrate some of the most beloved classics of all time, such as *Charlotte's Web* and *The Cricket in Times Square*.

Dear Houghton Mifflin Readers,

When I was asked to illustrate the "Little House" books, I was very pleased, but I had to see Mrs. Wilder and Almanzo to ask them many questions.

I lived in New York and it was a long drive to Missouri. Mrs. Wilder was working in her garden when I arrived, so I sat and watched her.

She was like a young woman, very busy trimming trees, cutting flowers, watering plants. She was very happy to meet me and hear about my drawings for her books, and invited me into her house. It was a lovely, cosy, cosy house and Almanzo was seated in a comfortable chair reading.

"You and Almanzo can talk while I make tea," she said. I explained to Almanzo that I was on my way to see all the places where they had lived, as told about in the stories. But Almanzo said it might snow any day, and advised me to go some other time.

We talked about everything in the books so that my drawings would be correct. Laura remembered everything in great detail, and Almanzo too. They told me where Plum Creek was and answered all my questions.

After three hours I drove to De Smet and saw everything there and met several people who knew Laura when she was very young.

When I had seen everything in South Dakota, I started back to New York. As I arrived at the first hotel, it began to snow. It snowed all that night and for two more days. I could not continue my trip; Almanzo was right. But I had seen everything and met Laura and Almanzo, so I was very lucky.

Garth Williams

Other Authors,

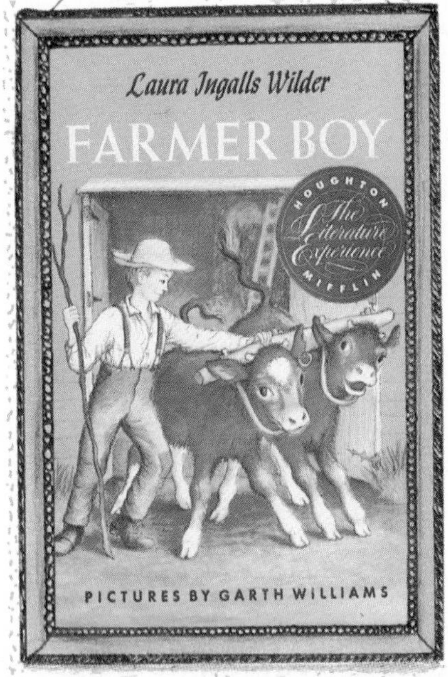

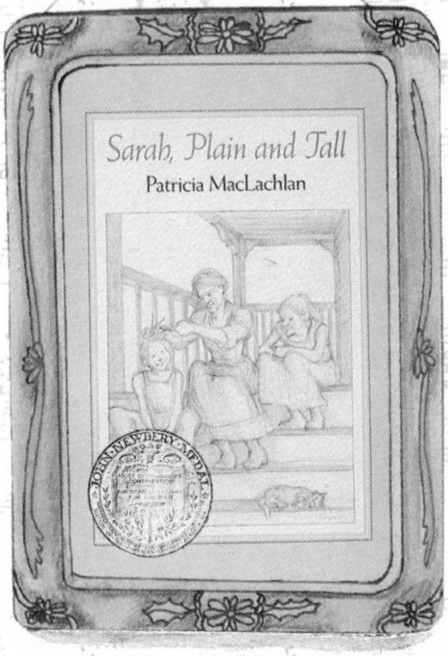

Farmer Boy
by Laura Ingalls Wilder

—

Hearty meals, sleek horses, and lively adventures with his brother and sisters are part of Almanzo's life on a New York farm in the mid-1800's.

Talk About a Family
by Eloise Greenfield

—

Now that Genny's brother Larry is home from the army, maybe he'll be able to bring their family together again.

Sarah, Plain and Tall
by Patricia MacLachlan

—

Can Sarah, who is used to living by the ocean, adjust to living on the frontier? Anna and Caleb hope Sarah will want to stay with them and be their new mother.

Other Families

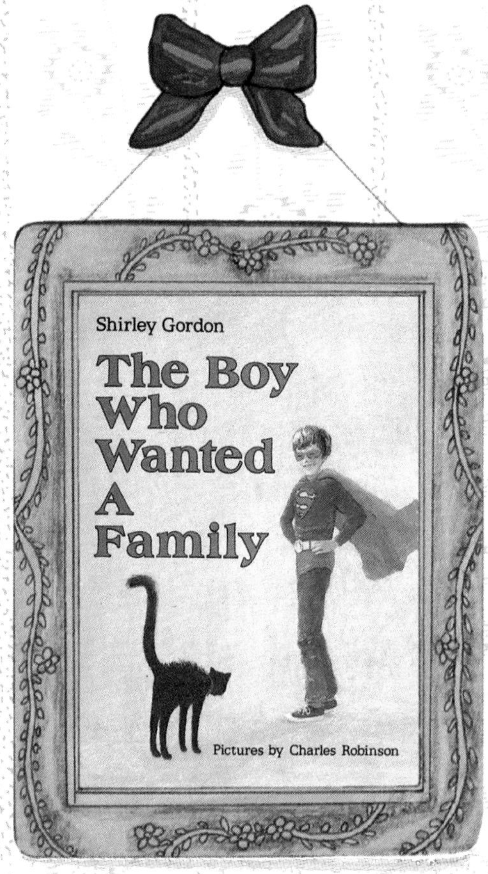

Blackberries in the Dark
by Mavis Jukes

—

Austin and his grandmother have lost something special they once shared. But they find something new, and a tradition lives on.

The Boy Who Wanted a Family
by Shirley Gordon

—

Michael wants a mother. Miss Graham wants a son. Can the two of them be a family — together?

All-of-a-kind Family
by Sydney Taylor

—

Collecting junk, going to the library, and visiting Coney Island are some of the ways five sisters spend their days in New York at the turn of the century.

Linking Literature to Social Studies

Reading a good book can make the reader want to find out more about the author, the characters, or the setting. Having read three stories by Laura Ingalls Wilder, you may want to learn more about what it was like to live on the Great Plains in the late 1800's.

The article that follows was taken from a chapter in a social studies textbook. It tells about some new ways of doing things that made living and traveling on the Great Plains much easier.

A Changing Nation

Changes in the West

READING FOCUS

What changes helped the West to grow?

Key Terms

- sod
- transcontinental railroad
- breadbasket

In the 1850's, many people left their homes in the East and journeyed west. Most of these pioneers traveled all the way to the Pacific coast. They settled in California, Washington, Oregon, Idaho, and Utah.

Many pioneers did not think of settling on the Great Plains because they thought of that region as a desert. The Plains were covered with a heavy layer of **sod,** which is thick grass and dirt mixed together. No iron plow could cut through sod. Also, water was scarce, and there were few trees on the Plains. How could settlers build homes without lumber?

In time two changes took place that brought more and more settlers into this region. Railroads were built across the Great Plains, and a way was found to farm the land. In this selection, you will read about these two changes.

Iron Rails Join East and West

A dream was about to come true. The dream was of a railroad that would cross the West. It was called the **transcontinental railroad**.

The work had started six years before. The Central Pacific Railroad Company began building east from California. Another company, the Union Pacific, built west from Nebraska. Soon the two would meet.

Many of the Central Pacific railroad workers were from China. They had come to America because of stories of great wealth to be found. According to those stories, there were mountains of gold in the land called California. By the time

Chinese workers helped to build the western railroads.

they arrived, however, most of California's gold had been mined.

The Chinese had settled in new cities like Sacramento and San Francisco. Life was hard for these newcomers. But some were successful in starting small businesses.

The railroad provided thousands of jobs for the Chinese. Most of the hard work had been in the mountains. People had said it was impossible to build a railroad through the Sierra Nevadas and the Rockies. But the workers were doing it. In some places, they had to build ledges on the side of a mountain. In other spots, dynamite was used to blast tunnels through solid rock. Now, the work on the railroad was nearly over. They had done the impossible.

The two railroads met on May 10, 1869, at a place called Promontory Point in Utah. A golden spike was driven into the railroad tracks at the point where the two lines joined. The first transcontinental railroad was complete.

The iron tracks joined East and West together. More railroads were built across the country. Now people could travel west in comfort. The days of the long, hard journey by covered wagon were coming to an end.

This map shows the railroad lines that crossed the West.

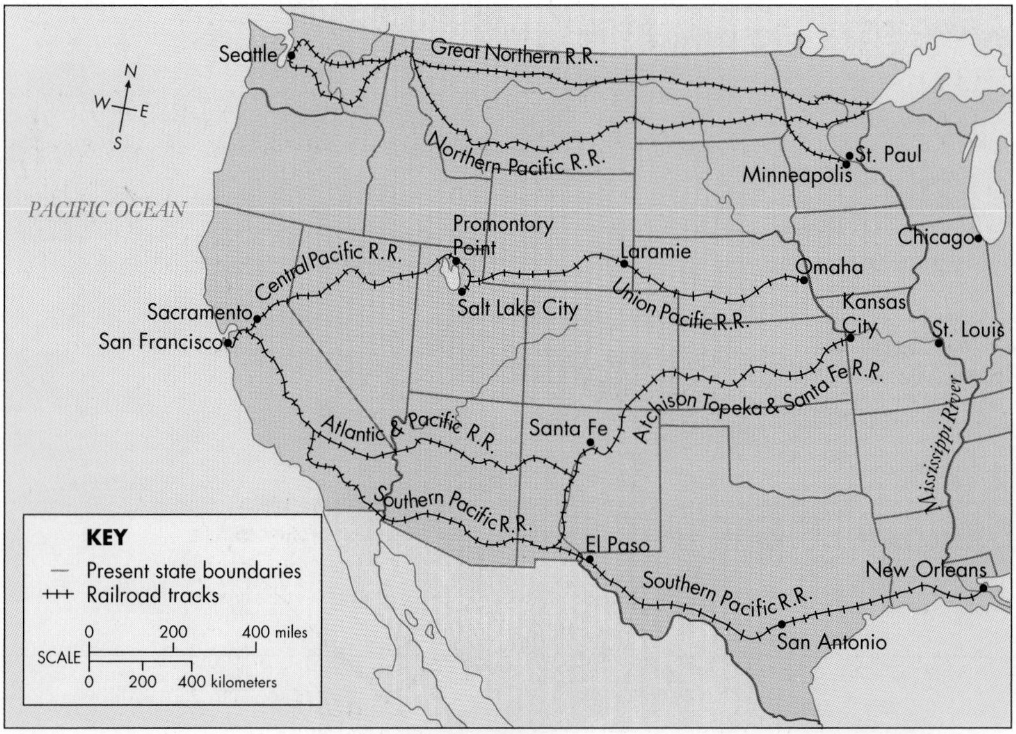

The Railroads Sell Land

The companies that built the railroads were in business to make a profit. They did this in three ways: (1) They collected fares from passengers. (2) They charged money for carrying freight or goods. (3) They sold land.

Congress had voted to give huge stretches of land to the railroad companies. That land ran along each side of the tracks. The companies had the right to sell the land to settlers.

More settlers meant more farms and towns, and this meant more business for the railroads. Since they wanted to attract settlers, the railroad companies sold their land at low prices. The companies sent agents to the eastern states and to Europe, urging people to move to America's western lands.

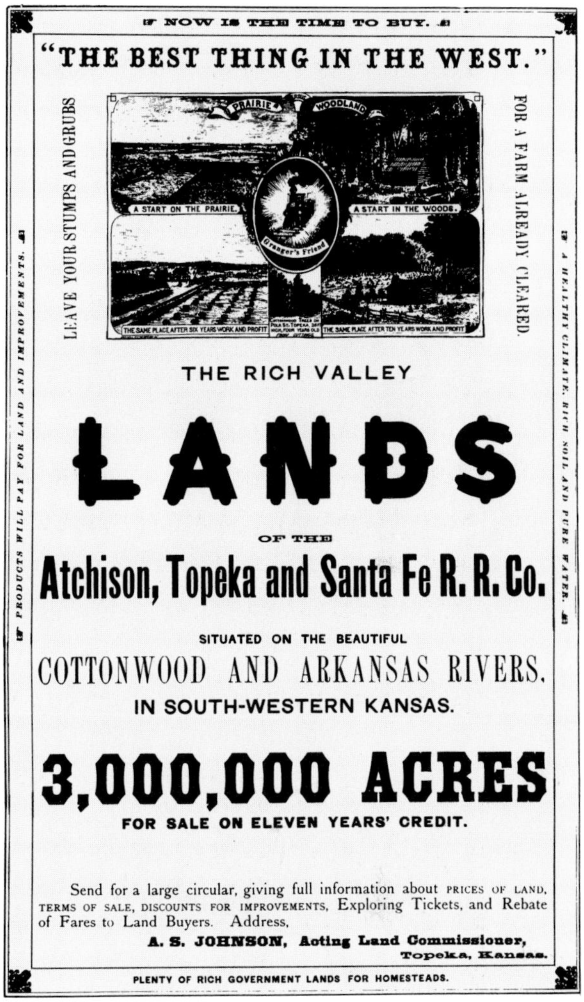

The railroad companies used ads such as the one shown here to try to sell land to the settlers.

Population of four Plains states, 1860–1900 (Kansas, Nebraska, North Dakota, South Dakota)

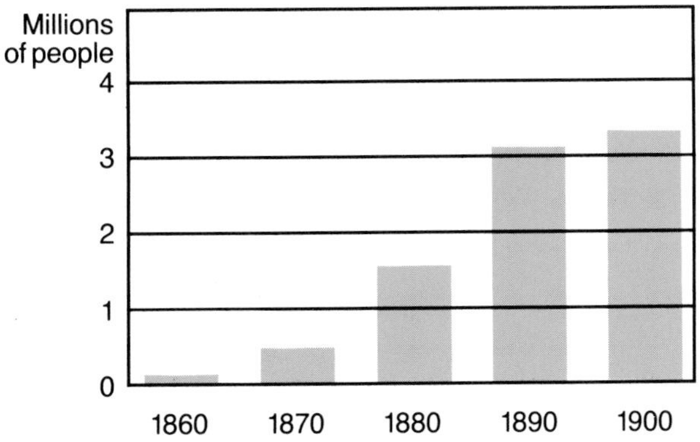

This graph shows how fast the population of four states on the Great Plains grew. In 1860 only 141,000 settlers lived in those states. About how many people lived there in 1880? In 1890? In 1900?

A family in front of their sod house near Broken Bow, Nebraska, 1886.

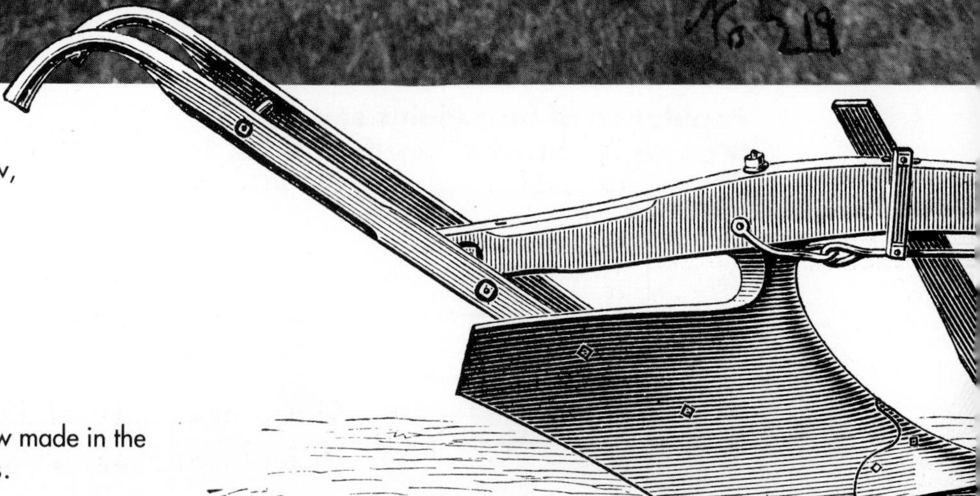

A steel plow made in the late 1800's.

New Ways of Farming

There were other changes in the late 1860's and 1870's that drew people to the Plains. A new invention, the steel plow, made it easier to farm the sod. Soil had stuck to iron plows. Steel was a much tougher and smoother form of iron. The steel plows could easily slice through the thick prairie sod.

The new farmers on the Great Plains used the steel plows to prepare their fields for planting. They also used them to cut through the sod to dig wells for water and to cut blocks of sod to build houses. Since wood was scarce, settlers built their first homes out of blocks of sod. The sod houses were warm in the harsh winters and cool under the hot summer sun.

Also in these years, new types of wheat were brought from Europe. The new wheat grew well on the Plains.

By the 1870's the wheat grown by the pioneer farmers was turning the Great Plains into the nation's **breadbasket**. This means that the wheat grown in this region was feeding the whole country.

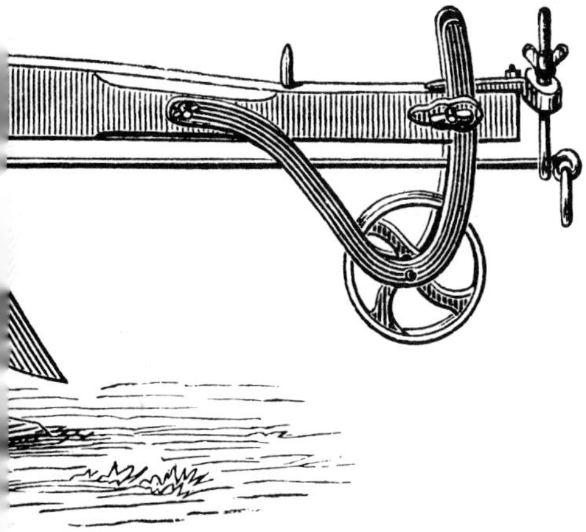

CHECK UP

- What changes helped the West to grow?
- Where was the first transcontinental railroad built?
- Why did the railroad companies want to sell land to settlers?
- What new ways of farming made it easier to settle on the Great Plains?

MYSTERY

BOOK 5

The Mystery Hour

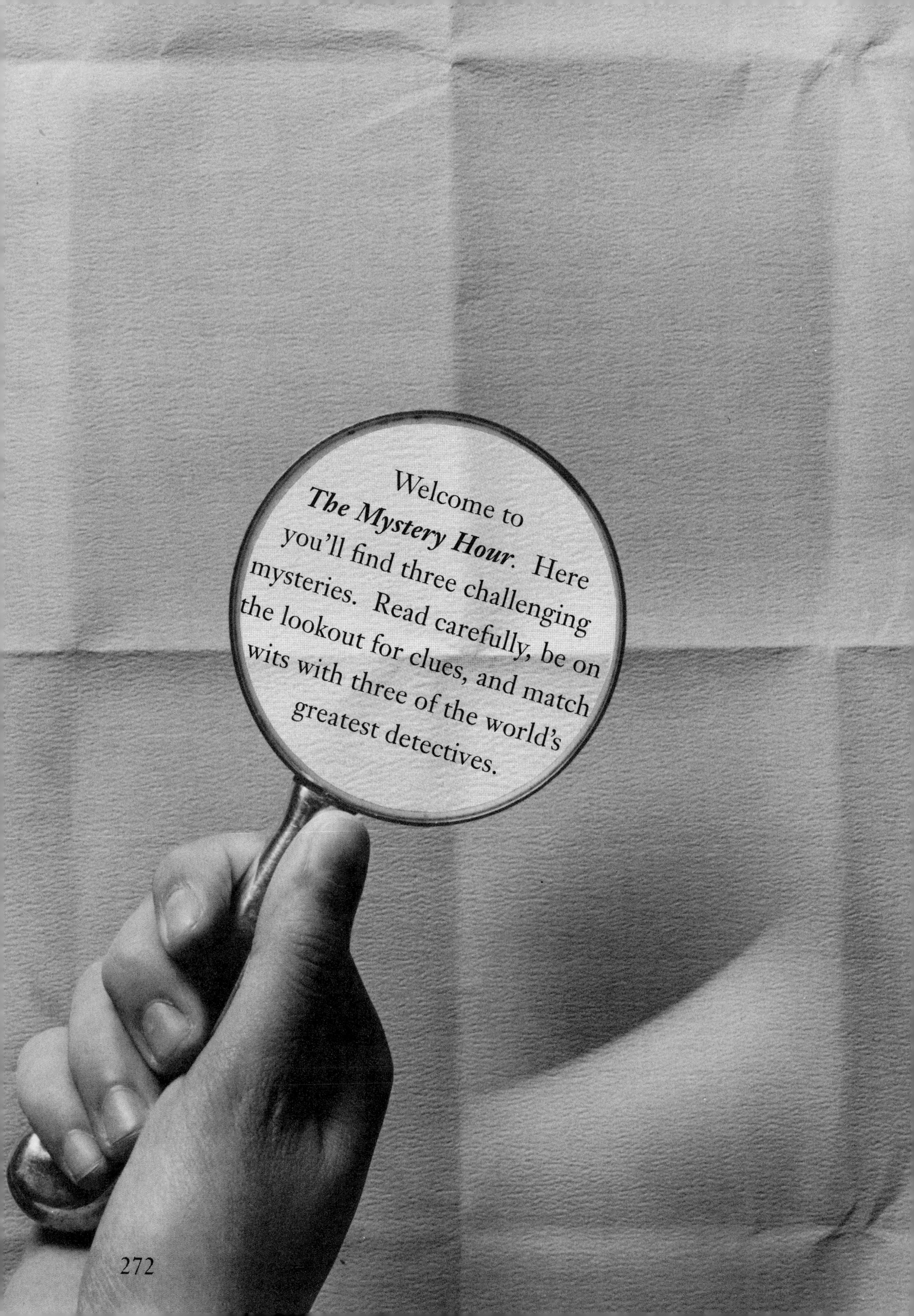
Welcome to
The Mystery Hour. Here
you'll find three challenging
mysteries. Read carefully, be on
the lookout for clues, and match
wits with three of the world's
greatest detectives.

Contents

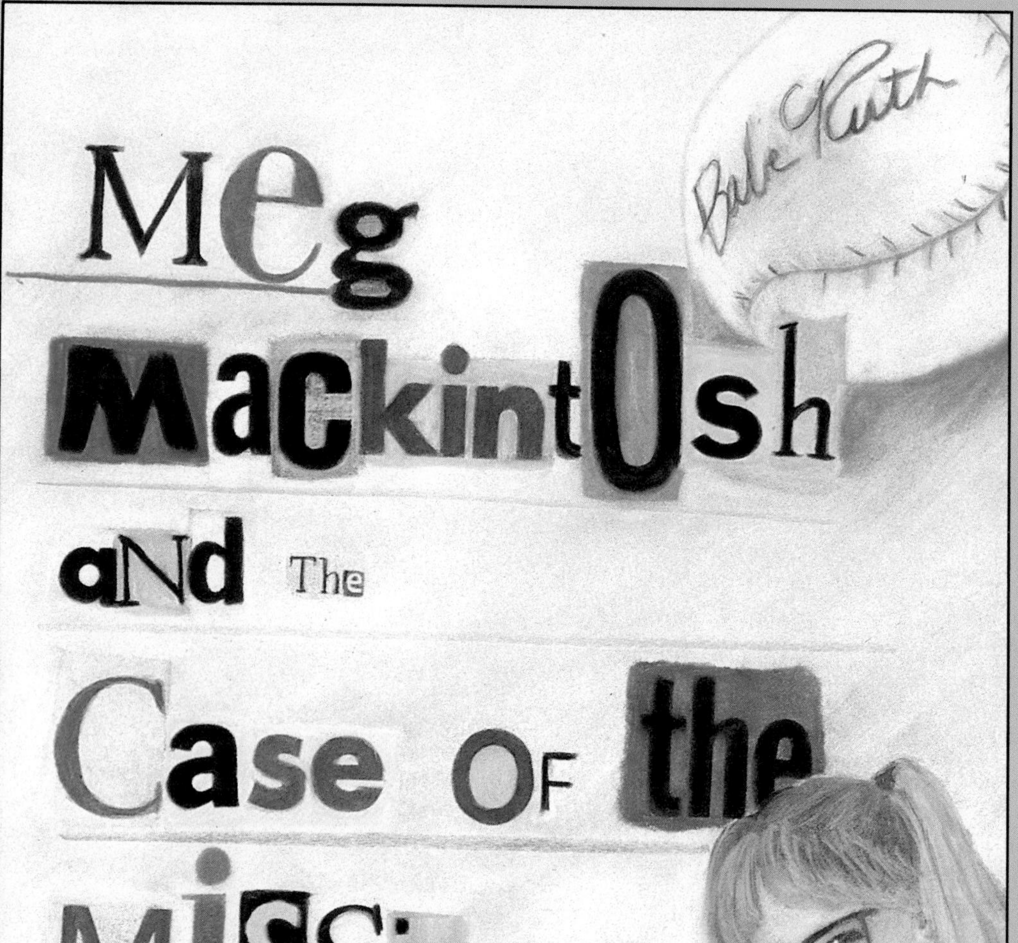

by Lucinda Landon ♦ illustrations by Hilary Mosberg

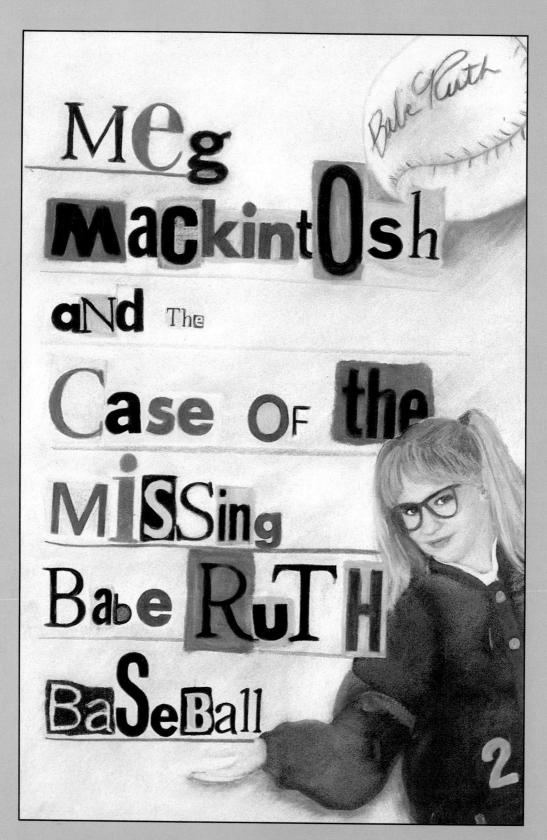

Hmm, I do detect a bit of family resemblance," said Meg Mackintosh, as she examined Gramps's old family photo album.

"You've got some funny-looking relatives," remarked Liddy. "And look at these pictures of you and Peter!"

Meg turned another page.

"Gramps, who's this?"

"That's me," explained Gramps, "and that's my cousin Alice. She was always bossing me around. She used to drive me crazy, teasing me about my little dog and calling me 'Georgie Porgie.' I called her 'Tattletale Al' because she was always getting me in trouble.

"I'll never forget the day that photo was taken. We went on a picnic," Gramps reminisced. "That was the day she lost my prize possession."

"What was it?" Meg asked.

"My baseball, signed by the Babe himself."

"A baby signed your baseball?"

"Of course not. Babe Ruth, the greatest baseball player ever. He autographed the ball and gave it to my father and my father gave it to me. I took it to that picnic and Alice lost it. I never saw it again."

OFFICIAL DETECTIVE'S REPORT
FILE #: 000001
CONFIDENTIAL
CASE: The Missing Babe Ruth Baseball
DETECTIVE: Meg Mackintosh, sister of Peter Mackintosh, president of the Detective Club
ADDRESS: Gramps's House
AGE: 10
HOBBY: Solving Mysteries

Meg examined the photo. Alice *did* look like a troublemaker. Then Meg spied something else.

The corner of a piece of paper was sticking out from behind the old photograph. Meg pulled it out and carefully unfolded it.

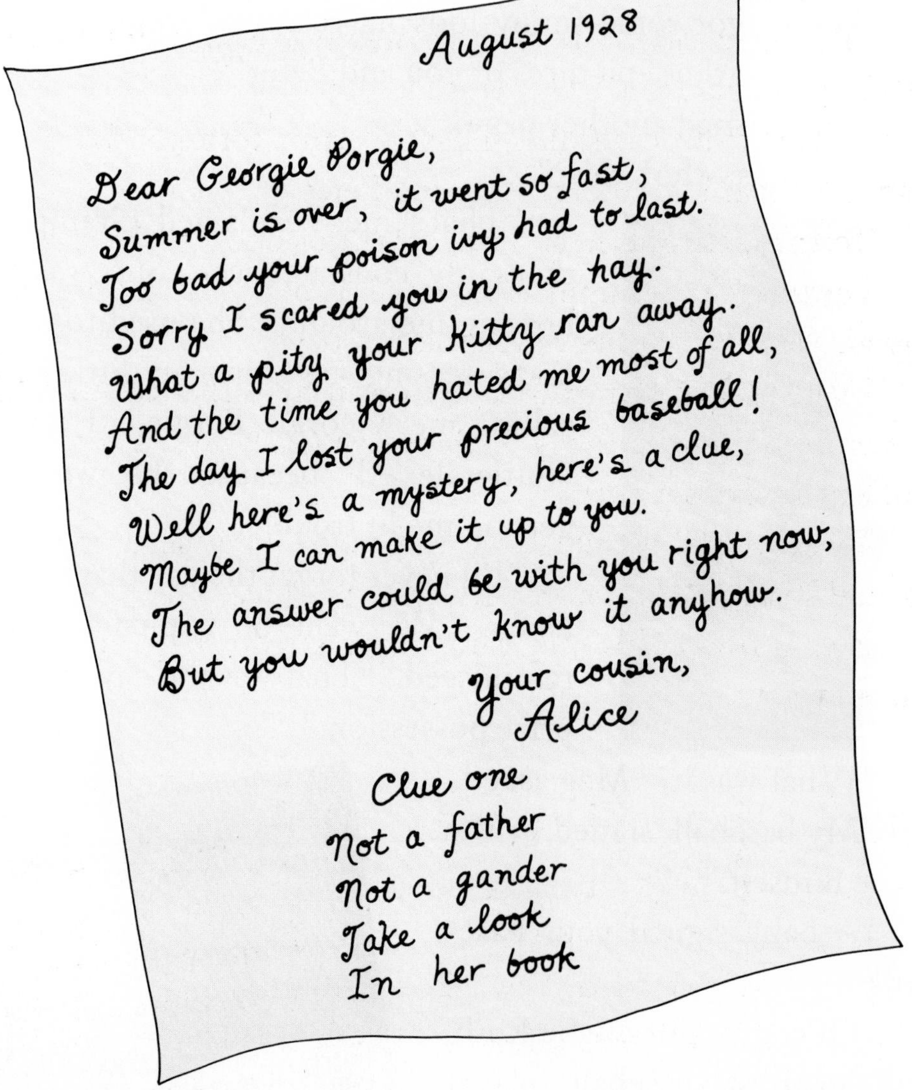
August 1928

Dear Georgie Porgie,
Summer is over, it went so fast,
Too bad your poison ivy had to last.
Sorry I scared you in the hay.
What a pity your kitty ran away.
And the time you hated me most of all,
The day I lost your precious baseball!
Well here's a mystery, here's a clue,
Maybe I can make it up to you.
The answer could be with you right now,
But you wouldn't know it anyhow.

Your cousin,
Alice

Clue one
Not a father
Not a gander
Take a look
In her book

"Hear that, Gramps? Maybe your baseball's not lost. Just follow the clue!" exclaimed Meg.

"I doubt it's that simple, Meg-O. Just another of her pranks. I saw that note years ago, but I couldn't make head nor tail of it," Gramps sighed.

"It's probably too old to make sense now," added Liddy.

"But it might really mean something. I've got to investigate," insisted Meg.

Just then the phone rang.

"Hey, Nut-Meg, Peter here. Remind Gramps that I'll be there in the morning."

"Take your time. I've found a mystery. Something to do with a Babe Ruth baseball," Meg teased.

"A Babe Ruth baseball? That's worth a fortune! Don't touch anything until I get there!" shouted Peter.

"Tough luck, Sherlock, I can solve this one myself. Bye."

Upstairs in Gramps's boyhood room, where Meg always stayed, she took out her notebook and pencil.

"Finally. The chance I've been waiting for!" Meg told Liddy. "Peter won't let me join his Detective Club until I have 'proof' that I can solve a mystery."

"Well, you'd better do it before he gets here tomorrow," warned Liddy. "He'll never give you a chance."

Meg knew Liddy was right. She sat down at the desk and started a list.

CLUE ONE
Not a father
Not a gander
Take a look
In her book
Not a father ?
brother
cousin
sister
baby
mother
Grandma
aunt
uncle ??
Not a gander?
duck
chick
geese
hen
duckling
goose
robin
rooster
Take a look
In her book ?

"Take a look in her book." Meg looked at the clue again. "Alice's diary? A nature book about birds?" She gazed up at the shelf of Gramps's old books.

"The Old Woman and the Little Red Hen," Liddy suggested as she squinted at the dusty titles. "Doesn't that fit?"

"I don't think so," said Meg, still jotting in her notebook. Suddenly she reached for a book. "I think I've got it!"

WHICH BOOK DID MEG REACH FOR?

"Not a father, that's mother. Not a gander, that's goose. The Mother Goose book!" Meg explained.

She carefully opened it.

"This is definitely Gramps's old book. We must be on the right track," Meg said. After a moment she added, "I think I know where to look."

WHICH RHYME DID MEG TURN TO?

"Georgie Porgie, pudding and pie . . ." said Meg.

"Kissed the girls and made them cry . . ." added Liddy as she twirled a pencil in her hair. "So?"

"Georgie Porgie. That's what Alice called Gramps," Meg reminded her. Sure enough there was a small note tucked tightly between the pages. Another clue!

"Little boy blue, come blow your horn," Meg recited.

"But what does a horn have to do with a baseball?" wondered Liddy.

"I don't know yet. First we have to find the horn. Let's see. Foghorn? Cow horn? Horn of plenty? Cape Horn?"

"Well, good luck with it. I have to get home," Liddy said.

Meg walked Liddy downstairs, then went to find Gramps.

"Gramps, did you ever play any musical instrument, like a French horn?"

"No, but I can sing a little. Why?" Gramps replied.

"I found another clue. Alice hid it in your old Mother Goose book, on the Georgie Porgie page. It has something to do with a horn."

"That's easy." Gramps grinned as he pointed to the bookshelf. Meg followed his finger to the old bugle there. She took it down to inspect it. She removed the mouthpiece, shook it, and peered inside with her flashlight. But no clue.

Gramps got up from the couch. "Well, my dear detective, it's time to turn in. I wouldn't get my hopes up over these clues. Old Alice, she was a sly one."

"Maybe this isn't going to be as easy as I thought," Meg whispered to Skip as they went upstairs to bed.

Meg checked her detective kit. Everything was in order — a magnifying glass, a pair of tweezers to pick up small clues, flashlight and extra batteries, tape measure, scissors, envelopes, and, of course, her detective notebook and pencils.

"I have to be sure to write everything down," she said to Skip as she got under the covers. "The tiniest fact can solve the biggest mystery. Track, write, decode, deduce . . . then I'll have plenty of proof to show Peter and his Detective Club." After a while she slid her notebook under her pillow and dozed off to sleep.

Yikes," shrieked Meg. "Stop! Please stop that awful noise!"

Gramps put the bugle down. "If you think that's bad, Meg-O, you should have heard your father play it. I got this bugle for him when he went to Scout Camp. He was a pitiful horn player. Ah well, rise and shine for breakfast."

When Meg got downstairs, Gramps was making pancakes. "All this talk about Alice reminds me of when we were kids. Once she challenged me to a pancake-eating contest. I ate sixteen, while she watched with a miserable grin on her face. When it was her turn, she ate three and forfeited the contest. She had decided from the start to let me win. All I won was a stomachache!" Gramps laughed. "Alice was always getting the best of me."

But Meg was only half listening. She was still puzzled over something Gramps had said earlier. Something had to be wrong with the horn clue.

WHAT WAS IT?

"Wait a minute!" Meg shouted. "Gramps, if you got this bugle for Dad when he was a kid, it *couldn't* be the right horn. It wasn't even *around* when Alice drummed up this whole mystery."

"Guess that's so," Gramps admitted sheepishly.

Meg looked at the clue again. "Whatever you do, don't blow this horn." Remembering another kind of horn, she raced into the living room.

"You wouldn't want to blow this horn, eh, Skip," Meg said as she took the old powder horn off the hook. She pulled off the cap. There was no powder inside, but there was something else. Meg took her tweezers out of her detective kit and slowly pulled out a small, tightly rolled piece of paper.

"I guess I'm not surprised that nobody has looked in there lately," said Gramps. "Maybe you really are onto something, Meg-O. What does it say?"

"I don't know. Does it mean anything to you, Gramps?"

"Never cared much for word puzzles myself," confessed Gramps, "but if you find one of those jigsaw puzzles with the pictures, I'll be glad to help you."

Meg shook her head and sighed. Peter would be arriving soon. She had to solve this mystery fast. Just then the back door slammed and Meg jumped.

"Whew, it's only you," Meg said with a sigh as Liddy came into the room.

"Only me? Only me might help you solve this," Liddy replied as she read the clue. "It looks like a secret-alphabet code. You know, when each letter stands for a different letter in the alphabet."

"Or maybe the letters in each word are just scrambled around," said Meg. She took out her notebook and began trying different combinations.

Before long the door slammed again. Peter was peering over their shoulders.

"Here's a clue for you, Nut-Meg, *drop it*!" Peter said. "I can have this solved in no time!"

"I found it, I followed it, and I'll finish it," protested Meg, covering her notes. But not quickly enough.

"What's this? A word puzzle? I could put it on my computer and have it decoded in a flash," Peter persisted. "What's it got to do with a Babe Ruth baseball, anyway?"

Meg snatched the clue back. "Don't bother. I've already figured it out with my own brainpower!"

And She Had. Have You?

"Well, what does it say?" asked Liddy, as Peter stomped out of the room. "I counted seven *E*'s, but what does that mean?"

"Nothing. It's not an alphabet code. It *is* a scrambled-letter code. The letters in each word are just mixed around."

"It says: 'Clue three little bo peep lost her' — her sheep, of course," said Meg.

"Why didn't I see that?" said Liddy, shutting the dictionary.

"Is it something to do with sheep's wool, or an old spinning wheel?" wondered Meg.

"Or a sheepskin?" suggested Liddy.

Meg and Liddy looked high and low. Meanwhile, Peter was eagerly searching the old photo albums, jotting down notes.

He was more nerve-racking than Alice and her crazy clues, thought Meg.

It wasn't until later in the afternoon, when Liddy had gone home, that Meg realized what the answer to the sheep clue was.

DO YOU KNOW WHERE BO PEEP'S LOST SHEEP CAN BE FOUND?

"Right in front of me all along," Meg sighed. She carefully unhooked the old painting. On the back, tucked tightly between the canvas and the frame, was another small note. But it had crumbled over time.

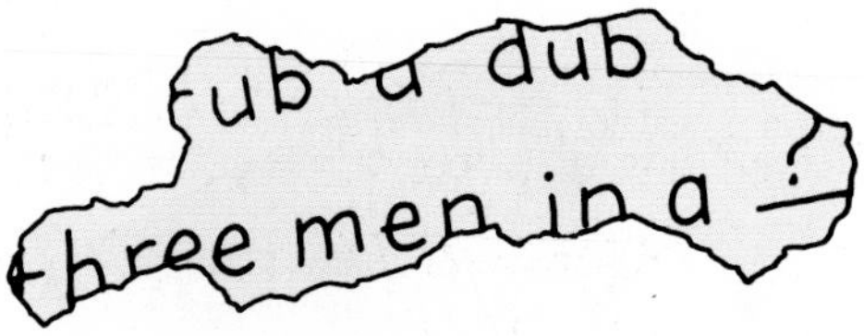

Meg wrote down what she could decipher.

"Aha! Another scrambled code," said Peter, and Meg jumped. She hadn't heard him come up behind her. "Wait until the guys see that baseball!"

"Stay out of this! You don't even know what it's all about," Meg answered. "Anyway, it's Gramps's baseball."

"I think I've got it unjumbled . . . B-U-D-D-H-A!" Peter raced to the statue in the living room.

But Meg knew he was wasting his time. Taking her notes with her, she slipped off to find the answer to the clue.

What Did The Clue Mean And Where Did Meg Look?

Peter was way off. It wasn't a scrambled-letter code at all. It was a line from another Mother Goose rhyme. Alice must have meant *tub*.

Meg was scouring the bathroom for clues when Gramps leaned in the door. "Sorry to disappoint you, Meg-O, but you won't find much here. You see, it's like the horn. This bathroom isn't as old as those clues."

"A new bathroom? Then where's the old one?" asked Meg.

"Well, we put a bathroom *in* the house, but we didn't take one *out*, so to speak. Back when I was a youngster, we just had an outhouse. We took baths in an old tub in the kitchen," Gramps said.

"This can't be a dead end," sighed Meg. "There's got to be a solution, after I've gotten this far."

"Alice was cunning," Gramps said.

Meg had to agree.

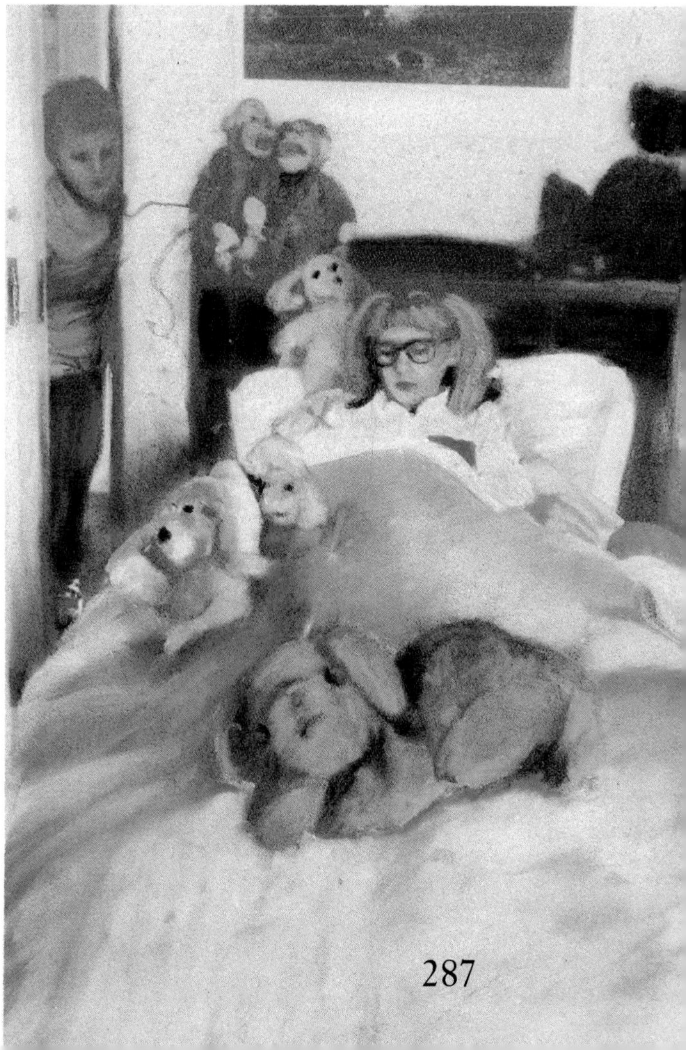

Later that night, Peter knocked on Meg's door. "Are you still sleeping with Gramps's old stuffed animals? A little babyish, don't you think? I gave up that pathetic old dog years ago."

"What do you really want, Peter?" Meg said suspiciously.

"Hey, Meggy, let's put our heads together on this mystery. I could help you out. For instance, the old outhouse, where Gramps keeps his gardening stuff now. I bet that has something to do with it. Well, see ya in the morning, Nut-Meg."

"I'd already thought of that," Meg said to herself, "but I'd better not wait until tomorrow to check it out. Peter might get there first." When she thought that Gramps and Peter were safely asleep, she pulled her raincoat and boots over her pajamas and tiptoed outside. The air was cool and the ground still damp from rain. Meg flicked on her flashlight and headed for the rickety old toolshed.

The flimsy door swung open. Meg spied a pile of tools and flowerpots and an old rain barrel. Was it an old washtub? It must be — there was a note wedged between the wooden slats! She pulled it out and opened it up.

But instead of reaching for the shovel, Meg sat back on her heels and thought. There was something funny about this clue.

HOW DID MEG KNOW?

HINT: THERE ARE FIVE TELLTALE SIGNS.

CAN YOU SPOT THEM ALL?

1. It was on lined paper. All the other clues were on unlined.
2. It was ripped out of a spiral notebook. None of the others were.
3. The handwriting slanted to the left. Alice's slanted to the right.
4. It said "Clue #4" — but Meg had already found the fourth clue.
5. It had nothing to do with Mother Goose rhymes.

Clearly, this was a fake clue. Someone was trying to throw her off the track. Meg was sure she knew who . . . and after looking around the toolshed again, she knew where.

Someone had been here recently. There were fresh, muddy footprints and the dust marks showed that the cabinet had been emptied. Ten to one, Peter was inside.

Meg picked up the shovel and scraped it around on the floor, pretending to dig. After a moment, she came up with the perfect plan to turn the tables on Peter.

"Yikes!" she said loudly. "Spiders — a whole nest of them! Come on, Skip, let's split!" She slammed the toolshed door behind her, then tiptoed around the side and peered through the window.

In a flash, Peter tumbled out of the cabinet and bolted back to the house.

Meg held her breath to keep from laughing. "I'm not scared of spiders," she said to herself, "but you-know-who is . . . Mr. Big-shot Detective! It serves him right for leaving that careless clue."

But, as she headed back to bed, she had to admit she was still no further along in solving the mystery. And time was running out. Mom and Dad would be picking them up the next day at noon.

In the morning, Gramps asked Meg to get some kindling for the wood cookstove. He kept it in a funny-shaped old metal bin. The old bathtub!

Meg searched the old tub for a clue, but there was no note, not a scrap of paper.

"Rats! How else could Alice have left a clue?" wondered Meg as she stirred figure eights in her oatmeal. Gramps always gave her huge spoons. This one had a fancy big *M* engraved on it.

As Meg stared at the spoon, she suddenly had an idea of how a message could have been left.

Just as she suspected, there was something scratched on the bottom of the tub:

"Another clue!" Meg exclaimed. This one looked too authentic to be one of Peter's tricks.

"Gramps, did you have any dogs when you were little?" Meg asked.

"Oh, yes," he replied, "probably a dozen or so. Let's see, there was Nippy and Nicky and Lucky and Flippy and twice as many cats. Gosh, we had a lot of pets — ducks, pigs, ponies, even a parrot."

Then the phone rang. It was Liddy.

"What's happening with the mystery?" she asked.

"Can't talk now," Meg whispered as she noticed Peter at the top of the stairs.

"Is that Lydia-the-Encyclopedia on the phone? Tell her I've got this case just about wrapped up," Peter said as he came down the stairs and glanced over Meg's shoulder. "So what's this latest clue?"

"It has something to do with Little Miss Muffet," Meg teased, "and the spider that sat down beside her, you know, scaring Miss Muffet away!"

"What are you talking about?" said Liddy. "Whatever you do, don't let him get it."

"Don't worry, he's bluffing." Meg hung up. She hoped she was right and that this wasn't all a wild-goose chase. She had some deducing of her own to do — fast. Her only hope was to go back to the beginning.

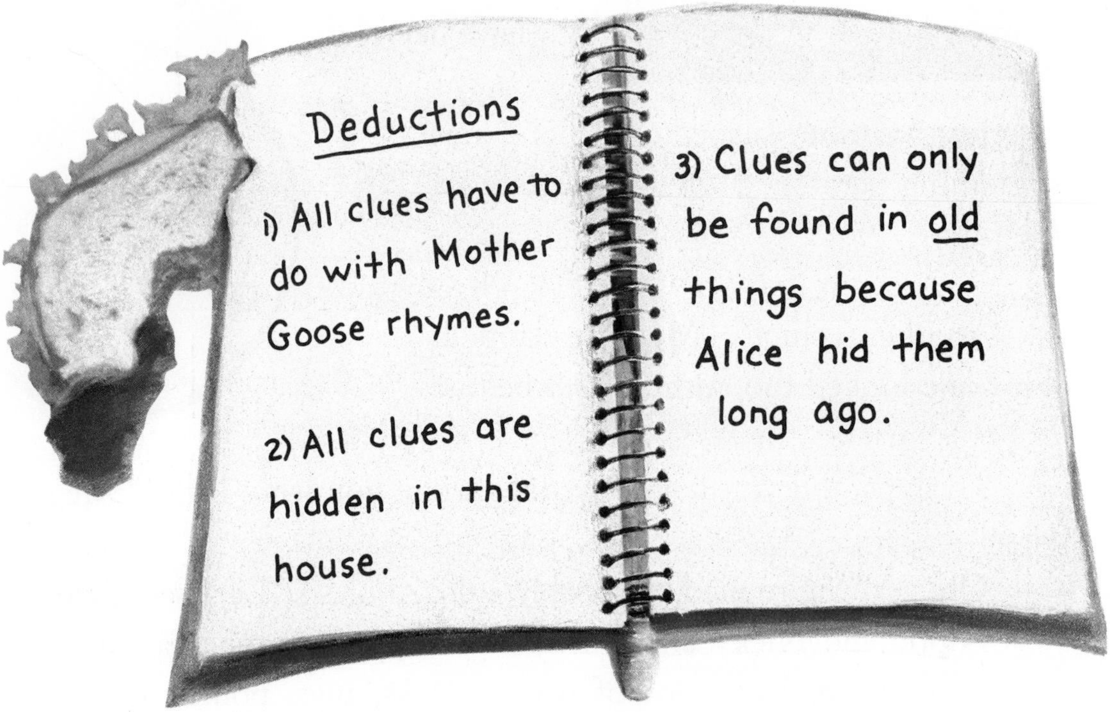

Deductions
1) All clues have to do with Mother Goose rhymes.
2) All clues are hidden in this house.
3) Clues can only be found in old things because Alice hid them long ago.

Meg studied the old clues, then looked at the new one. "'The little dog laughed.' If I'm right, it's part of a Mother Goose rhyme, too. And I think I know which one."

WHICH NURSERY RHYME WAS IT?

Meg found the rhyme in Gramp's Mother Goose book.

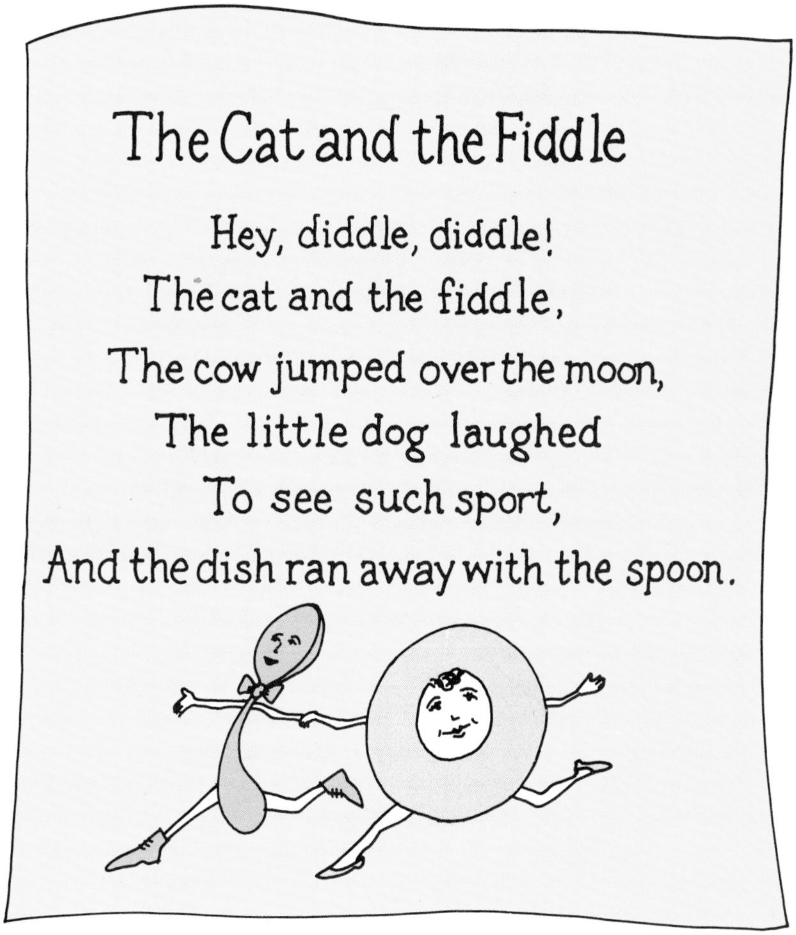
The Cat and the Fiddle
Hey, diddle, diddle!
The cat and the fiddle,
The cow jumped over the moon,
The little dog laughed
To see such sport,
And the dish ran away with the spoon.

"This could lead anywhere! Cat, fiddle, cow, moon, dish, or spoon?" Meg tried not to panic. She took out the old photo of Gramps and Alice that had started her on this investigation and reread Alice's letter and clues.

Peter had been upstairs and down, rummaging through all sorts of old stuff. Was he really onto something and was she the one off the track?

Meg was determined to solve the mystery. And as she stared at the photo and clue, it all fell into place.

WHAT WAS THE ANSWER?

Meg ran to her bedroom. Safely tucked under the covers was the old stuffed animal that had once belonged to Gramps. The old toy dog. It was the same one that was in the photograph, the one Peter had teased Meg about.

"The little dog laughed," Meg said to herself. "Of course! 'The answer could be with you right now, but you wouldn't know it anyhow' . . . just as Alice said in the letter."

Meg looked at the old toy intently. He was musty and worn. His body was very hard, stuffed with straw.

On his back was a loose thread. It was a different color, as if someone had tried to mend a seam but hadn't done a very good job.

Meg carefully pulled the thread. Sure enough, deep inside the old straw was something you'd never expect to find in an old doggie doll.

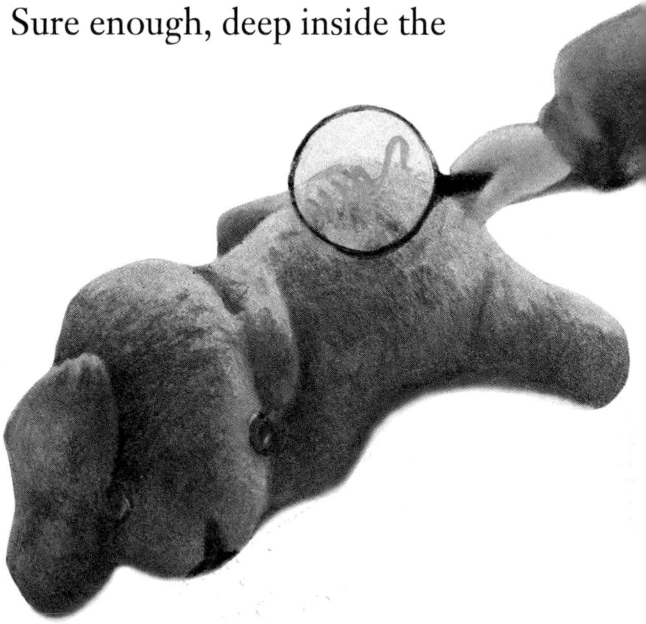

The baseball. Just as she had hoped! There was one final note with it, but Meg decided to let Gramps read it.

"What's this?" He woke with a start. "I must be dreaming. My baseball? It couldn't be!"

"It is," said Meg.

"It's what?" Peter burst in.

"It's my Babe Ruth baseball, long lost, and now Meg has found it," Gramps said with a big grin.

"That's right," said Meg. "Alice hid the ball in your old toy dog. With all that hard stuffing, no one ever noticed. She left the Mother Goose clues to help you track it down."

"Amazing," said Gramps.

"Amazing all right," grumbled Peter. "She just got lucky fooling around with those old baby toys."

"Sometimes he reminds me of someone, but I don't know who." Gramps winked at Meg.

"Maybe this will help you remember. It's a note from you-know-who," Meg said, winking back.

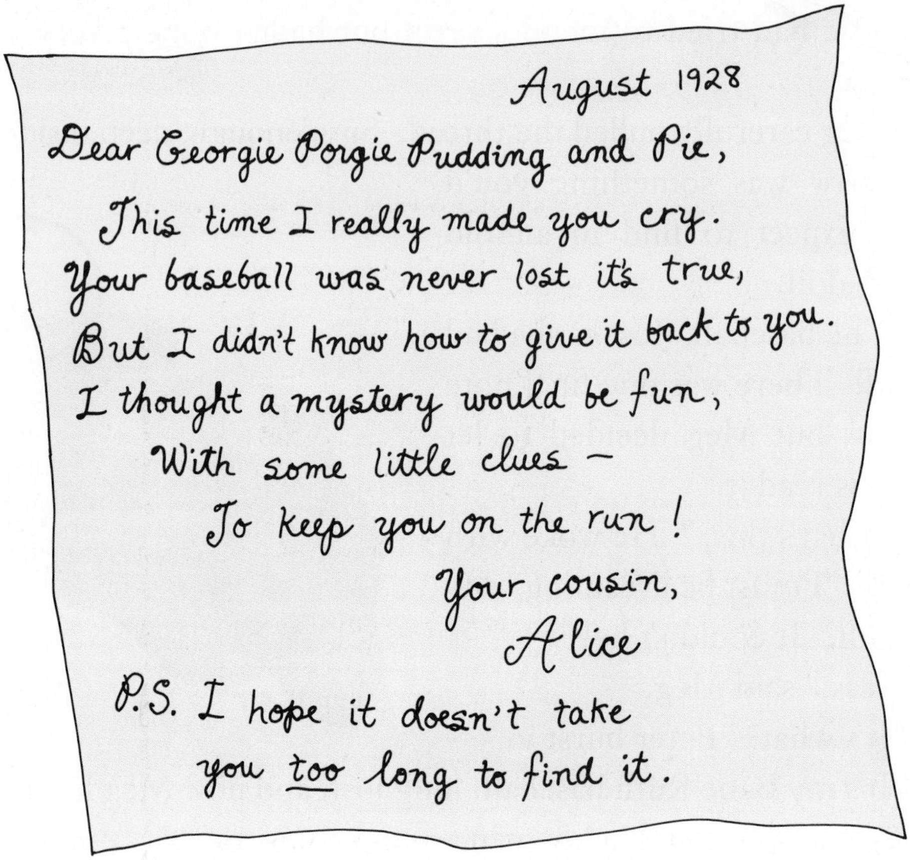

August 1928

Dear Georgie Porgie Pudding and Pie,

This time I really made you cry.
Your baseball was never lost it's true,
But I didn't know how to give it back to you.
I thought a mystery would be fun,
With some little clues –
To keep you on the run!

Your cousin,
Alice

P.S. I hope it doesn't take
you too long to find it.

"Not *too* long," said Gramps. "Only over fifty years! Wait until I call her and tell her the game is up! And Peter, you be sure to tell everybody back at the Detective Club how Meg-O the supersleuth cracked the case."

Peter groaned. "Oh, all right." Then he even smiled a little.

They heard Mom and Dad's car pull into the driveway. "And solved not a moment too soon," Meg said as she hugged Gramps good-bye.

"You'd better take this along for 'proof,'" Gramps replied, tossing her the baseball.

"Did you catch that, Peter?" Meg laughed. "Wait till the Detective Club sees this!"

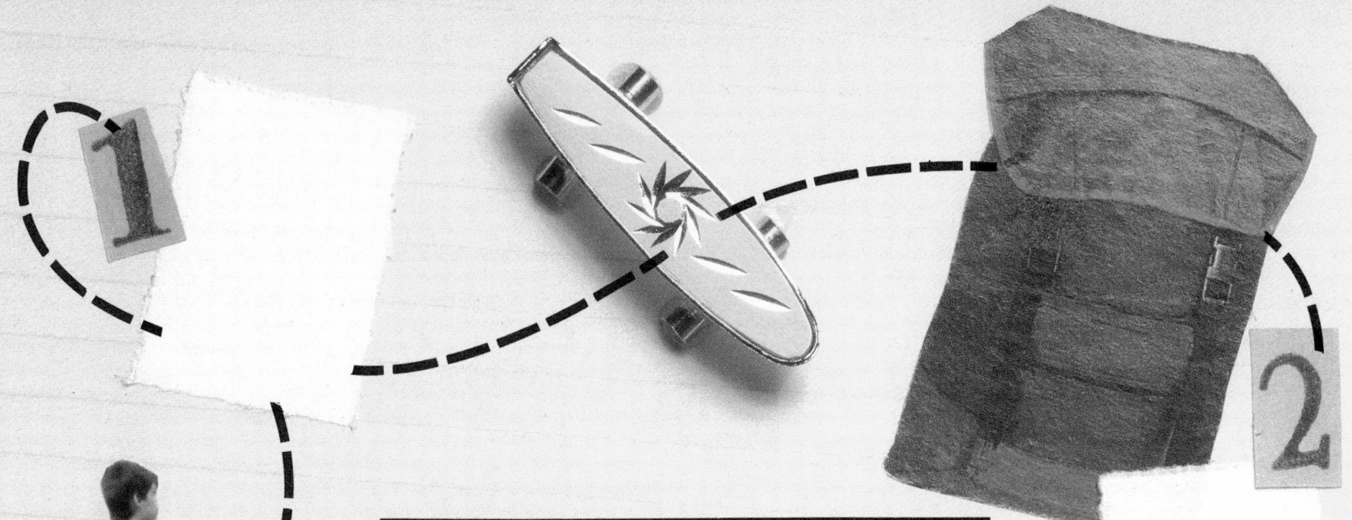

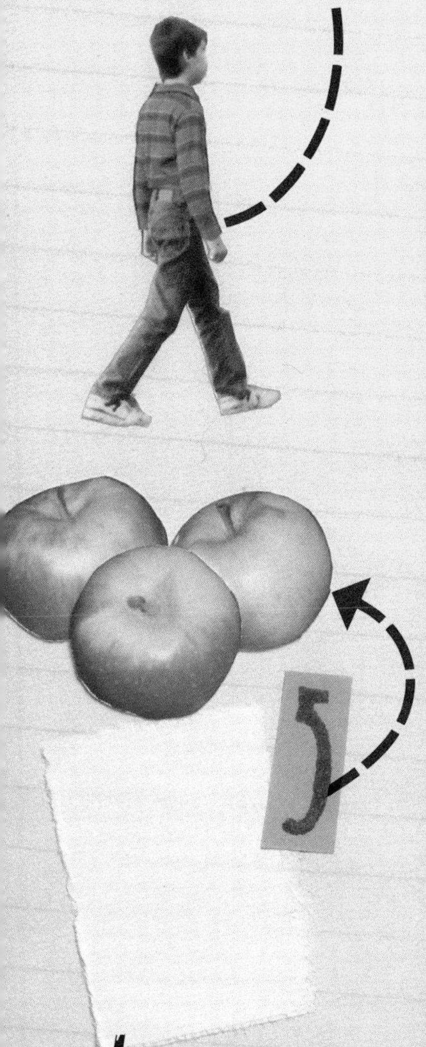

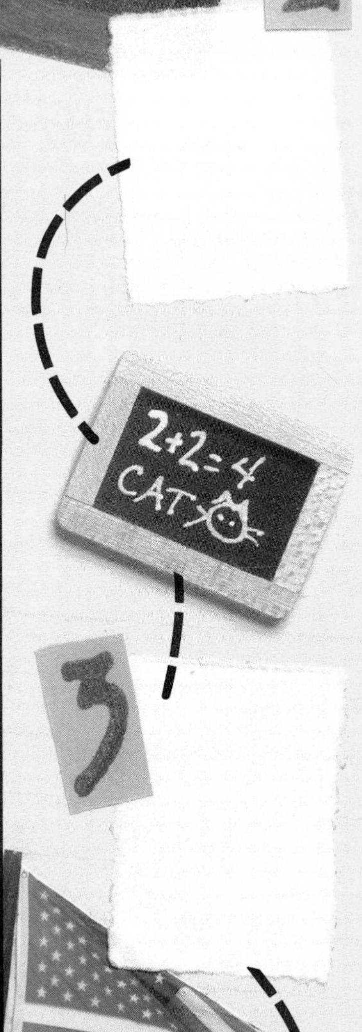

FOLLOW THOSE CLUES

Hide an object somewhere in your classroom. Then write a list of clues that tell your classmates how to find it. Remember that one clue should lead to the next one until the lost item is found.

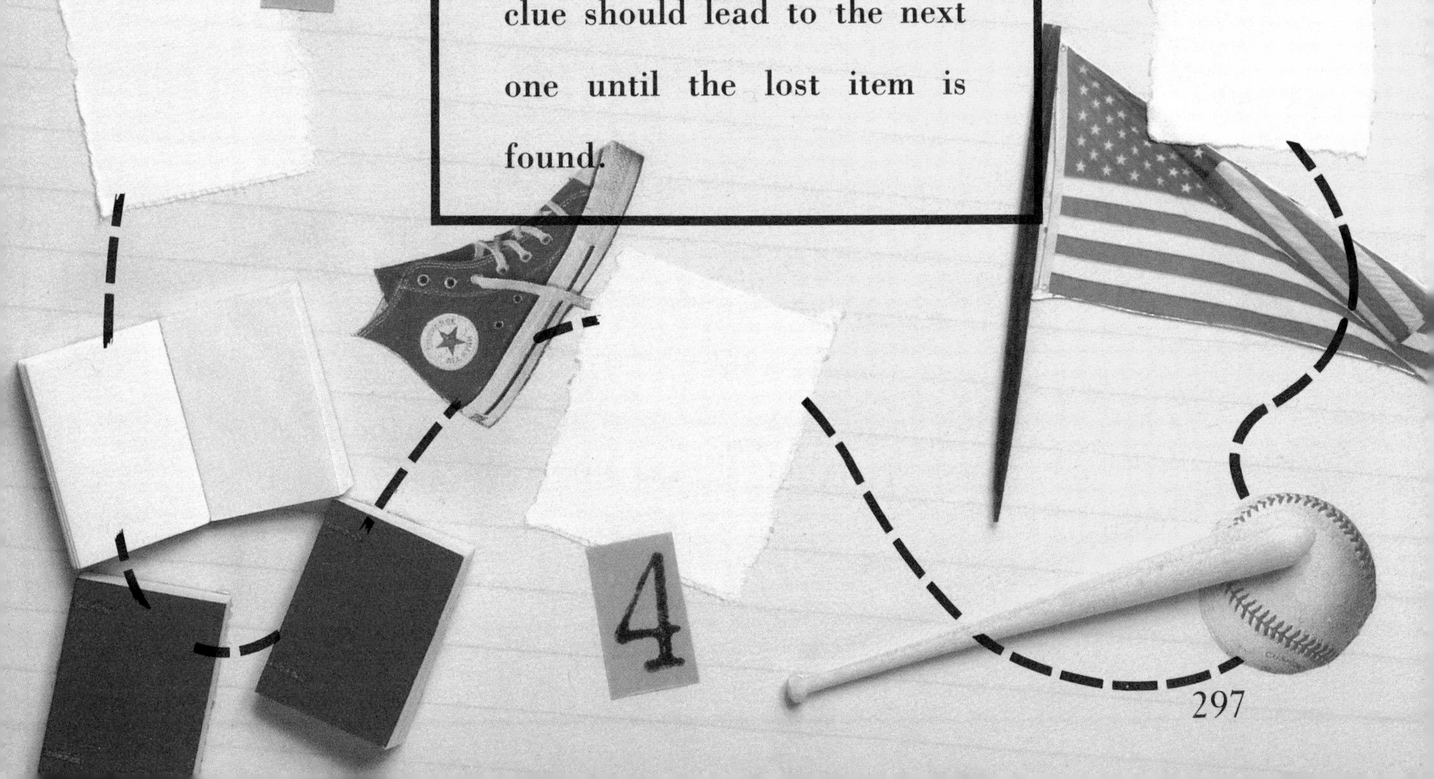

TEST YOUR POWERS OF OBSERVATION

Good detectives have to be very observant. That means they can look at the scene of a crime and see things that most people would miss.

Here's your chance to test your powers of observation. Look carefully at these two pictures. Can you spot at least twenty differences between them?

PADDINGTON TURNS DETECTIVE

From Paddington On Stage

Adapted by Michael Bond and Alfred Bradley ♦ Illustrated by Peggy Fortnum

CAST OF CHARACTERS

Mr. Brown
Mrs. Brown
Mrs. Bird
Paddington
Mr. Gruber
Policeman
Mr. Curry
Judy
Jonathan

PROPS

In the Browns' sitting room:
Table, chairs, etc.
Paddington's hat
Torch
Sandwich
Plastic clothes line
Battery
Pillowcase
Lantern

In Mr. Gruber's shop:
Chairs, bric-a-brac, etc.
Book
Cardboard box containing a magnifying glass, whistle, some small bottles, a pad of paper, and a false beard (could be made of yarn or cotton wool)
Large old coat

At Paddington Station:
Luggage and parcels
"Paddington Station" sign
Jar of marmalade
Photo-frame with picture of Aunt Lucy (with glass, if possible)

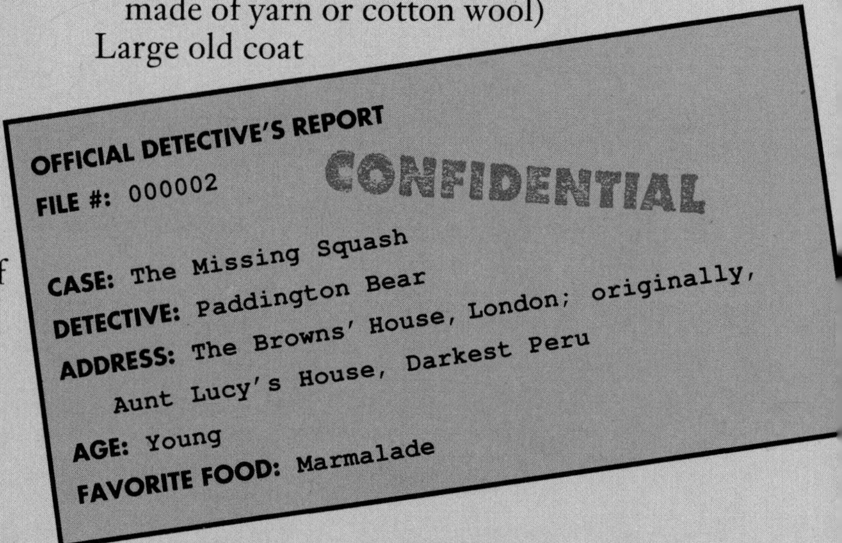

OFFICIAL DETECTIVE'S REPORT
CONFIDENTIAL
FILE #: 000002
CASE: The Missing Squash
DETECTIVE: Paddington Bear
ADDRESS: The Browns' House, London; originally, Aunt Lucy's House, Darkest Peru
AGE: Young
FAVORITE FOOD: Marmalade

SCENE 1

(The Browns' sitting room. Mr. and Mrs. Brown *are talking.)*

Mr. Brown: I can't think who would do a thing like that.

Mrs. Brown: Nor can I, Henry, it's never happened before.

Mr. Brown: I suppose it's too late to do anything about it now. It's very disappointing.

Mrs. Bird *(Coming in from the kitchen)*: What's the matter, Mr. Brown?

Mr. Brown: Someone's stolen my prize squash.

Mrs. Bird: When did that happen?

Mr. Brown: I don't know for sure. It was there on Wednesday. They must have stolen it during the night.

Mrs. Bird *(After exchanging a look with* Mrs. Brown*)*: Well, you've got several more.

*(*Paddington *comes in.)*

Mr. Brown: That isn't the point.

Paddington: Good morning, everybody.

Mrs. Bird: Good morning, Paddington.

Paddington: Is anything the matter, Mr. Brown?

Mr. Brown: Somebody has stolen my prize squash. I've several more, of course, but they'll never be ready in time for the show.

Paddington: Oh, dear! I'm sorry to hear that, Mr. Brown.

Mr. Brown: It's the biggest I've ever grown. I felt I was sure to win a prize. I've a good mind to offer a reward to anybody who tracks down the culprit.

(A thoughtful look comes into Paddington*'s eye and he makes for the door.)*

Mrs. Brown: Aren't you having any breakfast this morning, Paddington?

Paddington: No, thank you, Mrs. Brown. I want to see Mr. Gruber about something.

Mrs. Brown: What's that?

Paddington: I'm not sure until I see him. *(He puts on his hat and goes.)*

Mr. Brown: *Now* what has he got on his mind?

Mrs. Bird: I don't know, but I noticed a funny look came into his eyes when you mentioned a reward . . .

SCENE 2

(Mr. Gruber's shop. Mr. Gruber *puts down the book he is reading as* Paddington *comes in.)*

Paddington: Good morning, Mr. Gruber.

Mr. Gruber: Good morning, Mr. Brown. You're early today. It's only ten o'clock.

Paddington: Yes. I've got a problem and I wondered if you could help me.

Mr. Gruber: I'll do my best. Tell me about it.

Paddington: It's a flashing light.

Mr. Gruber: A flashing light?

Paddington: In the garden at Number thirty-two, Windsor Gardens — and Mr. Brown's squash.

Mr. Gruber: You'd better begin at the beginning.

Paddington: Yes, I suppose I had. You see, I've got a new torch[1] and last night, when I was in bed, I shone it at the window by mistake. Then I noticed that somebody was flashing a light outside in the garden — like a signal. So I flashed my light on and off three times and the light outside the window flashed three times as well.

---

[1]**torch:** A flashlight.

Mr. Gruber: What did you do?

Paddington: I pulled the bedclothes over my head and went to sleep!

Mr. Gruber: I see.

Paddington: Then, when I came down to breakfast this morning, Mr. Brown told me that somebody had stolen his prize squash.

Mr. Gruber: And you think that the two things are connected?

Paddington: That's right, and I thought I would like to catch whoever it is. Not just for the reward . . .

Mr. Gruber *(Twinkling)*: Oh, there's a reward, is there?

Paddington *(Casually)*: Mr. Brown did mention it. Do you remember that book you showed me once about the famous detective?

Mr. Gruber: Sherlock Holmes? Yes.

Paddington: I would like to be able to catch criminals like he did. But I may need to disguise myself. It'll make things a lot easier.

Mr. Gruber: I think I can help you there, Mr. Brown. *(He takes down a cardboard box.)* Somebody sold this to me a long time ago. You can borrow it if you like.

Paddington *(Reading from the lid of the box)*: Master Detective's Disguise Outfit. Thank you very much, Mr. Gruber. May I look inside?

Mr. Gruber: Of course.

Paddington: It looks very interesting. *(He takes out a magnifying glass.)* What's this, Mr. Gruber?

Mr. Gruber: That's a magnifying glass to look for clues.

Paddington: Very useful. And here's a police-whistle and some bottles and a pad.

Mr. Gruber: They're for fingerprints and one of the bottles is full of invisible ink.

Paddington: And a beard! Just what I need.

Mr. Gruber: Here. Try this old coat. It may be a bit big.

(Paddington *slips it on. It trails behind him.)*

Paddington: Thank you very much, Mr. Gruber. *(He hooks the beard over his ears.)* How's that?

Mr. Gruber: Splendid!

Paddington *(Putting his bush hat on)*: I don't think anybody will recognize me now.

Mr. Gruber *(As Doctor Watson)*: Do you think it will be a difficult crime to solve, Mr. Holmes?

Paddington: On the contrary, elementary, my dear Watson. *(He tucks the disguise outfit under his arm and sails out.)*

SCENE 3

(The living room at Number thirty-two, Windsor Gardens. There is a knock on the door. Mrs. Bird *goes to answer it.)*

Paddington *(In a deep voice)*: Good morning.

Mrs. Bird: Oh, hello, Paddington. I didn't expect you back so quickly.

Paddington: I'm not Paddington, Mrs. Bird. I'm Sherlock Holmes — the famous detective.

Mrs. Bird: Yes dear. Don't forget to wipe your feet.

Mrs. Brown *(Coming in from the kitchen)*: Is Paddington back already? I thought he would be having his elevenses[2] with Mr. Gruber.

Mrs. Bird: He's up to something, but I don't know what. He's just come back in a long overcoat, hidden behind a beard like Father Christmas, and he looked very thoughtful.

---

[2]**elevenses:** A light lunch.

Mrs. Brown: Oh, dear! Something always happens when he's like that.

*(*Paddington *enters minus his disguise.)*

Paddington: Hullo, Mrs. Brown.

Mrs. Brown: Hallo, Paddington.

Paddington: I wonder if I could have a new battery for my torch?

Mrs. Brown: Is the other one flat already?

Paddington: Yes. I've had to use it rather a lot lately.

Mrs. Brown: Here you are.

Paddington: Thank you very much, Mrs. Brown. *(He goes into the hall.)*

Mrs. Bird: I wonder why he needs his torch?

*(*Paddington *comes back suddenly, making them jump.)*

Paddington: Mrs. Brown, do you happen to have some rope I could borrow?

Mrs. Brown: I don't think I have any rope but I've a plastic clothes line. Would that be any good?

Paddington *(Gravely)*: That would do very well.

Mrs. Bird: Here you are. *(Gives him the clothes line.)*

Paddington: Thank you. *(He goes into the hall again.)*

Mrs. Bird: And what does he need those things for?

Mrs. Brown: I shudder to think.

Paddington *(Coming back suddenly again)*: There's just one more thing.

Mrs. Bird *(Wearily)*: Yes, Paddington?

Paddington: I wonder if I could take my elevenses to my room today. I'm not very hungry at the moment, and I may feel like a marmalade sandwich later.

Mrs. Brown: Here you are, all ready and waiting for you. *(She hands him the sandwiches on a plate.)*

Paddington: Thank you very much. *(He goes off as* Mrs. Brown *and* Mrs. Bird *shake their heads in amazement. After a moment they go off too.)*

(Blackout. After a moment the alarm clock sounds in the distance.)

Paddington *(Yawns as he enters)*: Midnight, that's the best time to catch criminals. *(He switches on his torch and shines it through the window.)* Nothing there, but I'd better be prepared. *(He puts on his beard, overcoat and hat and picks up his case.)* I'll go and hide in the greenhouse.

(He goes off. A moment later, a shadowy figure appears at the front of the stage. He is carrying a lantern, but is muffled up in a scarf so we don't see his face. As he reaches the front door, Paddington *comes along carrying the clothes line and pillowcase.*

The figure walks away and Paddington *creeps up behind him. The figure turns round suddenly, but* Paddington *ducks and isn't noticed. The next time the figure turns away,* Paddington *seizes his opportunity, pops the pillowcase and lassoo over his head and runs round him with the clothes line, pinning his arms to his sides so that he can't remove the pillowcase. When he is secured,* Paddington *blows his whistle.)*

Paddington: It's no good struggling. You've met your match! *(The figure answers with a muffled snort and struggles to get free.)* Be quiet, you will have your chance to speak when the police get here. *(*Paddington *leads him indoors just as the* Policeman *arrives on the scene.)*

Policeman: Hullo. Hullo. What's going on here?

Paddington: Good evening, Officer, that was quick.

Policeman: I just happened to be passing, sir, and I heard your whistle. What's the trouble?

Paddington: I've captured a burglar! I think he's the one who took Mr. Brown's squash.

Policeman: Mr. Brown's squash?

Paddington: That's right. I thought I saw a flashing light. Then I saw a shadowy figure. I couldn't see his face but from the way he walked, I'm sure it had a nasty look on it.

Policeman: Well sir, let's see, shall we? I'll switch the light on. *(He switches on the light and then jerks the rope which* Paddington *has been holding. The figure spins round until he comes to the end of it. The* Policeman *undoes the lassoo and the figure wrenches the pillowcase from his head.)*

Paddington: Oh, dear! *(He puts his torch down.)*

Mr. Curry: What is the meaning of this assault?

Policeman *(To* Paddington*)*: You were right. He *has* got a nasty look on his face. You are accused of acting in a suspicious manner.

Mr. Curry: Suspicious manner! I was going about my own business.

Policeman: At midnight? With a lantern?

Mr. Curry: I happen to collect moths and the light of the lantern attracts them. *(He suddenly sees* Paddington.*)* Bear! I might have known you would be at the bottom of this.

Paddington: I'm sorry, Mr. Curry. *(He takes off his beard.)*

Mr. Curry: Not as sorry as you will be!

Policeman: Hmmm. And what were you doing prowling round the house in disguise, young fellow-me-bear?

*(*Mr. and Mrs. Brown, *awakened by the din, come onstage.)*

Policeman: Unless you can explain yourself . . .

Mr. Brown: Whatever is the matter?

Paddington: Well, I'm afraid it's a bit complicated. You see, it all happened because of your squash, Mr. Brown . . . the one you were getting ready for the show. I was trying to catch the thief.

Mr. Brown: I don't see how my squash has anything to do with this noise.

Mrs. Brown: I think I'm beginning to understand . . . Paddington was trying to catch the person who took it. But I'm afraid he didn't stand a chance.

Policeman: Why not, madam?

Mrs. Brown: I was going to tell you sooner or later, Henry. It's my fault really, you see . . . I cut your squash by mistake!

Mr. Brown: You did? You cut my prize squash?

Mrs. Brown: Well, I didn't realize it was your prize one. And you know how fond you are of stuffed squash. We had it for dinner on Thursday.

Mr. Brown: We had it for dinner? How could you?

Policeman: Here, not so fast, sir, I can't get it all down. Has anybody else anything to say?

Mr. Curry: Yes, I have. I demand that this bear is punished. Springing out on an innocent member of the public. I shall demand damages.

*(*Paddington *is very unhappy at the trouble that he has caused. He decides to creep quietly away before anybody notices.)*

Policeman *(To* Mr. Brown*)*: What do you say to that, sir?

Mr. Brown: As my squash seems to have caused all this trouble, perhaps I had better try to find a solution to the problem. This morning I promised a reward to anybody who found out who took the squash. Now, through you, Mr. Curry, we have actually found the culprit. *(*Mrs. Brown *looks guilty.)* Suppose I gave the reward to *you.* Would that satisfy you?

Mr. Curry: Well, I don't know . . .

Mr. Brown: Say five pounds?

Mr. Curry *(After a moment's hesitation)*: Very well, but it mustn't happen again. And I demand an apology.

Mr. Brown: I'm sure Paddington didn't mean any harm, but, of course, he will apologize.

Mrs. Brown: Where is he?

*(*Judy *and* Jonathan, *who have appeared by this time, begin to look for him.)*

Mrs. Bird *(Enters)*: Whatever is going on here?

Judy: It's Paddington. He's missing.

Jonathan: He isn't in his room. I've just looked in there.

Judy: And all his things have gone.

Jonathan: His suitcase . . .

Judy: His clothes . . . and his picture of Aunt Lucy . . .

Jonathan: Everything!

Mrs. Brown: Where on earth can he have got to?

Mr. Brown: There's only one thing for it, we must organize a search party. *(He picks up the torch.)*

Mrs. Brown: But where can we look? We don't even know where to start.

Mrs. Bird *(Grimly, as she puts on her coat)*: I do . . . follow me. If you want my opinion, there isn't a moment to lose. *(*Mrs. Bird *hurries out followed by the rest of the family.)*

Mr. Curry: Hey! Hold on! Wait for me! *(He hurries after them.)*

SCENE 4

(Paddington Station. It is set with luggage and parcels. There is an announcement over the tannoy[3] *"The train about to leave from Platform One is the Boat-train Special." A Guard's whistle sounds. The* Browns *rush across stage, but the train is already moving off. A moment later they walk sadly back on.)*

Judy: Too late!

---

[3]**tannoy:** A loudspeaker.

Mr. Brown: We don't *know* he was on it.

Jonathan: I bet he was. I bet Mrs. Bird was right.

Judy: She usually is. Besides, you heard what they said . . .

Jonathan: It was the Boat-train Special!

Mrs. Brown: Goodness knows where he'll end up.

Mrs. Bird (*Following on behind*): If only I'd thought of it before.

Judy: Can't we ring up the station at the other end?

Mr. Brown: We can. But knowing Paddington, he might get off anywhere.

Mrs. Bird: Things just won't be the same without that bear.

Mr. Brown: You can say that again! *(He turns to leave, and as he does so,* Paddington *pops up from behind the parcels and raises his hat.* Mr. Brown *sees him and shines the torch in his direction.)* Paddington!

Paddington: Hullo, Mr. Brown.

The Browns *(Chorus)*: Paddington!

Judy: You didn't go after all!

Paddington: I did. But I missed the train. I seem to cause so much trouble that I thought you wouldn't want me to stay any more, so I thought I'd better go back to Darkest Peru. *(He reaches behind the parcels and takes a jar of marmalade, which he puts in his suitcase. Then he holds up his picture of Aunt Lucy.)* I haven't even had time to pack properly.

Mrs. Brown: Not want you to stay?

Mrs. Bird: Of course, we want you to stay.

Judy: Even Mr. Curry wants you to stay. Don't you, Mr. Curry?

Mr. Curry: Well, er . . . Hmmmmmmmph.

Mr. Brown *(Waving his torch in the direction of Paddington's photograph frame as he talks)*: Besides, if you go, who's going to eat all the marmalade?

Mrs. Bird: Exactly! The cupboard's full.

Paddington *(Peering at the glass on the photograph excitedly)*: Would you mind doing that again, Mr. Brown?

Mr. Brown: Do what again?

Paddington: Wave your torch about.

Mr. Brown: You mean . . . like that? *(He repeats the action.)*

Paddington: That's it! That's what I saw the other night! Oh, dear!

Judy: Can anyone join in?

Jonathan: Or is it a secret?

Paddington: It's a reflection, Mr. Brown. You see, when I shone that torch at my bedroom window the other night, I thought I saw someone signaling back at me. Only it wasn't . . . I thought it was the man who'd stolen your squash. But it must have been the reflection from my own torch all the time . . .

Mrs. Brown *(Looks at the others)*: Paddington . . .

Paddington: Yes, Mrs. Brown?

Mrs. Brown: You're incorrigible!

Paddington *(Hotly)*: I'm not, Mrs. Brown. I'm a bear!

Judy: And a jolly good bear at that. *(She takes his paw.)*

Jonathan: Hear! Hear! *(Nudges* Judy, *takes* Paddington*'s other paw, and together they lift him onto a box.)*

(Cue for song. Jonathan *and* Judy *lead the others into "For He's a Jolly Good Bear Cub" as the play ends.)*

CURTAIN

Dear Aunt Lucy...

Aunt Lucy is probably wondering how Paddington is doing. Write a letter to Aunt Lucy as Paddington would write it. Tell her all about the case of the missing squash.

The Browns' House
London, England
Dear Aunt Lucy,
I think my career
as a detective is over.
It all began when

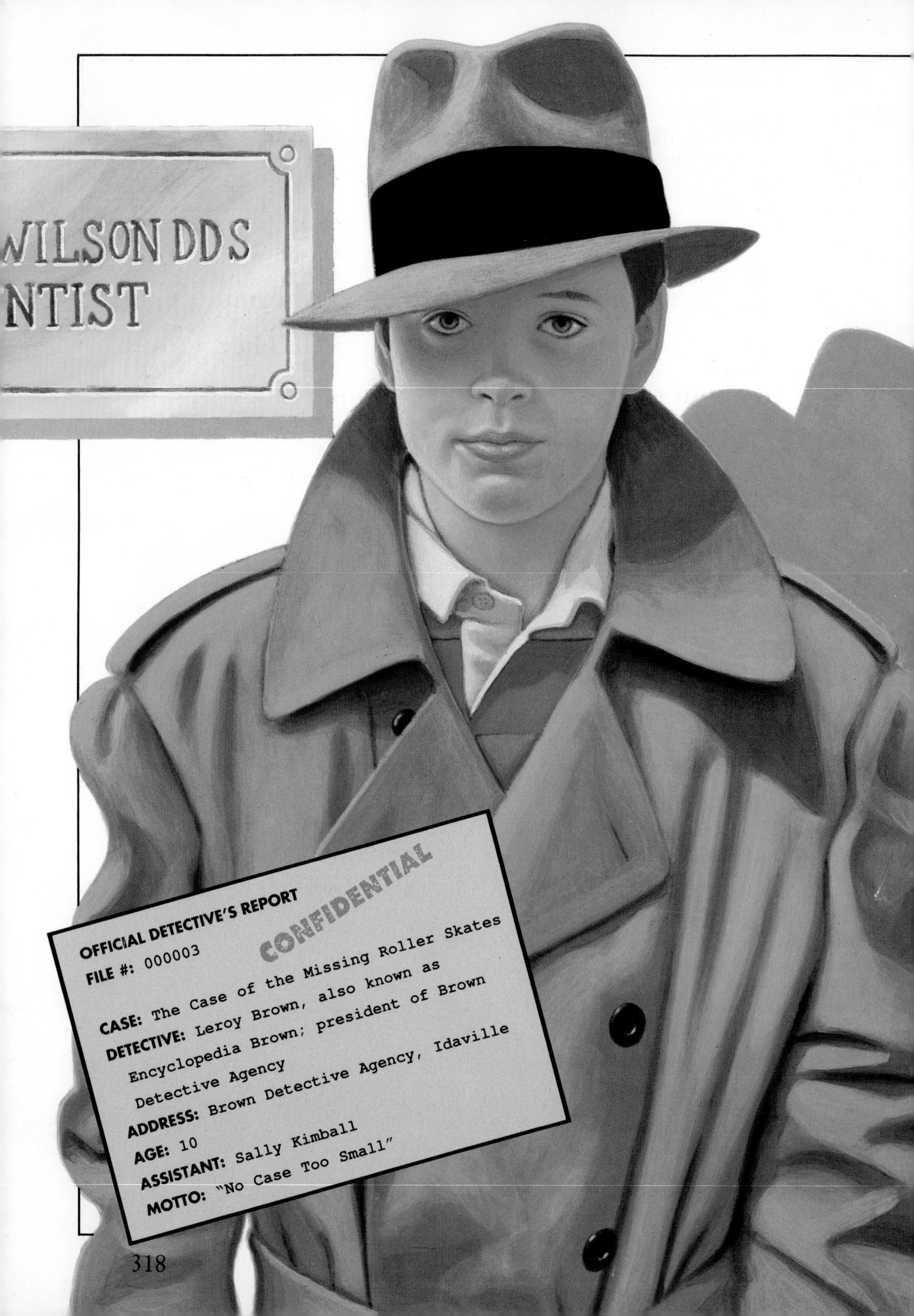
WILSON DDS
NTIST
OFFICIAL DETECTIVE'S REPORT
CONFIDENTIAL
FILE #: 000003
CASE: The Case of the Missing Roller Skates
DETECTIVE: Leroy Brown, also known as Encyclopedia Brown; president of Brown Detective Agency
ADDRESS: Brown Detective Agency, Idaville
AGE: 10
ASSISTANT: Sally Kimball
MOTTO: "No Case Too Small"

From

ENCYCLOPEDIA BROWN:

Boy Detective

by Donald J. Sobol
illustrated by Paul Van Munching

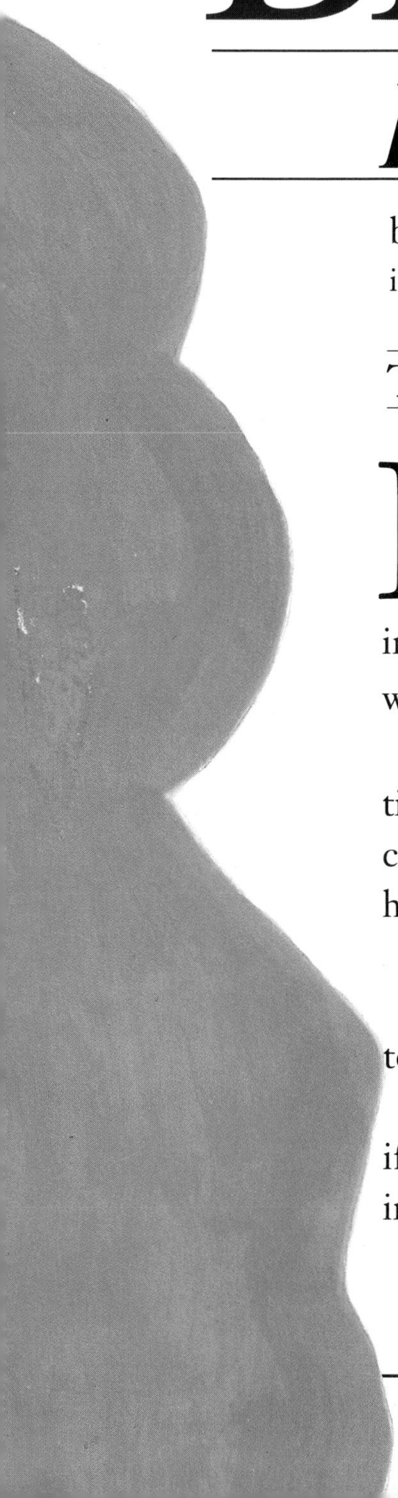

The Case of the Missing Roller Skates

Between nine and nine-thirty on Tuesday morning Sally Kimball's roller skates disappeared from the waiting room in Dr. Vivian Wilson's office.

And where was Encyclopedia Brown, boy detective? He was not ten feet away from the scene of the crime. He was sitting in a chair, with his eyes shut and his mouth wide open!

In a way, he had an excuse.

Dr. Wilson was pulling one of Encyclopedia's teeth.

"There!" said Dr. Wilson. He said it cheerfully, as if he were handing Encyclopedia an ice cream cone instead of a tooth.

"Ugh!" said Encyclopedia.

Dr. Wilson said, "All right. Hop down from the chair."

Encyclopedia hopped down and put the tooth in his pocket. He was going to give it to Charlie Stewart, who collected teeth and kept them in a flowered cookie jar.

Encyclopedia went into the waiting room. The chair on which he had left Sally's roller skates was empty!

He looked behind the chair. He dropped to his knees and looked under the chair.

"The skates — they're gone!" he exclaimed.

"Are you sure you brought them with you?" asked Dr. Wilson.

"I'm sure," answered Encyclopedia. "They were broken. I fixed them last night for my partner, Sally Kimball. I was going to take them over to her house on my way home from your office."

Dr. Wilson shook his head sadly. "I'm afraid you will never get them back."

But Dr. Wilson knew nothing about detective work. Encyclopedia liked the dentist, though he felt that Vivian was a better first name for a woman than a man.

"I'll find the skates," said the boy detective. He spoke with certainty. But he felt no such thing. What he felt was the blow to his pride; it hurt worse than his jaw.

Imagine a detective being robbed!

In the corridor outside Dr. Wilson's office, Encyclopedia leaned against the wall. He closed his eyes and did some deep thinking.

Dr. Wilson's office was on the ground floor of the new Medical Building. The building had three floors

and fifteen offices. All the offices were used by doctors or dentists.

What if the thief had followed him into the building in order to steal the skates? Then the case was closed. "I could spend the rest of my life looking through closets, school lockers, and garages all over Idaville," Encyclopedia thought.

But suppose the thief had simply come into the building to see a doctor. Suppose, on his way in, he had noticed a boy carrying a pair of roller skates. Well, that was something else!

Encyclopedia reasoned further. "The thief could be a grown-up, a boy, or a girl."

He ruled out a grown-up. First, because it was unlikely that a grown-up would steal an old pair of small skates. Second, because a grown-up would be too hard to catch. Too many men and women went in and out of the Medical Building every hour.

"I'll have to act on the idea that the thief is a boy or girl," he decided. "It's a long chance, but the only one I have."

He opened his eyes. The case called for plain, old-fashioned police leg work!

Encyclopedia began on the ground floor. He asked the same question in every office: "Were any boys or girls here to see the doctor this morning?"

The answer was the same in every office: "No."

Things looked hopeless. But on the top floor he finally got a lead. The nurse in room 301 told him a boy named Billy Haggerty had been there this morning to have a sprained wrist treated.

Encyclopedia asked in the last two offices, just to be sure. Neither doctor had treated children that morning.

Billy Haggerty became suspect number one!

Encyclopedia got Billy Haggerty's address from the nurse in room 301. He hurried back to Dr. Wilson's office to use the telephone. He called Sally. He told her to meet him in front of the Haggertys' house in half an hour.

"We may have some rough going ahead of us," he warned.

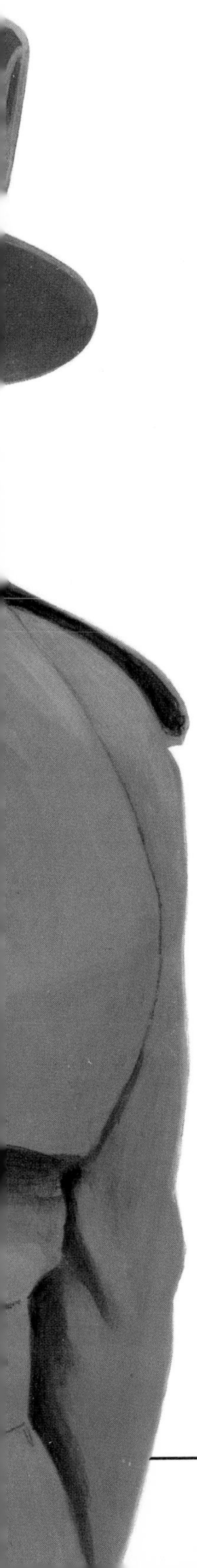

But Billy Haggerty turned out to be only an inch taller than Encyclopedia, and shorter than Sally.

Billy drew himself up to his full height at Encyclopedia's first question:

"Were you in Dr. Vivian Wilson's office this morning?"

"Naw," snapped Billy. "I don't know any Dr. Wilson."

"You didn't ask anyone about Dr. Wilson?" put in Sally.

"I never heard of him before you spoke his name," said Billy.

"Then you went straight to your own doctor on the third floor?" said Encyclopedia.

"Yeah. Dr. Stanton in room 301. What's it to you?"

"Dr. Wilson's office is down the hall from both the stairs and the elevator," said Encyclopedia thoughtfully. "You wouldn't pass his office going up or coming down."

"I don't know where his office is, and I don't care," said Billy. "It's none of your business where I was."

"We just want to be sure you weren't in Dr. Vivian Wilson's office this morning. That's all," said Sally.

"Well, I wasn't. I had a sprained wrist, not a toothache. So why should I go near his office?" demanded Billy. "I don't like snoopers. What are you after?"

"A pair of roller skates," said Encyclopedia. "Do you mind returning them? You've given yourself away."

WHAT GAVE BILLY AWAY?

Solution to *The Case of the Missing Roller Skates*

Billy Haggerty said that he had never heard of Dr. Vivian Wilson and that he didn't know where his office was. But he knew too much about him.

He knew that Dr. Vivian Wilson was (1) a man, not a woman, and (2) a dentist, not a doctor.

When he was tripped by his fibs, Billy returned the roller skates to Sally.

CASE CLOSED

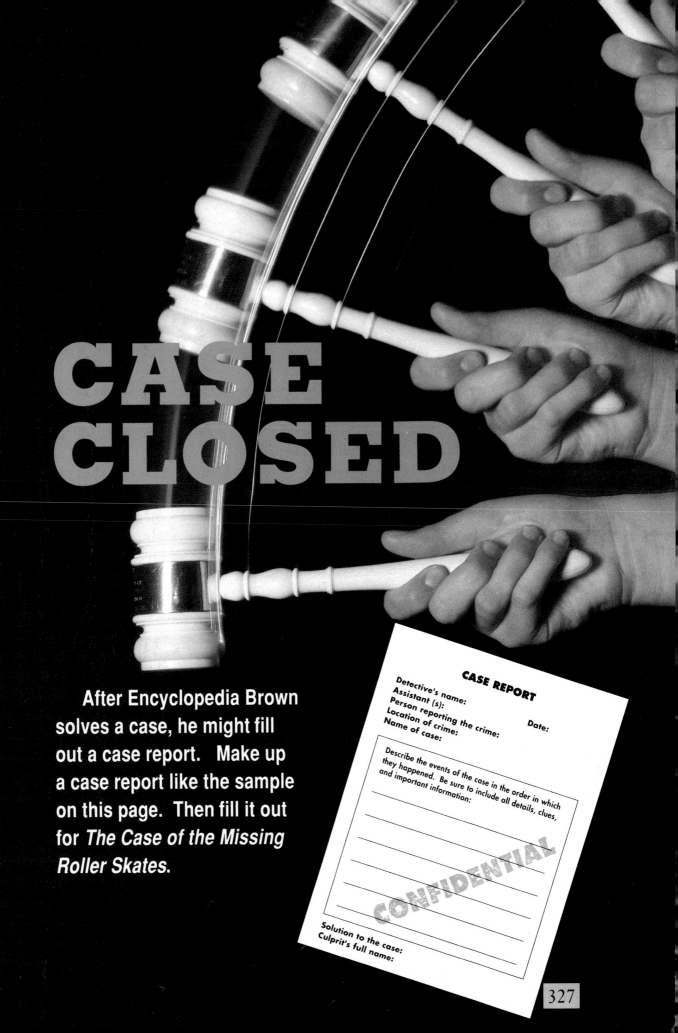

After Encyclopedia Brown solves a case, he might fill out a case report. Make up a case report like the sample on this page. Then fill it out for *The Case of the Missing Roller Skates*.

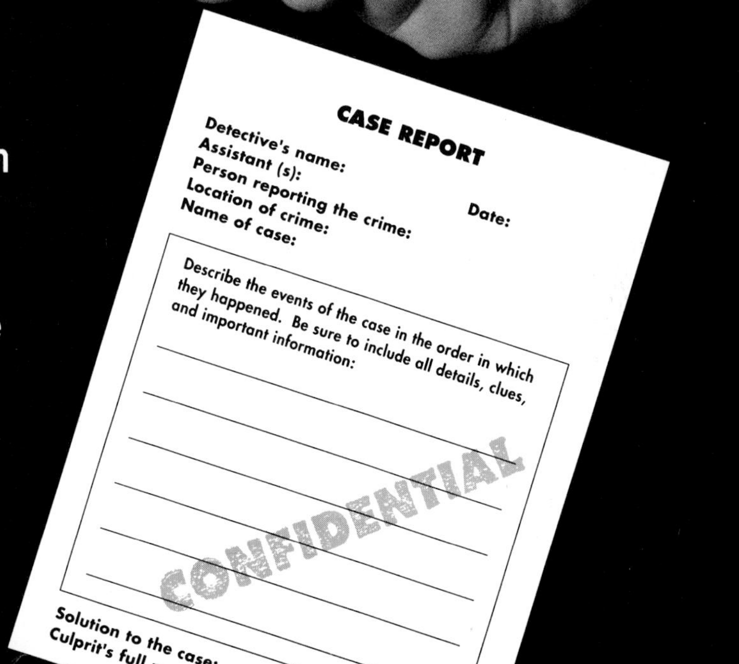

CASE REPORT

Detective's name:
Assistant (s):
Person reporting the crime: **Date:**
Location of crime:
Name of case:

Describe the events of the case in the order in which they happened. Be sure to include all details, clues, and important information:

CONFIDENTIAL

Solution to the case:
Culprit's full name:

Who Stole the Jewels?

Here's your chance to play detective. Read through the facts of this case and then see if you can figure out the identity of the jewel thief.

On a rainy afternoon, a thief breaks into a mansion and steals the famous Soapstone Diamonds. Some people near the scene of the crime see the thief scuttling away. The police interview these people. This is what they find out.

A saleswoman states that the thief was wearing dark glasses and had three buttons on his coat.

A little boy says he was carrying a stick in his left hand.

An old lady thinks the thief had a bald head and a briefcase.

An old man reports that he was wearing a spotted tie. A taxi driver thinks the thief had boots on.

Further police investigation shows that the saleswoman, the old man, and the lady were correct. The little boy and the taxi driver, however, were wrong.

Now that you have all the facts, help the police crack the case. Which one of these pictures shows the true thief?

Answer
The thief is number 3. He's wearing shoes, dark glasses and a spotted tie, has a bald head and three buttons on his coat. He is carrying a briefcase, and a stick in his right hand.

Lucinda Landon

Lucinda Landon loves mysteries as much as her heroine Meg Mackintosh does. Her eighteenth-century home has a hidden trap door leading to the basement and a secret hiding place behind the chimney.

When Landon was in art school, she would stay up all night just to finish reading a good mystery. Now she writes good mysteries, like *Meg Mackintosh and the Case of the Curious Whale Watch.*

Donald J. Sobol

Is Encyclopedia Brown a real boy? Readers of the more than twenty *Encyclopedia Brown* books constantly ask this question. Author Donald Sobol always answers no. "He is, perhaps, the boy I wanted to be — doing the things I wanted to read about but could not find in any book when I was ten," Sobol says.

The popular author didn't start writing until he was thirty. Sobol says he writes "to entertain, from the first paragraph to the last."

Other entertaining books by Sobol are *Angie's First Case* and *True Sea Adventures.*

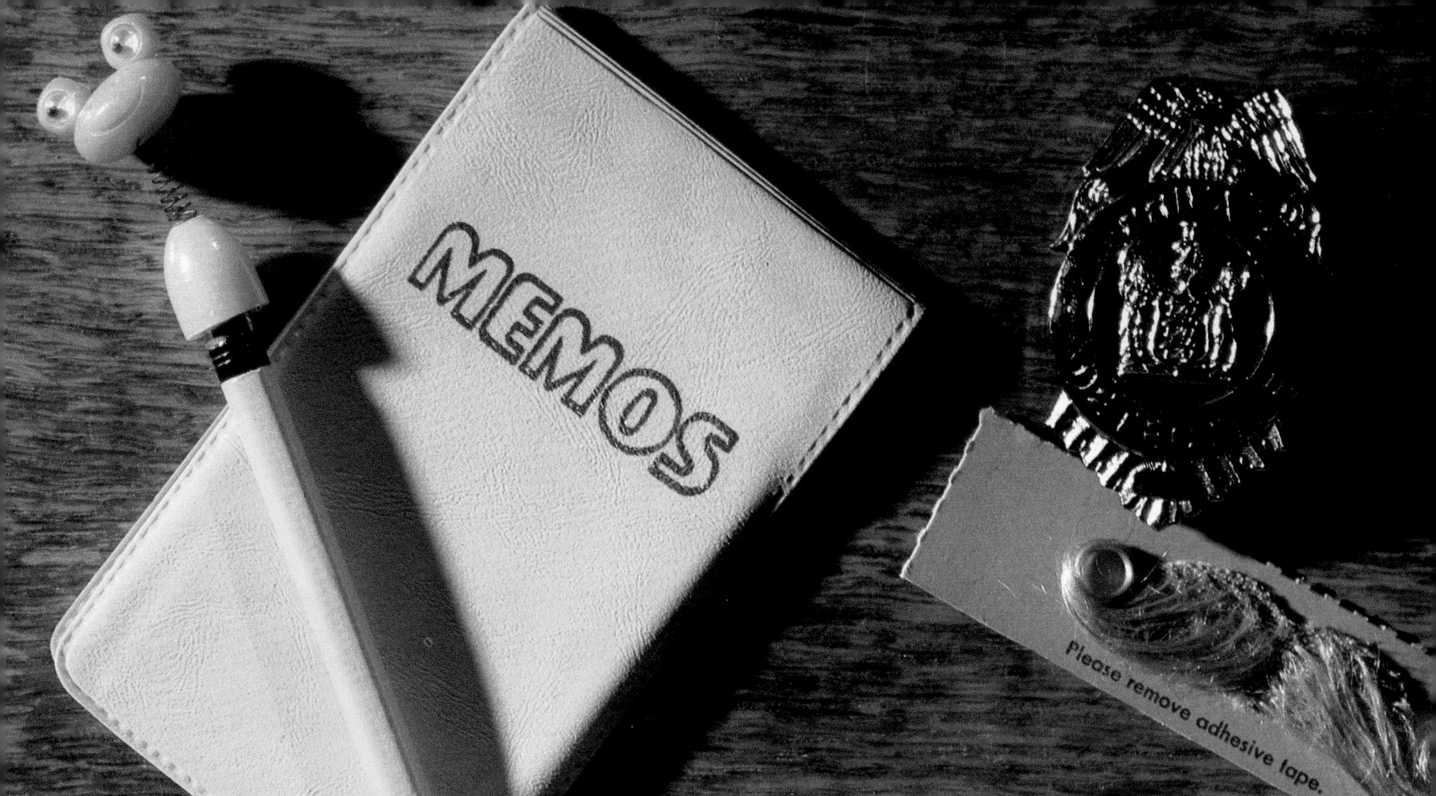

Michael Bond

On Christmas Eve in 1957, Michael Bond stopped in a London store to buy his wife a present. "On one of the shelves I came across the last toy bear that hadn't been sold. He looked very sorry for himself, so I bought him. Since we lived near Paddington Station at the time, I decided to name him Paddington," Bond says.

"One day I was sitting in front of my typewriter staring at a blank sheet of paper, wondering what to write, and I idly tapped out the words 'Mr. and Mrs. Brown first met Paddington on a railway platform.' Without intending it, I had become a children's author."

UNCOVER A MYSTERY

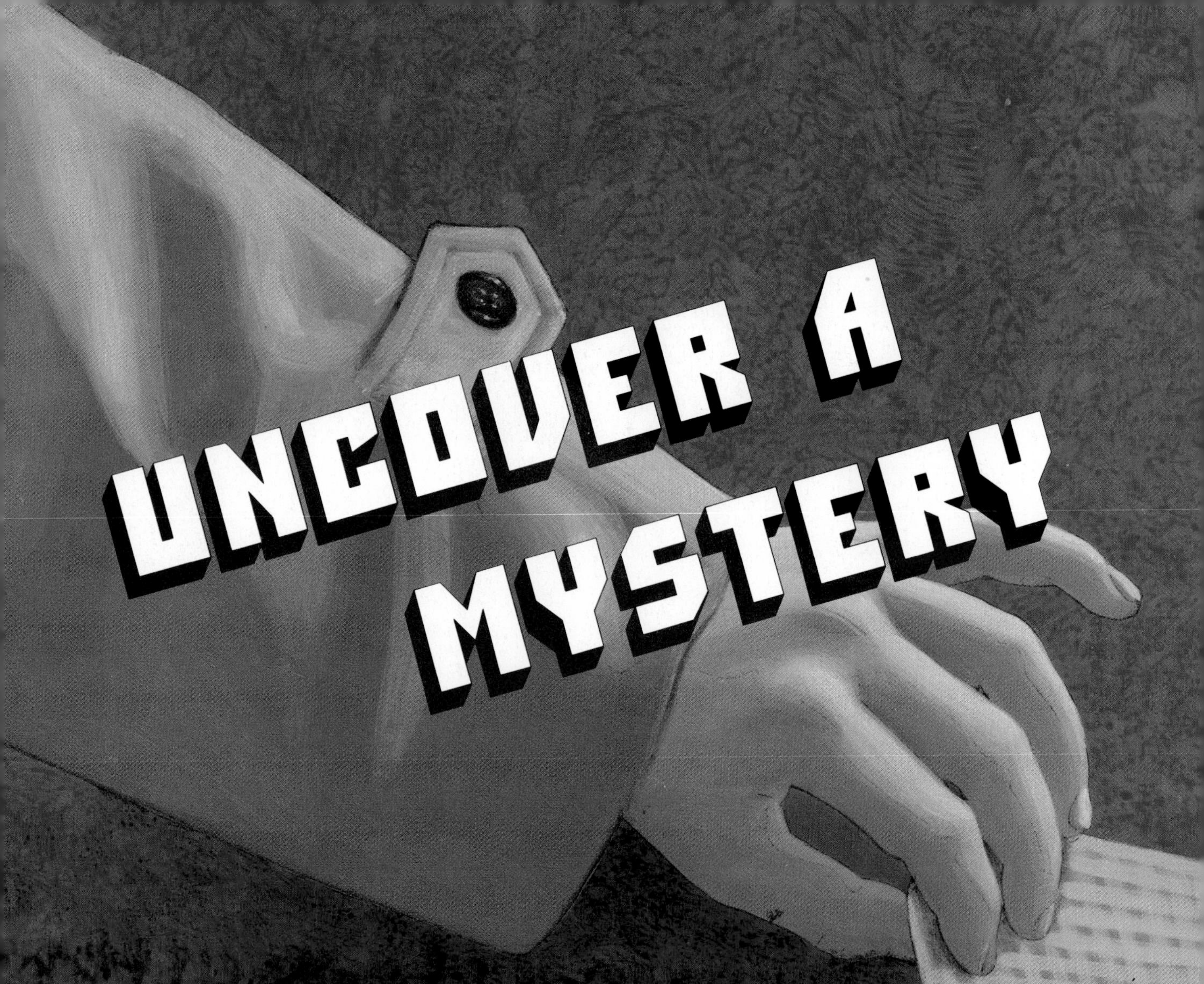

CAM JANSEN AND THE MYSTERY OF THE TELEVISION DOG
by David A. Adler
Cam Jansen, the fifth-grade detective with the amazing memory, is on the trail of a dognapper.

MEG MACKINTOSH AND THE MYSTERY AT THE MEDIEVAL CASTLE
by Lucinda Landon
A medieval castle, a suit of armor, and a dungeon combine in another puzzling case for ace detective Meg Mackintosh.

MYSTERY OF THE PLUMED SERPENT *by Barbara Brenner*
Twins Elena and Michael Garcia are hot on the trail of a stolen Mexican treasure.

WHATEVER HAPPENED TO UNCLE ALBERT? AND OTHER PUZZLING PLAYS *by Sue Alexander*
Who is haunting Plymouth Castle? What is the Mystery of the Stone Statues? These and other questions are answered by sleuth Blaylock Jones in four plays to read and perform.

THE YOUNG DETECTIVE'S HANDBOOK *by William Vivian Butler*
Tips for breaking secret codes, lifting fingerprints, and making clever disguises are included in this handbook designed to make you a successful detective.

A CLUE IN CODE *by Marilyn Singer*
Who took the class trip money? Twins Sam and Dave and their friend Rita track down the guilty party.

BIOGRAPHY

BOOK 6

The Dreamers

Walt Disney, Marian Anderson, Roberto Clemente.
Three extraordinary people. Three dreamers.
Three people who made their dreams come true.

There's a lot of the Mouse in me.
WALT DISNEY
Marian Anderson
" I think first about music, and of being where music is, and of music being where I am."

Contents

ROBERTO CLEMENTE
PIRAT
"I want to be remembered as a ballplayer who gave all he had to give."

WALT DISNEY

Master of Make-Believe

from the book by Elizabeth Rider Montgomery

Walt Disney was born in 1901. His family lived on a farm for a few years and later moved to Kansas City, Missouri, where his father bought a paper route. Life was hard for young Walt. He had to get up every morning at 3:30 to deliver papers, often in deep snow. But on Saturdays, after delivering papers, Walt took art lessons.

The Disneys eventually moved to Chicago, where Mr. Disney invested in a jelly factory. Walt worked at the factory, but also found time to study cartooning by mail.

By the age of eighteen, Walt had decided to become an artist. He packed his bags, gave his savings to his mother for safekeeping, and headed back to Kansas City to try to get a job at the Kansas City Star.

In Business for Himself

Walt did not get a job on the art staff of the *Star* when he arrived in Kansas City in the fall of 1919. But he did find work with the Gray Advertising Company, making sketches for their catalog.

When advertising slowed down, Walt was laid off. He turned to the post office for work. From 7:30 A.M. to mid-afternoon he delivered mail. He spent the rest of each day looking for another art job. In the evenings he made up drawing samples.

Just before Christmas Ub Iwerks, a fellow artist at Gray Advertising, came to see Walt. Ub had also been laid off.

After a brief conversation Walt said, "Why don't we go into business together, Ub?"

"Doing what?" asked Ub.

"We could do artwork for any business firm that doesn't have an art staff," Walt replied. "We'd make ads and letterheads — things like that."

Ub nodded thoughtfully. "You're good at cartooning, and I'm pretty good at lettering and airbrush painting. We'd make a real team."

Walt took some of Iwerks' samples and his own and showed them to businessmen who might need artwork. He got several orders. A newspaper publisher agreed to give them desk space in return for free artwork.

Walt wrote to his mother, asking her to send the $500 she was keeping for him. She answered promptly, but she sent no money.

"What do you want it for, Walter?" she asked.

Her letter made Walt angry. He was eighteen now — grown up — and the money belonged to him. Why should his parents treat him as if he were a child?

"I'm going into business," he wrote back. "I need my money for supplies. After all, I earned it. Why shouldn't I decide what to do with it?"

His mother sent only half of his money. It was soon spent on desks, drawing boards, an airbrush, and a tank of air.

The partnership got off to a good start. In its first month of operation it took in $135, and more orders were coming in.

Early in February 1920, Walt saw an ad in the *Star* for a cartoonist at Kansas City Film Ad

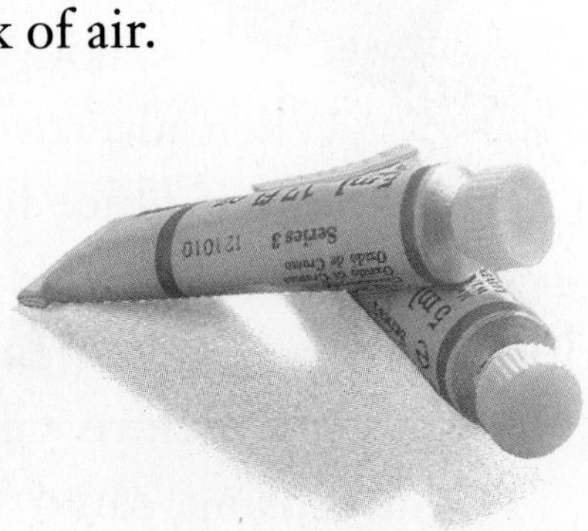

Company. He called on the firm, hoping to get an order, but they wanted a full-time artist.

"Our company makes one-minute, animated cartoon ads for local theaters," Walt was told. "The job pays $160 a month — full-time work."

Walt wanted the job, but if he took it he would have no time for Iwerks-Disney orders. He went back to the office to talk to Ub.

"It's too good an opportunity to pass up," Iwerks said. "That's more than the two of us together made last month."

The partners decided to separate. Walt would take the position at Kansas City Film Ad, and Ub would take over Iwerks-Disney work.

Two months later Ub telephoned Walt. "Can you get me a job there with you?"

"What about Iwerks-Disney?" Walt asked.

"I'm going broke," Iwerks confessed. "I'm no salesman like you." So Walt got Ub a job at Kansas City Film Ad.

Walt liked his job as a cartoon animator. The art of animation, or making a cartoon seem to move, was very new and very crude. Walt used little figures cut out of paper, with arms and legs fastened so they could be moved. A cutout was photographed in one position with a motion picture camera. Then the arms and legs were moved a trifle and another picture was taken. Again the figure was changed slightly and another picture taken, and so on. When the series of photographs was projected on a screen, the cartoon figure seemed to move.

In his spare time Walt tried to find better ways of making cartoons. He read all the books he could find on the subject in the public library. His boss lent him an old box movie camera, and night after night Walt worked with it in a neighbor's empty garage. He tried photographing a series of drawings instead of paper cutouts. It took much longer, but the animated figures were more lifelike.

Soon Walt made a sample reel of cartoon jokes, using drawings in place of cutouts, and sold it to the Newman Theater as a Laugh-O-Gram. The film was so popular that he was asked to make others. Walt decided to leave Kansas City Film Ad and go into business for himself again.

Grudgingly his mother sent him the rest of his money. But it was not enough. He needed thousands of dollars, not hundreds, to start his new business. So Walt visited all the people he had met in Kansas City and tried to get them to invest in his company.

Walt was a good salesman. He soon raised the $15,000 he needed. At not quite 21, Walt Disney became president of Laugh-O-Gram Films. Ub Iwerks was his chief assistant.

Failure

In spite of a promising start, the Laugh-O-Gram corporation had trouble making a profit. In less than a year it went out of business. Walt was left with nothing but his movie camera and a print of his latest movie, *Alice's Wonderland.* This film was a new idea of Walt's, which combined animated cartoon figures with pictures of a live girl.

Walt gave up his apartment and lived in the Laugh-O-Gram office, sleeping in an armchair. Often he had nightmares about delivering newspapers for his father.

He ate one meal a day, in a little Greek restaurant downstairs. Since there was no bathroom in the office, he walked downtown once a week to the Union Station and paid a dime for a tub bath in a public bathroom. He traded artwork for haircuts.

One day Walt got a letter from his brother Roy, now recovering from tuberculosis in a veterans' hospital in Los Angeles.

"I have a hunch, kid," Roy wrote, "that you could use a little dough. I'm enclosing a blank check. Fill it out for any amount up to $30."

Walt used most of the money to pay part of his bill at the Greek restaurant.

Walt tried everything he could think of to make money. He took photographs of news events. He made short movies of babies for parents to show in their living rooms. For the organist of the Isis Theater he made a cartoon that encouraged audiences to join in group singing.

Then a dentist asked Walt to make an animated cartoon that would teach children to care for their teeth. It was to be called *Tommy Tucker's Tooth.*

One evening the dentist telephoned and said, "Your money is ready, the $500 we agreed on. Come on over and get it."

"I can't," Walt replied. "My shoes are at the shoemaker's, and I can't get them until I pay him $1.50."

"Stay right there," the dentist said. "I'll bring the money to you." And he did.

For months Walt kept up this hand-to-mouth life. Once he lived for two days on beans and bread a neighbor gave him. Walt fed the crumbs to the mice that gathered in his wastebasket at night. He had become very fond of these little creatures and built cages for them. They kept him from getting lonely.

One mouse in particular seemed extra bright and curious. Walt named him Mortimer. From time to time Walt set Mortimer free on the drawing board and taught him tricks. Walt drew a big circle on a sheet of drawing paper. He taught Mortimer to stay inside that circle, tapping him gently on the nose each time the mouse tried to scamper across the line.

In the summer of 1923 Walt decided to go to California and join Roy, who would soon be getting out of the hospital. He sold his camera to raise the train fare. He packed his few belongings in a cheap suitcase — one shirt, two suits of underwear, some socks, a few drawing materials, and his film of *Alice's Wonderland.* Then he took the cages with his mice and rode to the end of the streetcar line. In an open field he let the mice go.

Walt turned to leave. After a few steps he looked back. Mortimer sat where Walt had left him. The mouse's eyes seemed very reproachful.

Two Partnerships

In July 1923, at the age of 21, Walt Disney arrived in Los Angeles in a badly worn jacket and mismatched pants. He had only $40 in his pocket. His prospects did not look bright. Walt boarded with one of his father's brothers, Robert Disney, paying him five dollars a week. Day after day he walked the streets looking for work. He also wrote to New York movie distributors, trying to interest them in *Alice's Wonderland.*

One day Walt got a letter that sent him hurrying to the veterans' hospital to see Roy.

"A New York movie distributor, Margaret Winkler, wants a series of *Alice* films!" he crowed, sitting on the edge of Roy's bed. "She'll pay $1,500 each! Think of that!"

"How many does she want?" Roy asked.

"Twelve. We'll do it, won't we, Roy? We'll go into business together. With $500 we could make a start, I'm sure of it!"

Roy shook his head. He was due to be discharged from the hospital in a few days, but he had no money except his $85-a-month pension from the government. "Who would lend us $500?"

However, Roy could not long resist Walt's enthusiasm. He soon found himself saying, "Okay, kid. Let's go!"

Roy persuaded Uncle Robert to lend them $500. Walt went to a neighborhood real estate dealer and asked to rent space for a studio.

"How much can you pay?" the realtor asked.

"About five dollars a month," Walt replied. The man laughed. "We don't need much space," Walt assured him hurriedly. "Just about room enough to swing a cat."

Still laughing, the man agreed to rent the Disneys a cubbyhole in the back of his office for five dollars a month.

Production costs ran higher than Walt had figured. He hired a girl from Kansas City to play "Alice." He worked night and day drawing cartoon figures, and he also built the scenes for the backgrounds. Soon he realized he must have help with the drawings, and he wrote to Ub Iwerks and offered him a job. Ub accepted.

At first Roy did the movie photography, but he could not master the steady cranking rhythm that the old-fashioned hand camera required. So Walt had to hire a real cameraman.

"We've got to raise more money," Roy said one evening as the partners sat down to their usual meal of beans in their little walk-up apartment. "Where can we get it?" Uncle Robert had announced flatly that he would not lend them money again.

"What about that girl Edna you went with in Kansas City?" Walt suggested.

"You leave Edna out of this," Roy snapped. "I'm not going to borrow money from my girl!"

Walt shrugged. "Maybe the organist of the Isis Theater in Kansas City would lend me a few hundred. He liked the animated song sheets I did for him."

Walt wrote to the organist, and he also wrote secretly to Roy's girl, Edna Francis. Both sent some money.

Although Roy was angry because Walt had gone against his wishes, he soon forgave him.

The Disney brothers made one *Alice* film after another, but there was little profit. Walt was always trying to improve the animation and photography, and improvements cost money. He also kept adding to his staff. He took on more artists and began to

train them in animation. Then he decided to hire a girl to do stenographic work and also ink the outlines of the pencil drawings and fill them in to make them ready for photographing.

One day while Walt was working, a pretty young woman appeared in the tiny Disney office and applied for a job.

"I'm Lillian Bounds, from Lewiston, Idaho," she told Walt. "I'm staying with my sister, just a few blocks from here."

"Good," Walt said, looking down at her approvingly. "You won't have to pay carfare."

Lillian took the job without bothering to ask what it paid. By the time she learned that her wages were only fifteen dollars a week, she had become so interested in her dynamic, hardworking boss that she stayed on.

Walt and Roy continued to live as cheaply as possible. They paid themselves salaries of $35 a week and put the rest of their income back into the business.

Walt admired Lillian Bounds, but he had no money or time for dates. Instead he would drive her home after they had worked late. When they reached her sister's house, they would sit in the car and talk.

"Come in and meet my sister," Lillian often urged, but Walt always refused. He was ashamed of his clothes — an old sweater and worn-out pants.

One day he asked Roy, the company's business manager, if he could draw enough money from their account to buy a suit.

Roy grinned. "We'll both buy suits, kid," he replied. "Edna is coming out from Kansas City, and we're getting married."

"That's swell, Roy," Walt exclaimed. "But I guess it means I've got to get a new cook!"

Roy and Edna were married in the spring of 1925. A few nights later Walt was dictating to Lillian in the office. Suddenly he paused. He leaned over and kissed her.

"Which do you think we should pay for first, Lilly, a new car or a ring?" he asked.

"A ring," Lilly replied promptly.

The wedding took place in July 1925, in Lillian's brother's home in Lewiston. Now Walt Disney had a marriage partner as well as a business partner.

The Lesson Oswald Taught

Lillian quickly learned that life with Walt Disney would never be dull, but it could be uncertain and upsetting. One day she worked for hours cooking dinner in their apartment kitchen. When dinner time arrived, Walt had not come home. Hour after hour Lillian waited, getting angrier and angrier.

Long after midnight the door opened softly and Walt tiptoed in. Before Lillian could say a word he said, "I'm sorry, Lilly. I forgot about dinner. I was drawing an awfully funny animation scene, and I didn't realize what time it was."

Lillian laughed helplessly. She just couldn't stay mad at Walt!

The following afternoon Walt came home early. He handed his wife a hatbox tied with a big red ribbon. "Here's a peace offering, Lilly," he said, smiling shyly.

Inside the box was a chow puppy, with another red ribbon around its neck!

Walt loved the puppy as much as Lilly did. He spoiled it with extra food, but he trained it with unlimited patience. Lilly was impressed with Walt's love of animals and his kindness to them.

The first two years of Walt's marriage saw many changes. The business outgrew the real estate office, so Walt leased a store building on Hyperion Avenue and converted it into a studio. He also bought a home near the studio.

After three years the *Alice Comedies* began to lose their popularity.

"I've got to think of a new series idea," Walt told Lilly. He began to spend every spare minute sketching different animals. Finally he drew a long-eared rabbit. His entire staff liked it.

"The rabbit can get into all kinds of scrapes," Walt said, "all of them very funny. It should be a good series."

"What will you name him?" Lilly asked. But Walt had not yet decided.

"Write names for the rabbit on slips of paper," Walt directed his staff. "We'll put them in a hat and draw one." "Oswald" was the name that was drawn.

Mintz, the eastern distributor, was delighted with Oswald Rabbit. He sent Walt a contract to sign, which named a price of $2,250 for each Oswald picture.

One day in 1927 Walt said to Lilly, "The Oswald contract will end soon. We'll go to New York, and I will bargain for a new contract personally. I'm going to ask for a raise in fees."

Instead of agreeing to a raise, Mintz told Walt bluntly, "I'll give you $1,800 a reel on a new contract."

Walt protested. "I'm not going to take a cut when Oswald is so popular!"

Mintz smiled unpleasantly. "Oh, yes, you are. If you don't, you lose Oswald entirely, and you also lose your best artists." He explained that he had copyrighted Oswald Rabbit in his own name

UNIVERSAL
presents
OSWALD
THE
LUCKY RABBIT
IN
"THE OL' SWIMMIN' HOLE"
A Winkler Production
by WALT DISNEY
HUGH
+MAX

instead of Disney's, so he owned all legal rights. He also showed Walt the contracts that four Disney artists had signed, agreeing to leave Disney and work for him.

It hurt Walt deeply that employees whom he had trained would desert him.

"If those men desert me now," Walt said, "they'll leave you in the lurch some day, too."

Mintz only smiled, sure that Walt Disney had no choice but to meet his terms.

However, Walt did not give in. "I can replace those artists easily," he boasted.

Walt wasn't as confident as he sounded. He and Lilly were sad as they packed for their trip home.

"I'll never work for anybody else again," Walt vowed. "Never!"

Before boarding the train, he sent a telegram to his brother: "Everything O.K. Coming home."

"How can you say that?" Lilly protested. "You know it isn't true!"

"I'll make it come true," Walt said.

The Birth of Mickey Mouse

On the long train trip across the continent, Walt Disney stared unseeingly out of the coach window. Day after day he tried to think of an animal character around which to build a new cartoon series. His mind went back to his childhood on the farm. He drew cows, horses, chickens, pigs, and geese. None of them satisfied him.

As the train reached the Middle West, Walt exclaimed suddenly, "I've got it!" He began to sketch furiously. Soon he thrust a sheet of drawings into Lilly's hands.

"See what you think of these," he said excitedly.

Lilly looked down at the sketches. She saw a cartoon of a mouse — a merry, appealing little creature. In a way the mouse, with his expressive eyes and his pointed face, resembled Walt. The body of the mouse was pear-shaped. He had pipestem legs in big shoes. He wore two-button short pants and gloves.

"I'll call him Mortimer Mouse," Walt said.

Lilly objected. "That's a horrible name for a character!"

"What's wrong with Mortimer?" Walt demanded. "I called one of my Kansas City mice Mortimer. He was smart. He learned to stay inside a circle on drawing paper. Mortimer learned . . ."

"I don't care what your Kansas City mouse learned!" Lilly snapped, her nerves on edge from days of worry and inactivity. "You've got to find a better name for that mouse!"

They argued about it while the train crossed wheat fields, deserts, and mountains. Before it reached the Pacific Coast, they had agreed to call the mouse "Mickey."

"Mickey Mouse is going to make a fortune for us," Walt assured his wife. "He's the kind of character who can cook up lots of mischief, like a bad little boy. I'll never run out of story ideas for Mickey."

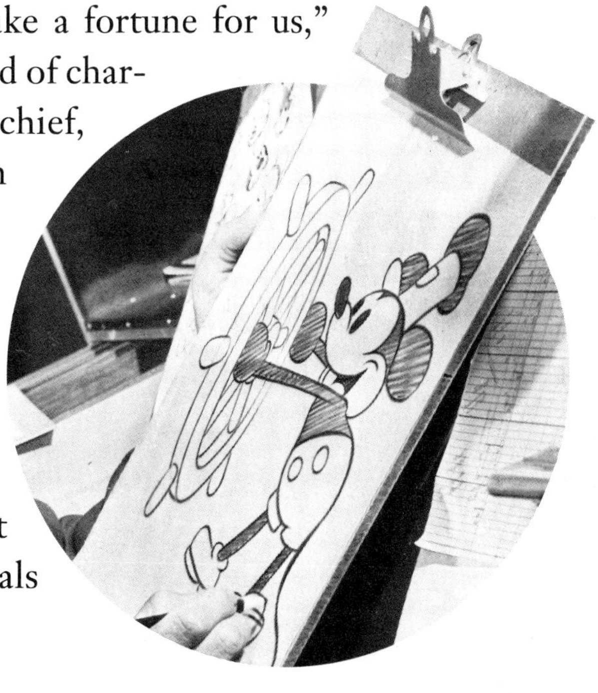

Walt started training new animators immediately, and he set to work on a Mickey Mouse film, *Plane Crazy*. He used farm animals as background and as sources of humor. Animators were sent to zoos and farms to draw animals from life.

The whole Disney staff worked night and day. Lilly and Edna, Roy's wife, helped by tracing the animation drawings on celluloid and inking them so they could be photographed. When *Plane Crazy* was finished, a second Mickey Mouse film was started, and then a third. But nobody would buy them! Something had happened that changed the whole movie industry!

In October 1927 a "talking picture," *The Jazz Singer*, had been shown. Before that date, movies had been "silent." That is, the actors moved their lips, but they made no sound in the theater. Movie audiences had to read signs flashed on the screen to find out what characters said. In *The Jazz Singer* audiences really heard for the first time what actors on the screen were saying. The picture was a sensation! After it appeared, owners of movie theaters no longer wanted to show "silent" films.

Walt Disney had spent a great deal of money on his silent Mickey Mouse pictures. Now they seemed worthless.

"What are we going to do with these films?" Roy asked at last, very discouraged.

"We'll make them over," Walt said. "We'll add sound to the film."

Roy stared at his brother. "That's impossible," he said.

"I'll find a way," Walt insisted. "Sound will make our pictures much better." He began to experiment with sound in the third Mickey Mouse film, which he called *Steamboat Willie.*

Lean months followed. It took time and money to solve the problems of adding sound to a film. And when it was accomplished at last, the brothers ran into more trouble. Distributors wanted to buy the Disney films outright.

Walt refused. "Nobody is ever going to own any of our

pictures again," he said stubbornly, remembering Oswald Rabbit. "We'll rent our films, we won't sell them."

Although the Disney Studio needed money badly, Roy stood by his brother.

Walt drove his staff unmercifully. Every detail of every picture had to be perfect, no matter how many times each drawing had to be done over. He drove himself even harder than he did his staff. Often he worked up to fourteen hours a day.

"I have a little work to finish," he told Lilly one evening after dinner. Lilly went with him to the studio. She stretched out on the sofa and watched her husband working at his drawing board. Soon she drifted off to sleep. The next thing she knew Walt was bending over her, shaking her gently.

"What time is it?" Lilly asked sleepily.

"Ten-thirty," Walt replied, glad that she didn't have a watch. He drove her home and somehow managed to keep her from seeing a clock before she went to bed. It was 2:30 in the morning!

The first Mickey Mouse film opened in New York in November 1928. Mickey Mouse, using Walt Disney's voice, quickly became a star. Audiences laughed at Mickey and loved him.

Fame

Walt could not enjoy his success. He had worked too hard too long. He became cross and irritable. He shouted at his staff, at Roy and Edna, and even at Lilly, whom he adored. Finally he went to a doctor.

"You need a long rest," the doctor told Walt. "Drop everything and get away from the studio. Take a trip, and when you come back stop working such long hours. Find yourself some hobbies. Otherwise your health will fail again."

Walt followed the doctor's orders. During several months of leisurely travel he regained his health, his cheerful disposition, and his zest for living.

Soon after he returned from his vacation, Walt learned about a process for color photography.

"That's what I've been waiting for," he exclaimed. "We'll scrap *Flowers and Trees* and reshoot the whole thing in color."

"We've already finished half of that picture in black and white!" Roy protested.

"*Flowers and Trees* is a natural for color photography," Walt insisted.

"But think how much more color photography will cost!" Roy exclaimed.

"Oh, you'll find some way to raise the money," Walt replied cheerfully.

They quarreled about it, but Walt would not give in. Roy finally raised the necessary money, and Walt rushed into color production of *Flowers and Trees*. However, he took time out to buy a peace pipe and place it on his brother's desk. Roy hung the pipe on the wall of his office.

When *Flowers and Trees* was finished, Roy admitted that Walt had been right to gamble on color. The picture won a Motion Picture Academy Award as the best cartoon of 1931–1932, and again the Disney Studio led all of its competitors.

Walt continued to search for perfection. He constantly looked for ways to improve animated cartoons. One day he stopped in to see Webb Smith in the Disney story department. Webb's office wall was covered with a series of sketches that told the story of the picture then in progress.

"I just had these offices redecorated, Webb," Walt complained. "You're ruining the wall with those thumbtacks."

"Sorry, Walt," Webb replied. "I didn't think of that."

Walt stopped frowning at the offending thumbtacks and studied Webb's sketches.

"Um," he murmured thoughtfully. "You can follow the story from these sketches better than from a written outline."

The next day a truckload of corkboard was delivered to the Disney Studio, and a permanent storyboard was installed in each office of the story department.

In the early 1930s the Great Depression swept over the nation. More than 18 million people were out of work. Disney Studio, however, continued to prosper. In five years Walt's staff increased from 150 employees to more than 750. The studio on Hyperion Avenue was enlarged, and Walt started a training class for cartoon artists.

During these years Walt Disney made many cartoon shorts. He made Donald Duck pictures and Silly Symphonies like *The Tortoise and the Hare* and *Three Little Pigs*. These were all very popular.

***Three Little Pigs* (1933)**

Still Mickey Mouse was Walt's best-known character. He had become more than a movie star. He was seen everywhere — on school tablets, watches, toys, and children's clothes. There was also a Mickey Mouse comic strip, printed in 1,000 newspapers, and there were hundreds of Mickey Mouse Clubs in 40 different countries. In 1935 the League of Nations presented a medal to Walt Disney, calling Mickey Mouse "a symbol of international good will." Walt and his cartoon characters had become world famous.

If you want to discover more about the man who created a mouse named Mickey, read the rest of *Walt Disney: Master of Make-Believe*.

CREATE A CARTOON

Walt Disney based the character of Mickey Mouse on his pet mouse. Create your own cartoon character based on a pet or even a person in your life. Draw a picture of your character and give it a name. Then, if you wish, create a four-panel comic strip featuring your new character.

THE STORY OF DISNEYLAND

Walt Disney used to take his daughters to amusement parks. His daughters would ride the roller coaster and Ferris wheel, but Disney was bored. He dreamed of building a clean, interesting park with imaginative rides — a place that adults as well as children could enjoy.

For many years Disney worked hard to make his dream come true. He hired designers and engineers to create imaginative rides. He bought a large piece of land in California and began construction. Many people doubted that the park would be a success.

Disney proved them wrong. In 1955 he opened Disneyland. At the park's grand opening, Disney said that Disneyland would never be completed "as long as there is imagination left in the world."

Marian Anderson

by Tobi Tobias

In a small house in Philadelphia a three-year-old girl was singing. She sat at a little table that she liked to make believe was her piano. The walls of the room were covered with flowered paper. The child thought she saw friendly faces in the flowers, looking down at her as she played and sang. The child's name was Marian Anderson. When she grew up, she became one of the world's best-loved singers.

Marian was born on February 27, 1903. Her father, John Anderson, worked long hours delivering coal and ice. Her mother, Anna Anderson, had been a schoolteacher once. Now she was busy keeping the house comfortable for her husband and their three daughters: Marian, Alyce, and Ethel. The Anderson family did not have much money, but they cared about each other and had many happy times together.

As Marian grew older, her father took her to church with him every Sunday. The Union Baptist Church was important to the people in Marian's neighborhood. Often their lives were unhappy. Many of them were poor. Some of them had trouble getting jobs. In church they heard words and music that said to them: "Yes, you have troubles. We know that life can be hard. We must hope for good things to come."

Marian joined the children's choir of the church. As she sang with this group, the choirmaster noticed her beautiful voice. He asked her to practice a duet with her best friend, Viola Johnson. The next Sunday the two girls stood up to sing for the whole congregation. It was Marian's first public performance. She was six years old.

Marian was finding out about music in other ways, too. When she was eight, her father bought an old piano. But there was no money for music lessons. After weeks of trying, Marian taught herself to play simple tunes. She wished she could learn more.

Then one day she saw a used violin in a store window. She went in and asked the man how much it cost. "Three dollars and ninety-five cents," he said. "Is it a good violin?" Marian asked. She knew how hard it would be for her to get that much money. "Oh, it's a very fine instrument," the storekeeper said.

Marian went to work after school. She scrubbed steps for her neighbors and ran their errands. If someone gave her a few cents for candy, she put the money carefully away. At last she earned and saved enough nickels and pennies. Proudly she went back to the store and bought the violin. A friend of the family taught her to tune it and to play a few notes. But before long the strings snapped and the wood of the violin cracked. It was no good at all. Marian was sad and disappointed. She wanted so much to make music well.

Still she was never downhearted for long. She loved singing in the choir. Her full, rich voice poured through the church. The sound she made was so loud the choirmaster sometimes laughed and said, "Hold back a little there, Marian. We want to hear the other singers, too." Friends and neighbors in the congregation, though, had nothing but praise for Marian.

Her voice was deep and velvety, the kind musicians call contralto. But she could reach up to the high soprano notes, too, and even down to the low music of the baritone. When the choir prepared a new song, Marian learned all the different parts, high and low, not just her own. Then, if a singer could not come to church on Sunday, she helped out by singing in his place. It made her happy to know the choir needed her, and she learned a lot about music this way. Secretly she dreamed of being a singer when she grew up.

At home, life was good. The Andersons were a warm, close family. Even though Marian's father worked hard and came home tired, he was always ready to laugh and joke with his daughters. Sometimes he surprised them with special treats, like new Easter hats or tickets to the circus. And Mrs. Anderson was there whenever the girls needed her, teaching them and loving them.

But when Marian was twelve, her father died. Life changed then. Harder times began. Marian's mother had to go out to work. She got a job cleaning other people's houses and bringing their laundry home to wash and iron. Mrs. Anderson was a frail, gentle woman, but she had great spirit. No matter how difficult her tasks were, she never complained. Somehow she found the extra strength to make a good home for her children.

As the years went by, Marian began to realize how hard her mother worked to provide for her family. "I'm getting old enough now," she thought, "I must do something, too." When she entered high school she tried to study useful subjects, like typing. She knew this would help her get a job as a secretary in an office. But all the time her heart was really set on singing.

If only she could earn enough money at it, she could make singing her life's work. Of course she was not paid for singing in church. Ever since she was eight, though, she had been invited to sing in other churches, too. People all over Philadelphia got to know about her splendid voice. They began asking her to perform at their parties and club meetings. By the time Marian was in high school, she was getting $5.00 every time she sang at one of these gatherings.

This seemed like a lot of money to her. Yet she knew she was still a long way from being a professional singer. She had been born with a fine voice and she sang with deep feeling.

But Marian saw how much she still had to learn. The best way, she decided, would be to have lessons, at a music school.

Early one morning she took the trolley car to a well-known school in uptown Philadelphia. She went into the building and got in line with a group of girls who were waiting to apply. When Marian's turn came, the pretty, blue-eyed woman in charge paid no attention to her. Marian stepped aside. After everyone else had been taken care of, the woman said, "What do *you* want?" in a sharp voice. "I'd like to arrange for lessons, please — " Marian began politely. "We don't take colored," said the woman coldly, and turned away.

Marian felt hurt and confused. She had often heard that white people sometimes behaved in this cruel, thoughtless way toward Negroes. But it had never really happened to her before. In her neighborhood black people and white people lived side by side. Most of the time they were comfortable and friendly with each other. True enough, their skins were different, Marian thought, but not their feelings.

Sadly she went home to tell her mother what happened at the school. "The way that woman spoke," she cried, "it bit into my soul." Her mother listened quietly. Was she wrong to think a Negro girl could become a singer? Marian asked. Maybe her dreams were foolish.

Mrs. Anderson thought for a while. Then, in her calm, sure way, she said, "Of course you can be a singer, Marian. You must have faith. There will be another way for you to learn what you need to know."

And there was another way. The people at the Union Baptist Church believed in Marian's talent. These friends and neighbors planned a concert to help her. Every bit of money they got from the tickets was set aside to pay for private singing lessons for Marian.

Marian performed at the concert herself, but the main star was Roland Hayes. Mr. Hayes was the first Negro singer to become famous in the concert halls of America and Europe. He sang the spirituals Marian and her people knew so well. These were powerful songs of sorrow, of joy, and of hope that the Negroes made up when they were slaves. Mr. Hayes also sang lieder, poems set to music by the great European composers. Marian could not understand the French or German languages they were sung in. Still she was quick to hear the beauty of the music. She longed to learn such songs herself.

Roland Hayes

Then, as she listened to Mr. Hayes's pure tenor voice, she suddenly realized, "His skin is dark, like mine. And he has gone so far. They say he has even sung for kings and queens. If he can, perhaps I can too." Slowly, from this time on, Marian's pride began to grow. It was never an angry pride, but full of faith and hope. Throughout her life, no matter what happened, it kept her strong.

With the money raised at the concert, Marian started taking music lessons. She quickly learned everything her teachers could show her. Then Giuseppi Boghetti agreed to listen to her. He was a well-known voice coach with studios in Philadelphia and New York. At first he spoke to her gruffly. "I am seeing you just as a favor," he said. "I don't want any new students. I have too many already."

Marian sang for him. The deep beauty and feeling in her voice instantly changed Mr. Boghetti's mind. "I will make room for you right away," he declared. "Don't think it will be easy, though. You have a grand voice. But it must be trained, so that it can do whatever you want it to do. For this you need many exercises and much hard practicing. We will work together. After that you will be able to go anywhere and sing for anybody."

That year Marian finished high school. With more free time, she could do more performing. She began to travel farther from home to sing in churches, colleges, and small theaters. Finally she earned enough money to make one of her greatest wishes come true. The day came when she could say to her mother, "I can take care of you now. You don't have to work any more." Afterward Marian always said that was the happiest day of her life.

Marian with her mother, Anna Anderson, after receiving an award

When Mr. Boghetti thought Marian was ready, he let her enter a contest of three hundred young singers. The first prize was a chance to perform with the New York Philharmonic Orchestra. By now Marian's amazing voice was well trained. And, as always, she put her whole spirit into the music. After she sang, the other contestants clapped and cheered. Then the judges announced that she had won.

Marian hoped this prize would prove she was ready to sing in America's best concert halls. The people who wrote about music in the newspapers and magazines were beginning to say fine things about her. But several years passed and still she was not often asked to sing in the really important theaters. Most Americans just did not want to believe that a Negro could be an excellent concert singer. They would not give Marian a chance to show them how good she was.

Marian felt that her career was standing still. "What can I do about this?" she wondered. Finally she decided to go to Europe. There she would study with famous singing masters. Then, if she performed for European audiences, and these people liked her work, perhaps America would welcome her back and realize what she could do.

She studied first in England. Then she went to Germany, to learn the language of her favorite lieder. There she met Kosti Vehanen, a pianist from Finland. "Let me become your accompanist," he offered. Marian agreed. Kosti would play the piano while she sang. Together they set out on a tour of the Scandinavian countries in the north of Europe. Here — in Norway, Sweden, Finland, and Denmark — Marian was immediately accepted as a great singer by everyone who heard her. It did not matter to these people that Marian was black and most of them were white. They loved her voice and they loved her.

Arturo Toscanini

A tour of Europe followed. Once again Marian was a huge success. Arturo Toscanini, the famous orchestra conductor, came to one of her concerts. He was so moved by her singing that he went backstage afterward to speak to her. Marian could hardly believe what he said: "A voice like yours is heard only once in a hundred years."

Ordinary people had the same feeling about her. It was Marian's way to end each of her concerts with a group of Negro spirituals. Often the Europeans could not understand the English words. It made no difference. Marian poured the heart and soul of her people into this music. When the songs she planned to sing were over, the audience would not leave the theater. They called for her again and again. Some of them rushed down the aisles and pounded on the stage, shouting out the names of the spirituals they liked best. " 'Deep River'!" they yelled. " 'Heaven, Heaven'!"

Never in America had she had a welcome like this. And yet Marian thought it was time to go back to her own country. Her stay in Europe helped her find her place as a singer. But America was her home. Her family was there. All the people who first believed in her and helped her were there, waiting. She knew she must return to them.

Marian sailed back to the United States on a large ocean liner. Every day she and Kosti practiced together for the important homecoming concert in New York. One morning, as Marian was going down the staircase to the rehearsal room, the rough sea made the ship lurch. Marian lost her balance and fell. She was in great pain. The doctor told her she had a broken bone in her foot. He put her leg in a bulky plaster cast.

But Marian did not disappoint the people who came to her concert. On December 30, 1935, she sang at Town Hall. Her cast was hidden by a long evening dress. And this time her American audience let themselves understand what a wonderful singer this black woman was. Marian sang about the beautiful things in the world, and the ugly things. She sang about happy times and sad ones. She sang about the deepest thoughts and feelings that all people share. When she finished there was a long silence. Then the audience rose to its feet and burst into wild applause.

Marian Anderson performing in Bombay, India

In the next thirty years Marian sang all over the world. She traveled across the United States again and again. She went back to Europe many times. She gave concerts in Russia, Israel, and Japan. She was almost always accepted as she deserved. Sometimes, though, there were difficulties because she was black. But when others were mean-spirited, Marian knew how to be generous and understanding. Once, when she faced this kind of trouble, the whole world was watching.

In the spring of 1939 she planned to give a concert in Washington, D.C., the nation's capital. She hoped to appear in Constitution Hall. It was owned by the Daughters of the American Revolution, a group of women whose families had, long ago, fought for freedom in the United States. But the D.A.R. refused to let Marian Anderson sing on their stage. Why? There could be only one answer. She was a Negro.

Fair-minded people all over America said this was wrong. Throughout the world men and women waited to see what would happen. Marian was not a fighter. But through her music she would do whatever she could to gain freedom and justice for her people. Leaders of the United States government invited her to give her concert outdoors for everyone who wanted to come.

On Easter Sunday Marian came to the Lincoln Memorial. She stood before the statue of Abraham Lincoln, the president who freed the Negro slaves. There she sang for 75,000 people. Black and white together, they joined her in the opening song — "The Star-Spangled Banner."

Marian Anderson singing at the Lincoln Memorial in 1939

Four years later Marian married Orpheus Fisher. They had known each other for a long time. Together they chose some beautiful land in the Connecticut farm country. On it they built the simple, comfortable house Marian had always dreamed of. Close by, near a running brook, was a separate studio for Marian to work in. Mr. Fisher, who was an architect, designed everything himself.

Marian with her husband, Orpheus Fisher, at Marianna Farm

Now, although Marian might be on tour most of the year, she always came home to Marianna Farm for the summer. There, with her new accompanist, Franz Rupp, she prepared her concerts for the next season. First Marian and Franz carefully picked out the songs they wanted to do. Then they studied them and practiced them over and over again. They tried to make their performance of each song as close to perfect as they could.

Marianna Farm was also a place of rest. Here Marian could relax with her husband. She enjoyed sewing things for her home and caring for the pet animals they kept. Here, too, her mother and sisters often visited with her.

After twenty years as a successful concert singer, Marian was given a chance to try another kind of music. In 1955 she was asked to appear with the world-famous Metropolitan Opera Company in New York. She took the part of Ulrica, the gypsy fortune-teller, in Verdi's opera *The Masked Ball.* It was the first time a Negro had sung an important role at the Metropolitan as a regular company member.

Marian's part was not easy. She had to reach very high and very low notes, and join in difficult group singing. And as she sang, she had to make the audience believe she was truly a gypsy sorceress. The whole company worked with her. Marian said it was like being part of a big family. Together they gave a wonderful performance of the opera.

That night, as the gold curtain came down at the Met, people called excitedly, "Anderson, Anderson!" Some of them even cried, thinking of all Marian had done to reach this great moment. That night a new audience discovered her glorious voice. More important, Marian opened a door for her own people. From that time on, Negro singers were welcome on the great opera stage.

Marian's talent and her simple, beautiful spirit brought her many honors. Like Roland

Hayes, she sang for kings and queens, and for three presidents of the United States. Two of her best rewards, though, were jobs she was invited to do.

In 1951 the American government asked her to tour the countries of Asia. She sang to the people and then spoke with them. These men and women found it easy to talk to her, to tell her the thoughts deep inside them, to explain what their countries needed and what they hoped for. Marian understood people from different places so well that she was then sent to the United Nations. There she joined the leaders of many countries in trying to bring peace to the world.

Now Marian was growing older. Her singing voice was not as rich and full as it used to be. Of course she would always sing at home, for her family and friends. But it was best to end the days of performing.

In 1956 she made a farewell tour of Europe and America. As she took her last bows from the stage, she thought, "My work is not over. There is still much I can do. I want to help people of different groups come to understand each other. I can make the way easier for young singers. I want to do something for children all over the world — with my hands, and my heart, and my soul. In a way, my work is just beginning."

A Someday Dream

As a young girl, Marian Anderson
secretly dreamed of being a singer when she grew up.
What do you dream of being someday?
Write a paragraph or a poem telling about your dream.

Poetry

GERTRUDE

When I hear Marian Anderson sing,
I am a STUFFless kind of thing.

Heart is like the flying air.
I cannot find it anywhere.

Fingers tingle. I am cold
And warm and young and very old.

But, most, I am a STUFFless thing
When I hear Marian Anderson sing.

Gwendolyn Brooks

DREAMS

Hold fast to dreams
For if dreams die
Life is a broken-winged bird
That cannot fly.

Hold fast to dreams
For when dreams go
Life is a barren field
Frozen with snow.

Langston Hughes

HOLD FAST YOUR DREAMS

Hold fast your dreams!
Within your heart
Keep one still, secret spot
Where dreams may go,
And sheltered so,
May thrive and grow —
Where doubt and fear are not.
Oh, keep a place apart
Within your heart,
For little dreams to go.

Louise Driscoll

Roberto Clemente

by Kenneth Rudeen

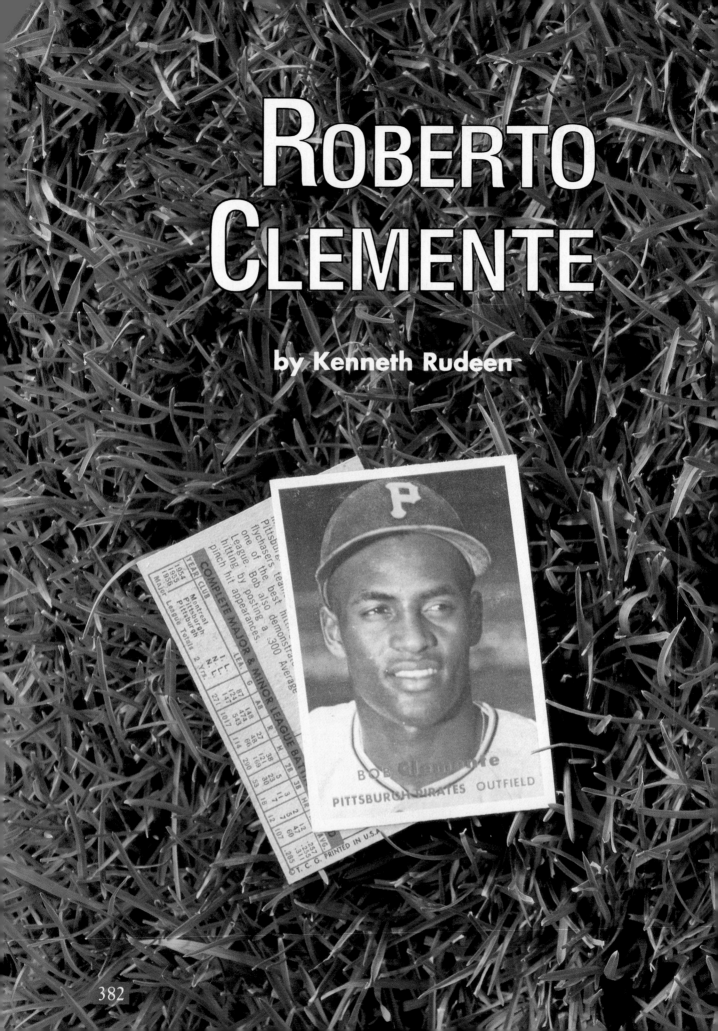

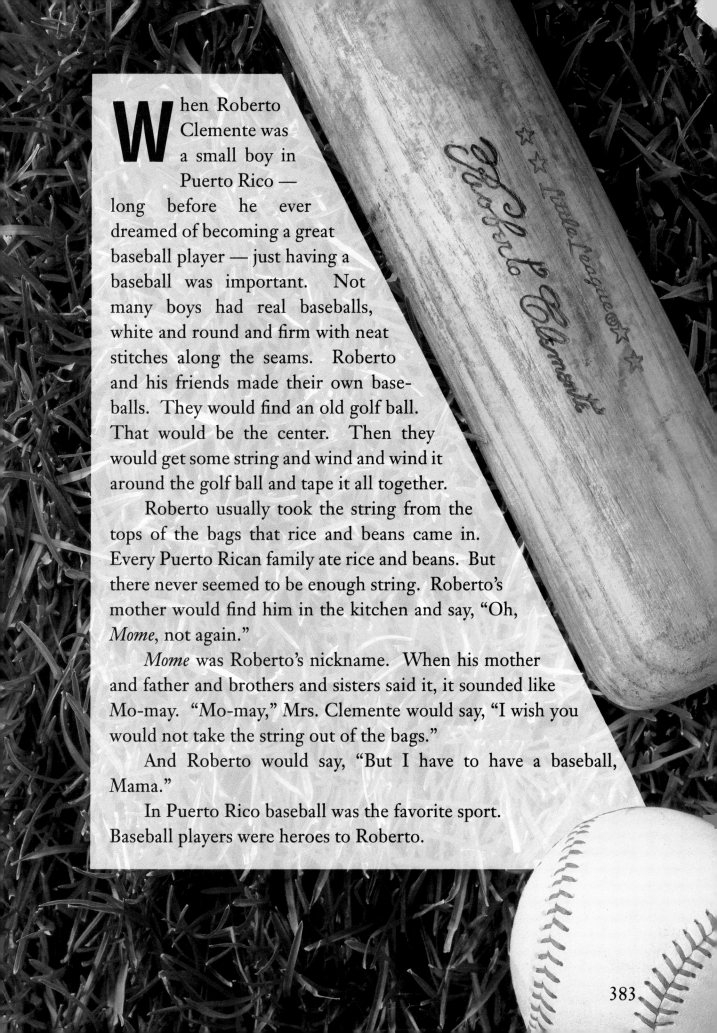

When Roberto Clemente was a small boy in Puerto Rico — long before he ever dreamed of becoming a great baseball player — just having a baseball was important. Not many boys had real baseballs, white and round and firm with neat stitches along the seams. Roberto and his friends made their own baseballs. They would find an old golf ball. That would be the center. Then they would get some string and wind and wind it around the golf ball and tape it all together.

Roberto usually took the string from the tops of the bags that rice and beans came in. Every Puerto Rican family ate rice and beans. But there never seemed to be enough string. Roberto's mother would find him in the kitchen and say, "Oh, *Mome*, not again."

Mome was Roberto's nickname. When his mother and father and brothers and sisters said it, it sounded like Mo-may. "Mo-may," Mrs. Clemente would say, "I wish you would not take the string out of the bags."

And Roberto would say, "But I have to have a baseball, Mama."

In Puerto Rico baseball was the favorite sport. Baseball players were heroes to Roberto.

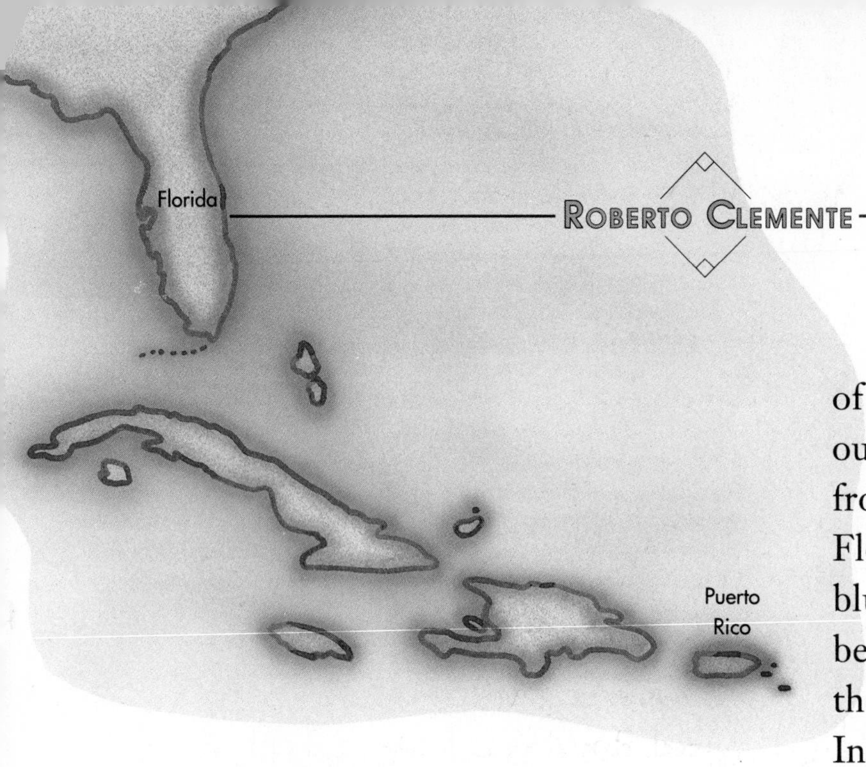

Puerto Rico is one of the islands that stretch out like steppingstones from the southern tip of Florida into the warm, blue sea. The island is beautiful, but for most of the people life is hard. In the sky the sun shines brightly. Foamy waves splash against the shore. Green mountains rise up from the sea. Birds with gaily colored feathers sing in the trees.

But men are not free to fly like birds. They must work long hours in the cities or in the fields. To be a baseball player is to be like a bird. That is a way to fly up from the hard life.

Roberto Clemente was born in the town of Carolina on August 18, 1934. The town is nestled in a valley not far from the big city of San Juan. When Roberto was growing up, there were large fields of sugar cane all around Carolina. They looked a little like the cornfields of the United States. The canes were slender and tall, growing to a height well above a man's head. They had sharp, narrow leaves that cut like a razor if you brushed against one by mistake.

To Roberto and his friends the sugar cane was like candy. They would peel back the bark on a piece of cane and bite and suck on the chewy pulp inside to get its sweet taste.

Roberto knew the fields especially well. His father was a foreman for a big sugar cane company. He saw that other workers in the fields did their jobs properly.

A man did not get rich working in the cane fields. An ordinary worker received only $2 a day. A foreman like Roberto's father received $3 or $4 a day.

In Roberto's family there was no money for luxuries like new baseballs. But there was always enough rice and beans and chicken and pork on the table. Roberto's small house, which was made of wood and had a zinc roof, stood near a grove of bamboo trees.

Roberto's father was strict. When he gave his sons jobs to do, they did them. One day he asked Roberto and another son to move a large pile of sand. It was hard work to shovel the heavy sand, and the sun was hot.

"Roberto, I feel sick," his brother said.

Roberto looked at his brother. Sweat stood out on his forehead and his face was pale.

"Go on home," Roberto said. "I will finish the job."

It was easy to say, but when his brother was gone, Roberto had to face the pile of sand all by himself. It looked so high he wanted to give up. But he didn't.

Roberto worked harder than he ever had before. When he was finished at last, he ran for home, because his father had told

sugar cane

him not to be late for dinner. He was tired and he ached, but inside he felt good.

From Monday to Friday, Roberto went to school. Often his thoughts were tugged from his books by the warm sun and gentle breezes outside the classroom window — tugged to the ball park, where someday he hoped to play.

In the meantime he had to be content, after school, with balls made of string and tape and games played in a rough clearing that was not even level.

There were other boys much better at baseball than Roberto. People did not say, "Roberto is going to be a great ballplayer." He was small and thin. He could not hit the ball as hard or throw it as far as the bigger boys of his age.

Roberto and his friends played a game that was more like softball than baseball. They did not have the gloves or catching masks and pads to handle the hard, stinging baseball that the big-leaguers use.

But they saw the real game played in the park in Carolina — and they longed to play there, too, someday.

While he loved baseball and played as much as he could on the field the boys used, after school Roberto always ran first to the sugar cane fields. There he met his father and rode home with him on his horse. Papa Clemente climbed into the saddle and Roberto scrambled up behind him. Then off they rode to the house with the bamboo trees.

One day, when Roberto was nine years old, he was late. Papa Clemente rode off without him. A car came along and crashed into the horse. Papa Clemente was thrown. He was badly hurt and had to spend two months in a hospital.

"It is a miracle Roberto was spared," his father said. "If he had been riding with me as usual, I am afraid he would have been killed."

When time came for Roberto to go to high school, he was happy. The high school had a real baseball field. It had real baseballs, gloves, and masks.

Roberto played in the outfield. He had to run fast to get to balls that were hit in his direction and throw hard to keep the hitter from running to extra bases.

Roberto had always been a fast runner. Now he worked hard to become a good thrower and a good hitter. Roberto's high school had a track team. Besides running on the team, Roberto also threw the javelin, which is like a spear. When you throw it, the javelin sails through the air and then comes down and sticks in the ground.

Roberto threw the javelin to make his arm strong for baseball. In time he became one of the best throwers on his baseball team.

In high school Roberto was a quiet and serious boy. "He did not want to be just an ordinary person, he wanted to be the best," one of his friends says.

Just before Roberto was graduated from high school he was chosen to play for the team in Santurce. Santurce is a town near

Roberto (kneeling, second from left) with the Santurce team

Carolina. Roberto was paid to play baseball for this town. He did not make a great deal of money, but it was more than anyone in the sugar fields could make.

Even better, now Roberto was *somebody*. People turned their heads to look at him when he walked in the plaza. To his old friends he was still *Mome*, but to everyone else he was the new young ballplayer, Roberto Clemente.

It was a name soon to be heard in the United States, where the best players in baseball perform in two major leagues. They are called the National League and the American League.

Roberto wanted to be the best. He wanted to play in the major leagues. Men who look for new players for the major leagues came to see him in Puerto Rico. They saw him hit the ball hard. They saw him catch it in the outfield with sure hands. They saw him throw the ball fast and true. They saw him run swiftly.

In 1954, when Roberto was nineteen years old, he was chosen by one of the most famous teams in the National League, the Brooklyn Dodgers.

He was happy to have this chance. The Dodgers was the team of Jackie Robinson. Jackie was the first black man to play in the major leagues. He was a wonderful player, but he had many problems with white people who did not accept black men as equals.

Like Robinson, Roberto Clemente was black. But while growing up in Puerto Rico, he did not think about the color of a person's skin. Black men and men with light skin had always played baseball together in Puerto Rico.

So while Roberto was happy, he was also scared. He was going far from home for the first time in his life, and to places where black men still were not always treated fairly.

First Roberto was sent to Montreal in Canada to play for a farm team of the Dodgers. A farm team helps prepare young players for the major leagues.

Roberto probably was good enough to be on the Dodgers. But this was still a time when there were not very many black men in the major leagues. Some people said that the major leagues did not want to have more than four black players on any one team.

The Brooklyn Dodgers already had four black players. That was one of the reasons, people said, why Roberto was sent to the Montreal farm team.

But now the Dodgers had a problem. They wanted to keep Roberto for the future, but by sending him to a farm team just then they ran the risk of losing him. Scouts for other teams might discover him. One of these teams might take him.

The Dodgers did not want that to happen. They wanted to hide Roberto from these scouts. But how were they to do it? The Dodgers could not put him in a cave, or a closet. They had to try to hide him right out in the open as he played baseball for Montreal. They tried to do this by making it look as if Roberto were not as good a player as he really was.

It was not easy to hide Roberto. The manager of the Montreal team did his best. When Roberto was doing fine in a game, the manager would take him out. When Roberto was having just an ordinary day, the manager would leave him in.

Roberto did not know why he was being treated this way. He became confused and angry. He was lonely, anyway, living among strangers so far from home. He had grown up speaking Spanish. The people on his team spoke English, and the people in Montreal mostly spoke French.

There were trips to other cities to play other farm teams, so there were new sights for Roberto to see and new people to meet. He had money to spend. He had a good-looking uniform, and he had time to practice batting and throwing and running.

Roberto might have enjoyed all these things, but life seemed upside-down. The better he played, the quicker he was taken from a game. The worse he played, the longer he stayed in. At times he thought about quitting baseball and going home to Puerto Rico.

But his desire to play, and to be the best, was stronger than his loneliness and his anger. He kept on playing.

The Dodgers just could not make him look bad enough. Other teams could see that he was a fine player. Scouts for the Pittsburgh Pirates, another team in the National League, watched Roberto closely. They decided to take him and have him play for them.

Pittsburgh is not a place of tall sugar cane fields and gaily colored birds. It is a big, smoky city. But its people do have one thing in common with the people of Carolina, Puerto Rico. They love their baseball team.

Right from the start they loved Roberto. He was tremendous as a fielder. He had a trick of catching a ball way up in the air, with both of his feet off the ground, and then whirling to throw the ball back to the infield before his feet came down to earth. He thought nothing of crashing into walls and fences if he had to do that to catch a ball.

He became an excellent hitter. In baseball a really good hitter is one who gets three hits in every ten chances at bat. If he does that, he is said to be batting three hundred. In his second year with Pittsburgh, Roberto was batting better than three hundred.

More and more black men, more and more Spanish-speaking players like Roberto were coming into major league baseball. Soon there was no more talk of keeping the number of black players on a team down to four.

But still there were times when Roberto felt that he and other Spanish-speaking players were treated unfairly. He believed that they were not given as much praise and publicity as the others, even when they were just as good. Roberto was the kind of man who could make people listen to him. He asked for equal treatment for Spanish-speaking players. Whenever he could help one of them, he did.

Once the regular Pittsburgh shortstop could not play. A Spanish-speaking player was put in his place. This player was new to the team and nervous. He made some mistakes. Other players on the team were angry with him.

Roberto found him later, crying in the dressing room. "You are coming to dinner with me tonight," Roberto said. At dinner Roberto cheered him up. Then he asked the other Pirates to be more patient with the shortstop. They were, and he played well in some very important games.

By 1960 Roberto's Pirates were strong enough to win the championship of the National League. They played the American

P
P
P
PIRATES
ATES

League champions, the New York Yankees, in the World Series. There were seven games in that World Series. Roberto made a hit in every game and the Pirates won.

Roberto was getting better and better as a player, but he was not always happy. Often he was sick or injured. Playing as hard as he did, he would tear muscles. Once he had malaria, an illness of chills and fevers.

Even so, Roberto went on to win four batting championships in the National League. Nearly every year he was a member of the All-Star team — the best players from all the teams in the National League.

Every winter, after the major league baseball season ended in the United States, Roberto went home to Puerto Rico. Once when he was in Carolina he met one of his old high school teachers in a drugstore. As he was talking to her, a lovely girl walked past.

"Do you know her?" Roberto asked his friend, the teacher.

"Yes, I do," the teacher said. "That is Vera Zabala."

"Will you introduce me?" Roberto asked.

That is how Roberto met the woman he married. They built a beautiful house in the town of Rio Piedras, which is near Carolina, and in time they had three little boys.

Roberto with his sons
Enrique, Luis, and Roberto, Jr.

The basement of the house in Rio Piedras was Roberto's workshop. As a child he had liked to make things of clay. He had shaped small figures of people and animals and let them bake in the Carolina sun until they were hard. Now in Rio Piedras he took clay and made it into baseball gloves and bats.

When Roberto talked to young Puerto Ricans, he remembered the rough playing field of his boyhood and he began to dream of a sports city for the island. There young people would be able to play baseball, basketball, tennis, and soccer with the best equipment.

Each spring he returned to the United States to play for the Pirates. But not until 1971 did he and the Pirates win another National League championship and go into another World Series.

Now the Pirates faced the Baltimore Orioles. Nearly everybody thought Baltimore was a better team than Pittsburgh, and the Orioles won the first game easily. The next day they won again. Those games were played in Baltimore on the Orioles' home field. It is often easier to win at home than on the opponent's field.

There were to be three games in Pittsburgh. To the great joy of that city, the Pirates won all three games. To win a World Series one team must win four games. So now the Pirates needed just one more victory. But the next game would be played in Baltimore.

Baltimore won that game by the close score of 3 to 2. The winners of the next game would be the world champions. And again the game would be played in Baltimore.

The stadium in Baltimore was packed with cheering fans. Millions of people were watching the game on television.

The score was zero to zero when Roberto stepped up to bat in the fourth inning. He made a twisting motion with his head to relieve the pain he had been feeling all week in his neck. He looked out at the Baltimore pitcher, Mike Cuellar.

Cuellar was a man who threw slow, tricky pitches that were difficult to hit. He threw. The ball floated in toward Roberto. Crack! went the bat. The ball flew over the outfield and into the seats beyond. It was a home run. Pittsburgh was ahead in the game, 1 to 0.

Roberto connects for a home run in the 1971 World Series.

In the eighth inning the Pirates scored another run. Baltimore scored a run in the eighth inning, too, but the Orioles could do nothing after that to draw even. The game ended. The Pirates had won the Series in the last possible game by the score of 2 to 1. Without Roberto's home run, who knows what might have happened?

Just as he had in 1960, Roberto made a hit in every game of the World Series. He was voted the most valuable player of the Series by the reporters who wrote about it. Of all the players on both teams, Roberto Clemente was the very best.

Roberto rounds the bases after homering in the Series.

He went home to a hero's welcome in Puerto Rico. A huge crowd was at the airport in San Juan to meet his plane. The governor of the island presented him with a gold medal.

There was just one more thing left in baseball for Roberto to do. That was to make 3,000 hits. He would soon be thirty-eight years old — very old for a ballplayer. Only ten men in the entire history of baseball had ever played long enough or well enough to make 3,000 hits. These were special heroes.

At the very end of the 1972 season, on September 30 in Pittsburgh, Roberto hit Number 3,000.

Roberto went home to his family in Rio Piedras. He wanted to rest and also to plan for the sports city for the boys and girls of Puerto Rico.

Roberto hits Number 3,000.

In December he heard terrible news. In the city of Managua in the Central American country of Nicaragua there had been an earthquake. The ground trembled and shook beneath the city. Buildings cracked and fell. Fires broke out. More than 10,000 people were killed. More than 200,000 people lost their homes.

Around the world people began sending money and food and medicine and clothing to help the earthquake victims. Roberto asked the many Puerto Ricans he knew to help out as much as they could. He did more.

On December 31 he climbed aboard a plane loaded with supplies to take them to the people of Managua. The plane, heavily laden, rose slowly from the San Juan airport and headed out to sea. Then, when it was just a mile away, it plunged into the ocean.

That night was New Year's Eve, usually a time of gaiety and celebration, but there was no gaiety in Puerto Rico. Thousands of people went to the beach to look for the wreckage of the plane. When it became clear that Roberto had drowned, Puerto Ricans and many people in the United States felt sad. A great player — and man — was gone.

In the United States Roberto was elected to baseball's Hall of Fame. This is the greatest honor a baseball player can receive. The Hall of Fame building is in Cooperstown, New York. In it there are pictures of the best players, and things like their bats and caps.

A sign was placed on the door of the room Roberto had lived in during spring training with the Pirates in Florida. It read, "I want to be remembered as a ballplayer who gave all he had to give."

It was signed, Roberto Clemente

ROBERTO WALKER CLEMENTE
PITTSBURGH N. L. 1955-1972
MEMBER OF EXCLUSIVE 3,000-HIT CLUB. LED NATIONAL LEAGUE IN BATTING FOUR TIMES. HAD FOUR SEASONS WITH 200 OR MORE HITS WHILE POSTING LIFETIME .317 AVERAGE AND 240 HOME RUNS. WON MOST VALUABLE PLAYER AWARD 1966. RIFLE-ARMED DEFENSIVE STAR SET N. L. MARK BY PACING OUTFIELDERS IN ASSISTS FIVE YEARS. BATTED .362 IN TWO WORLD SERIES, HITTING IN ALL 14 GAMES.

plaque from the Hall of Fame

CLEMENTE'S DREAM

This is my dream. I do not know exactly what this sports city will be like . . . but it will be beautiful. It will be open to everybody. No matter who they are.

Roberto Clemente

Roberto Clemente's dream of opening a sports center for young people in his homeland became a reality. Thanks to the efforts of Clemente's wife and the people of Puerto Rico, *Ciudad Deportiva* (Sports City) is now open. The center has baseball fields, basketball and tennis courts, a recreation area, and a swimming pool. *Ciudad Deportiva* is free and open to all.

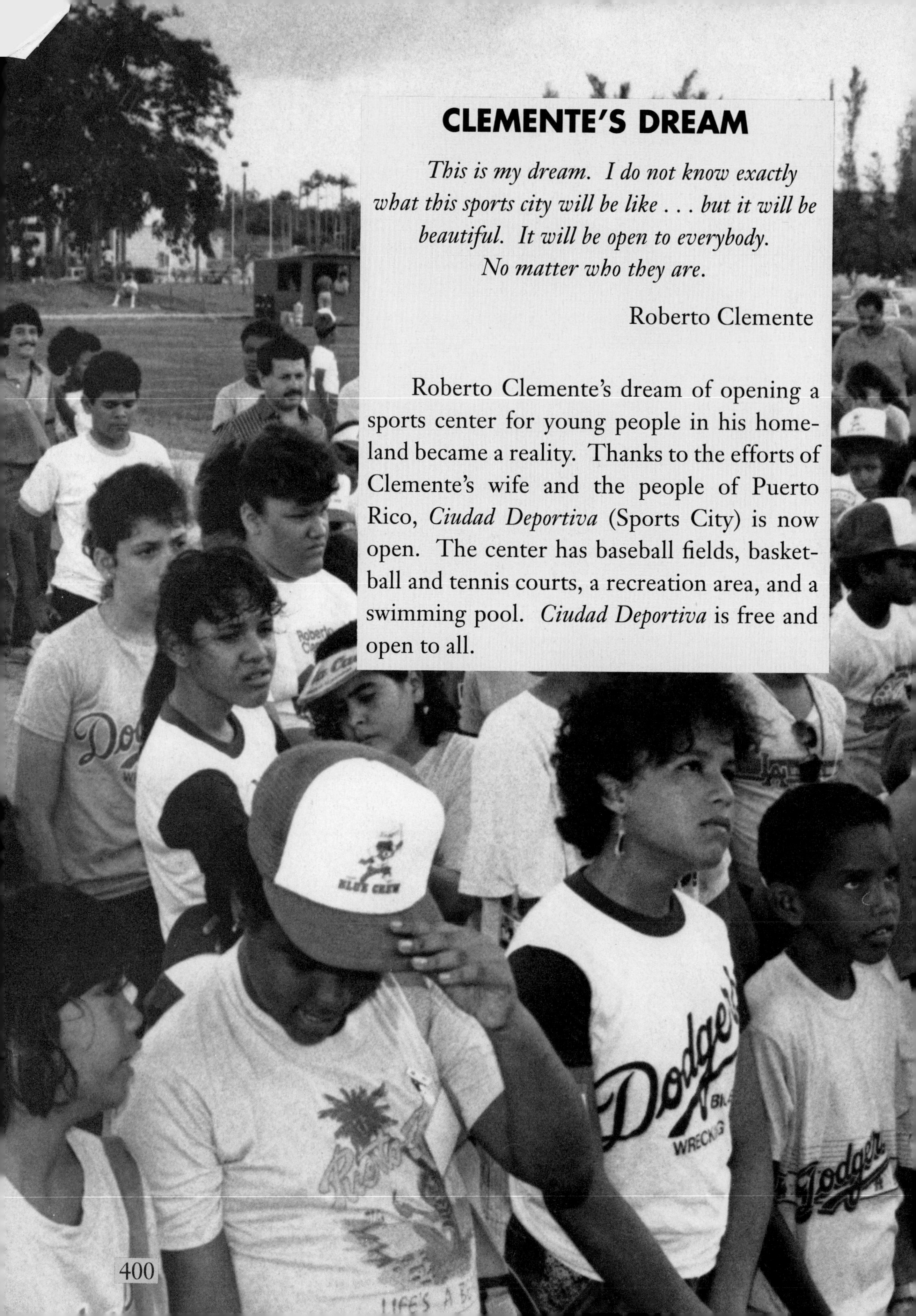

MY HERO

As a boy in Puerto Rico, Roberto Clemente admired baseball players. When he grew up and played baseball himself, Clemente became a hero to many people.

Who are your heroes? They might be famous people or they might be people who are close to you. Write a paragraph about one of your heroes and tell why you admire that person.

The Authors

ELIZABETH RIDER MONTGOMERY

Elizabeth Montgomery never intended to be a writer. She wanted to illustrate books, not write them. Winning an essay contest at age six for "The Good and Bad Uses of the Apple" didn't convince her. Winning several other writing contests didn't convince her either. Finally, her parents convinced her that she couldn't make any money as an illustrator. So she gave in and became a writer.

Montgomery wrote many biographies, including these:

- ***Hans Christian Andersen, Immortal Storyteller***
- ***Alexander Graham Bell: Man of Sound***

TOBI TOBIAS

When Tobi Tobias was nine years old, her father predicted that one day she would become a writer. She made his words come true.

Tobias has written many books, including several other biographies. Her love for the performing arts, especially dance, is seen in books such as these:

- ***Maria Tallchief*** — the story of the Osage Indian who became a ballerina.
- ***Arthur Mitchell*** — the biography of the man who became a star with the New York City Ballet.

KENNETH RUDEEN

Kenneth Rudeen, the author of *Roberto Clemente*, had something in common with Walt Disney. While Rudeen was still in high school, he worked in the mailroom of the Kansas City *Star*, the same newspaper that Disney once delivered. By age seventeen, Rudeen had become a reporter for the *Star*. Rudeen has written several biographies of sports heroes. Here are two you might enjoy:

- ***Jackie Robinson*** tells the story of the man who broke the color barrier in major league baseball.
- ***Wilt Chamberlain*** tells how one of the greatest basketball players got his start.

They Lived Their Dreams

Take Me Out to the Airfield!
by Robert Quackenbush

Long before airplanes existed, two brothers dreamed of flying. Their names were Wilbur and Orville Wright.

Grandma Moses: Painter of Rural America *by Zibby Oneal*

Although she did not start painting until she was nearly eighty years old, Grandma Moses became one of America's best-loved artists.

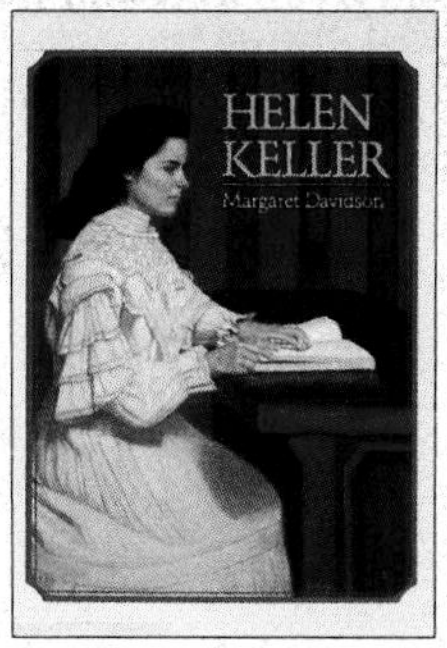

Helen Keller *by Margaret Davidson*

W-A-T-E-R. *Water* was the first word Helen Keller learned to spell, despite being deaf and blind. She became an inspiration to the world.

Martin Luther King, Jr. *by David A. Adler*

"I have a dream that my four little children will one day live in a nation where they will not be judged by the color of their skin but by the content of their character."

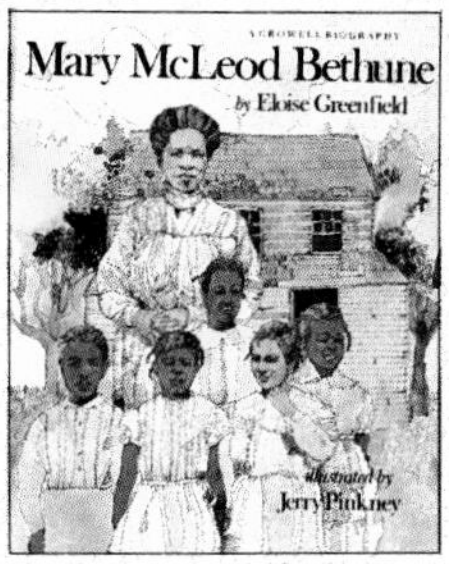

Mary McLeod Bethune *by Eloise Greenfield*

She dreamed of learning to read. She dreamed of going to school. She dreamed of starting a school. She did all that she dreamed.

Lou Gehrig, Pride of the Yankees
by Keith Brandt

"Today I consider myself the luckiest man on the face of the earth," Lou Gehrig told the fans at Yankee Stadium.

FICTION

BOOK 7

Dear Diary

Nov. 5
Dear Diary,
I'm going to prove once and for all that I'm the smartest girl in my class.
July 16
Dear Diary,
Uncle Joe came to live with us today.
Aug. 25
Dear Diary,
Grandpa took me to the festival, and did we have a great time!
1
May 1
Dear Diary,
Guess what? Annie Alpert likes me! (well, maybe.)

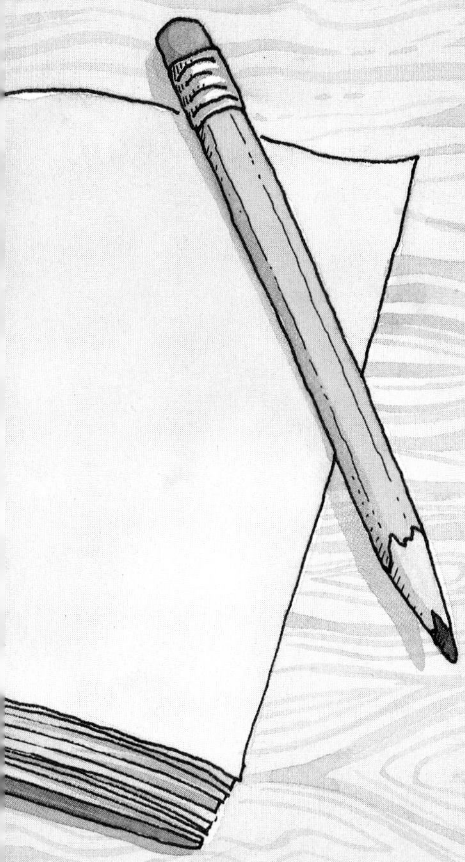

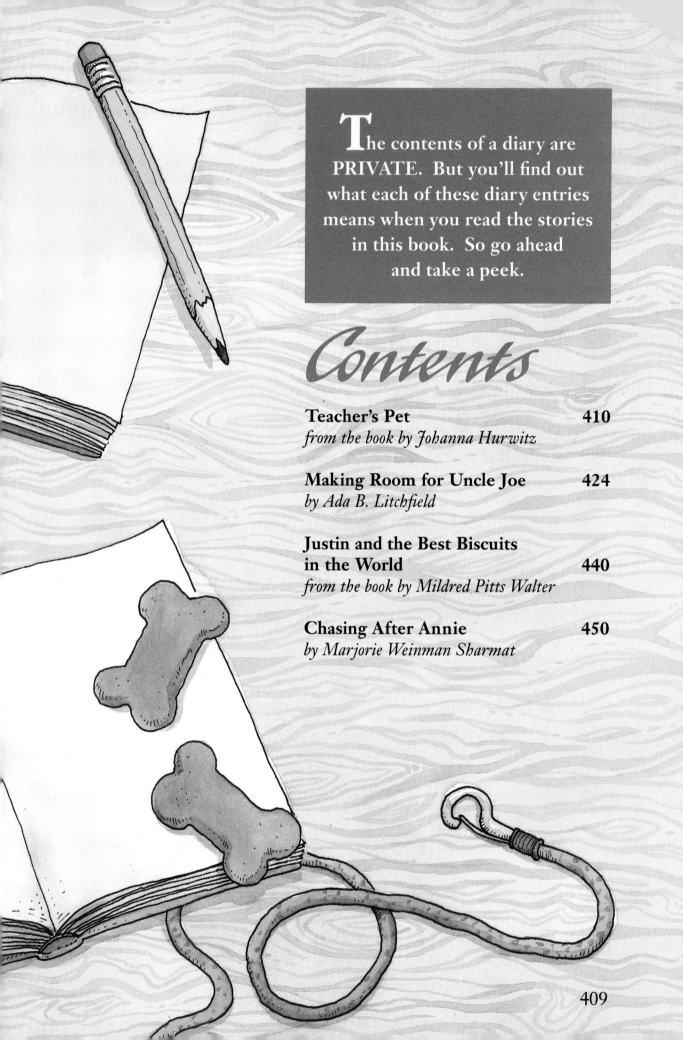

The contents of a diary are PRIVATE. But you'll find out what each of these diary entries means when you read the stories in this book. So go ahead and take a peek.

Contents

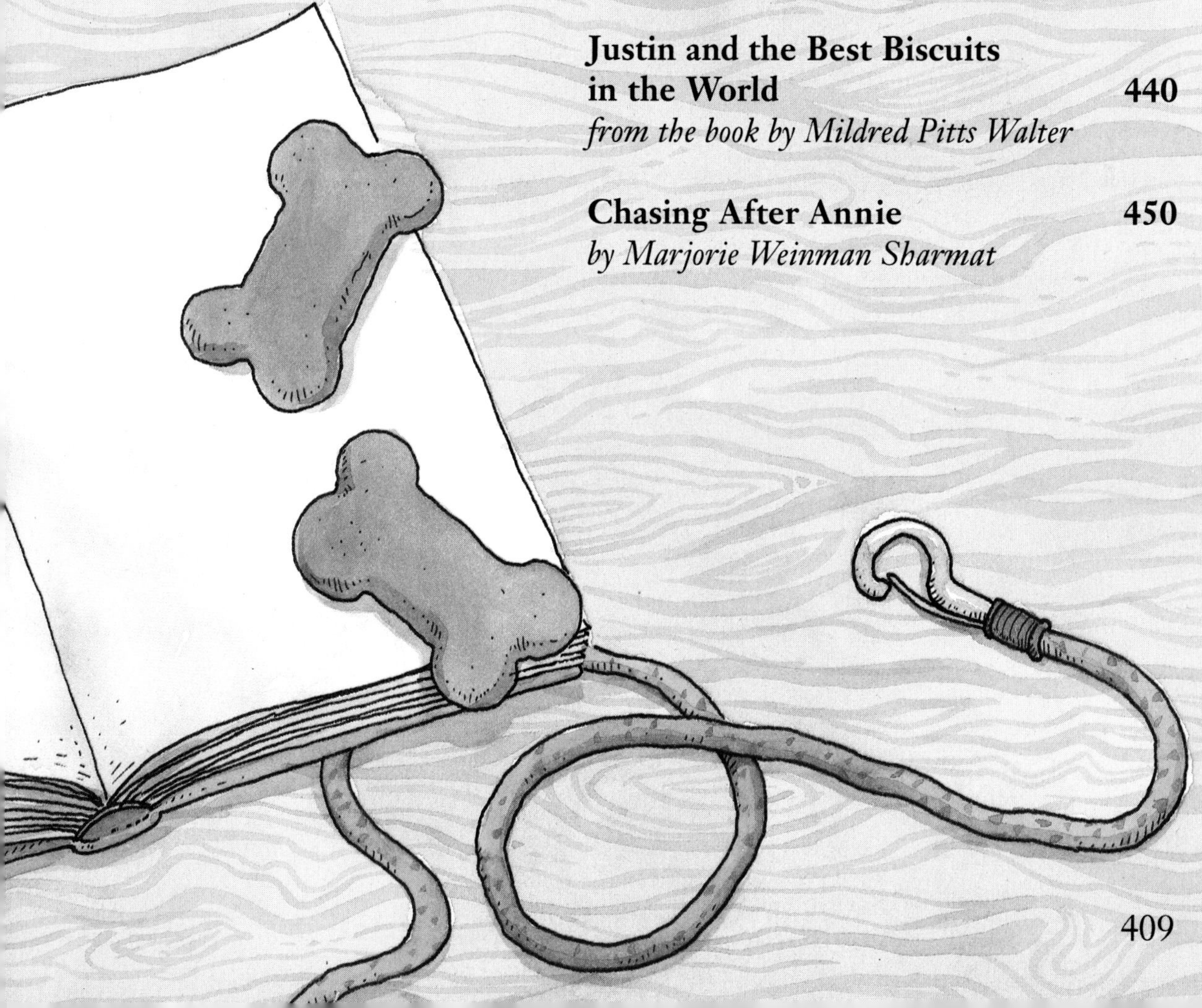

ssignments
k Report is
Tomorrow!!
Pages 12-

Teacher's Pet

from the book by Johanna Hurwitz
illustrations by George Courage

There was no doubt about it. Zoe Mitchell was just as smart as Cricket Kaufman. Everyone who had known Cricket since she had been the star of the morning kindergarten class, back when she was five years old, agreed. Finally, she had met her match.

In some ways, it made Cricket feel strange not to be the best student in the class. But at the same time, she worked harder than ever and found that she liked school better and better. She was learning so many new things. It was hard to decide if it was because now she was in fourth grade or because she was working not to let Zoe get ahead of her. Lucas Cott was smart, too, but it wasn't the same thing. Maybe it was because he was the smartest boy in the class and she had been the smartest girl. Now, whenever test papers were handed back, Cricket craned her head to see what mark Zoe had gotten. Almost always, the two girls had performed equally well.

Mrs. Schraalenburgh beamed proudly at them both when they each got 100 percent on the fractions test in arithmetic. But she also congratulated Julio for improving his score. When Cricket walked to the back of the room to use the pencil sharpener, she was able to see that Julio had almost as many problems wrong as he had gotten right. Mrs. Schraalenburgh was a funny teacher. She always said she was proud of all her students and to prove it she never singled one person out above the others. Maybe that was why it wasn't quite so bad that Zoe Mitchell was such a good student. If Cricket wasn't the teacher's pet this year, neither was Zoe. No one was. With a different "personality of the day" selected each morning, and students being congratulated even when they could only answer half the questions, everyone was treated equally.

Still, when Mrs. Schraalenburgh said that once a month everyone had to write a book report, Cricket was delighted. She loved reading and a book report would be fun for her to write. She would do one that was so much better than everyone else's that Mrs. Schraalenburgh would have to admit that she was the very best student in the class. Although Cricket was pleased with the new assignment, there were loud groans from the back of the room.

"Quiet!" Mrs. Schraalenburgh scolded. "If you have something to say, raise your hands and I will call on you." She looked at Lucas, who had made the loudest groan.

"Don't you like to read, Lucas?" asked the teacher.

"Sure," said Lucas. "But I don't like writing book reports."

"A book report is a way of sharing something that you have enjoyed with the rest of the class," said Mrs. Schraalenburgh. "It should tell your classmates whether or not they too should read that book."

Lucas did not look convinced. Cricket knew he read a lot of books. She saw him checking them out of the school library when the class had library time. But she also knew he was lazy about doing homework. She, on the other hand, couldn't wait to begin. She would make the best book report that anyone ever did. Then, perhaps finally, Mrs. Schraalenburgh would know what a great student she was.

Cricket had read so many books since the school year had begun that at first she couldn't make up her mind which to use for her report. Finally, she decided to write her report on the book that she had given to Zoe. It was *Dear Mr. Henshaw* by Beverly Clearly. It was too bad she couldn't find a copy of it in the library. But Cricket remembered the story very well, and she thought she could write a report from her memory. Her memory was very good and it had been only a couple of weeks since she had read the book.

Cricket sat down and wrote, covering both sides of a sheet of loose-leaf paper as she told all about the book. Then, very neatly, she copied it over. She used a razor-edged marking pen that she had bought with her allowance last week. The letters came out clear and neat, but near the bottom of the page, she made a mistake. Cricket didn't want to have any crossing-out on her report. So she took a fresh piece of paper and copied her report over again, very slowly this time so that she wouldn't make another error. When she was finished, it looked beautiful. It was the neatest piece of homework that she had ever done.

Then, to enhance the report, she decided to make a special cover for it. She took two sheets of red-colored paper. With her pencil and a ruler, she drew lines across the top of the page. She did it very, very lightly so that afterward she would be able to erase the lines. Then, using the block letters that they had been learning to do in art class, she wrote the title and the author.

<u>Dear Mr. Henshaw</u>, by Beverly Clearly

Book Report by Cricket Kaufman

Underneath, she drew a picture of a boy sitting at a desk and writing. People who hadn't read the book might think it was supposed to be a picture of Cricket writing her book report, but if you read the book or at least read Cricket's report about it, you would know that it was supposed to be Leigh Botts, the main character in the story. He was always writing letters to his favorite author, who was named Mr. Henshaw. Cricket colored in the picture with her markers, and she erased the lines from the top of the paper.

Cricket had her own stapler. She used it to staple the top cover and the back cover to the page with her report. When she was finally finished, it was time for bed. She had missed her favorite Thursday evening television program. But she was so proud of her completed book report that she didn't even mind. Wait until Mrs. Schraalenburgh sees my wonderful report, she thought. She knew that the teacher would have to be very impressed with her careful work.

The next morning Cricket proudly handed in her report.

"You didn't tell us we had to make covers," said Connie Alf when she saw Cricket's masterpiece.

"We didn't have to make covers," said Julio. Cricket looked at the paper he was putting on the teacher's desk. Wait until Mrs. Schraalenburgh saw that he had written a report about *Mr. Popper's Penguins*, which she read to them at the beginning of September. It was cheating to write a report about a book that you hadn't even read. Listening didn't count. And besides, everyone in the class already knew about the story. Julio will be in big trouble, Cricket decided.

"I wrote about the book that you gave me," Zoe whispered to Cricket as she put hers in the pile. "It was a great book and it was fun to write about it." She smiled at Cricket. But Cricket did not smile back. It hadn't occurred to her that Zoe would use the same book that she did for her report.

"How long was your report?" Cricket asked her.

"It was all one side and a little bit of the other side of the paper," said Zoe.

Cricket began to feel better. Her report was longer and her report had a fancy cover. Her report had to be a lot better than Zoe's. In fact, having another report on the same book to compare with hers would make Mrs. Schraalenburgh realize all the more how much effort Cricket had put into the assignment. She smiled at Zoe. It was a good thing that they had both written about the same book, after all.

Mrs. Schraalenburgh took all the reports and put them inside her canvas tote bag. "I'll take these home to read over the weekend," she promised. "On Monday, I'll give them back and we'll share them together."

All weekend Cricket glowed inside as she thought about her wonderful book report. She just knew that her teacher was going to love it. She couldn't wait until they were returned on Monday. Mrs. Schraalenburgh would probably write on the report how fabulous it was.

The reports were not returned to the students until after lunch on Monday. Cricket could hardly sit still as the teacher walked about the room handing them back. She decided that she would try and keep a straight face. It would be hard not to grin from ear to ear when she was reading the teacher's comments. But on the other hand, it would look as if she were showing off when other students got bad marks on their reports. She held her breath as Mrs. Schraalenburgh stood at her desk and sorted through the remaining papers in her hand.

"Here's yours, Cricket," said the teacher. She patted Cricket on the back. "I'm sure you'll do better next time, so don't worry too much about your grade."

Cricket couldn't imagine what the teacher was referring to. There was nothing written on the red cover of her report, but when she opened it up, she saw a B– written on the top of the page. Cricket couldn't believe it. How could she possibly have gotten such a low mark? This was an A+ report. It didn't make sense. Then Cricket noticed that on the inside of the back cover, Mrs. Schraalenburgh had written a message.

It is careless of you to misspell the name of the author whom you are writing about. The author of this book spells her last name CLEARY. Also, the award that this book won is called the NEWBERY Medal, not NEWBERRY. If you read your report over, you will see that you said the same thing three different times. It is better to say what you have to once and not bore your readers. I am glad you liked this book and I am sure next time you will write a better report to prove it.

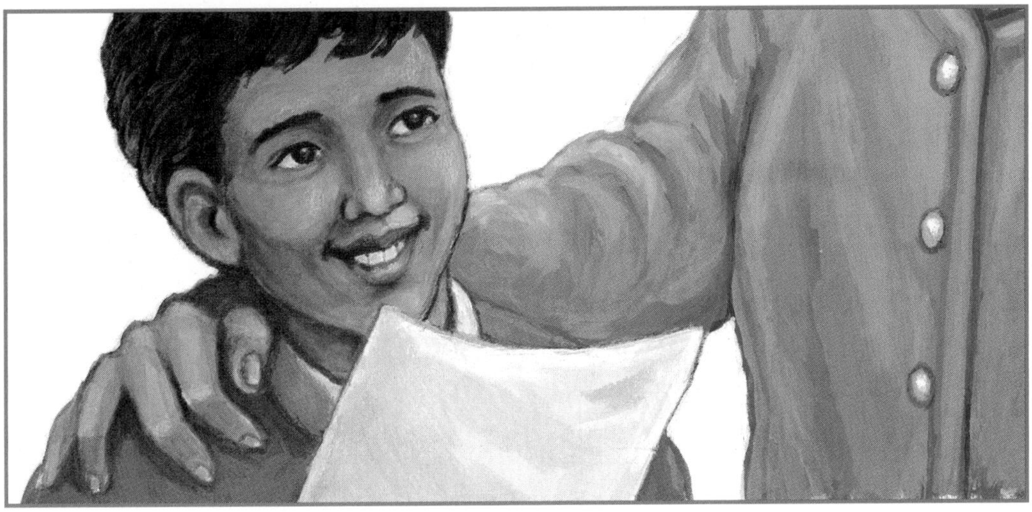

Cricket's eyes blurred with tears. She couldn't believe it. Mrs. Schraalenburgh didn't like her report. So what if she had spelled the author's name wrong? What did it matter? She had never said that spelling was going to count in their book reports.

"I am going to have a few people read their reports out loud to share them with us now," said Mrs. Schraalenburgh. "Let's start with Julio," she said.

Cricket blinked back her tears. If she had gotten a B–, Julio must have gotten a D.

"I gave Julio an A for his report," the teacher said as Julio walked proudly up to the front of the room.

"Even though Julio wrote about a book that we have already read and talked about in class this year, he has captured the humor of the story and what he has to say about the book will make anyone who hasn't already read it want to read it," she said.

Julio cleared his throat and waited until he had everyone's attention. Then he read his report. It was short, Cricket noted. But he made everyone laugh when he reminded them of one of the funny scenes in the book.

"Suppose you wrote about a book you didn't like," said Connie.

"Why would you bother to do that?" asked Mrs. Schraalenburgh. "If you didn't like the book, you should have stopped reading it and looked for another one."

All the children looked at each other. They had never heard a teacher say that you should stop reading a book.

"Do you know how many books are in the school library?" Mrs. Schraalenburgh asked.

"One hundred," guessed Julio.

Cricket raised her hand. She had once asked the librarian, so she knew the correct answer.

"Many, many more than a hundred," said Mrs. Schraalenburgh.

"Two hundred," someone called out.

"No speaking out," Mrs. Schraalenburgh reminded the students. "Cricket, do you know?" asked the teacher.

"Eight thousand," she said.

There were loud gasps. Eight thousand was a big number.

"That's right," said Mrs. Schraalenburgh. "And don't you think that if there are eight thousand books right here in this school building you could find one that you would like? So why would you waste your time reading a book you don't like?"

"But if we have to make book reports every month from now on, we'll need to find more than *one* book," Lucas pointed out.

"That's right," Connie agreed.

"I suspect that if you gave it a try, you could find many, many books that you will like among the eight thousand books in the school library. And what about the public library? Do you know how many books they have there?"

"Eight thousand," someone guessed.

Mrs. Schraalenburgh shook her head. "The next time you go, ask the children's librarian how many books are in the collection there," she said.

"And next time, Julio will write about a new book. One that he hasn't read or heard read to him before," Mrs. Schraalenburgh added. "Right, Julio?"

Julio grinned at the teacher. "Right," he said. "I want to see if I can make an A every time."

"That's the spirit," said Mrs. Schraalenburgh.

Next she called on Zoe.

Zoe went to the front of the room and began reading. Cricket was surprised to hear her name in the report. Zoe read, "I picked this book because it was given to me by my friend Cricket Kaufman. At first I thought I wouldn't like it because it was all in letters. But before I knew it, I was right in the middle of the story of Leigh Botts and his problems . . ."

Cricket could hardly believe that Zoe considered her to be her friend. Just because she gave her that book it didn't make them friends. That hadn't been her idea. Her mother had insisted that she bring a gift when she went to Zoe's party. And now Zoe had gotten an A writing about it when Cricket had only got a B–. It just didn't seem fair.

Zoe finished reading her report. "How many people want to read that book, now that they have heard about it?" asked Mrs. Schraalenburgh.

Every hand in the class except Cricket's went up.

"Now you know why Zoe got an A on her report. She has done an excellent job of sharing her pleasure with all of us. I notice that Cricket didn't raise her hand. But she doesn't have to read the book. She already did," said the teacher, smiling at Cricket. "And when she gave a copy of it to Zoe as a present, she was sharing her pleasure of the book in still another way."

Cricket could have said that when she bought the book for Zoe, she hadn't even read it yet. But she didn't. She liked what Mrs. Schraalenburgh said about her sharing her pleasure of the book by giving it as a present. It almost made up for the bad mark she got.

Mrs. Schraalenburgh wrote Beverly Cleary's name on the chalk board so that everyone could copy it and said "Now when you go to the library, you'll know who the author is." Cricket blushed to see the correct spelling on the board. It had really been foolish on her part to write a book report when she didn't have the book right in front of her to copy the author's name. She wouldn't make that mistake again.

A few other students read their book reports, too. Cricket noticed that none of them had made covers for their reports. It had been silly of her to waste her time making a fancy cover if Mrs. Schraalenburgh didn't give her extra credit for it.

"There isn't time to read any more reports," said Mrs. Schraalenburgh after a while. "This was just to get us started. Next month, we will have oral book reports and everyone will have a turn. So start looking for a good book to read. Don't wait until the last minute."

The bell rang for dismissal. Zoe edged over to Cricket. "Thanks again for the book," she said.

Cricket nodded her head. She was relieved that Zoe didn't ask her what grade she had gotten on her report. If the situation had been reversed and Cricket had received an A and Zoe had not read her report aloud, Cricket knew she would have been dying to ask.

"I'll bet we have the same taste in books," said Zoe. "Maybe we could go to the library together after school sometime. You could show me the books you've read and I could show you the ones I've read."

Cricket found herself smiling at Zoe. It sounded as if it might be fun. There had never been another girl in school who liked to read as much as she did. Maybe Zoe was right. Maybe she would be a friend to her.

"Okay," she agreed. And suddenly, it didn't matter so much what grade she had gotten on her report. Next time she would get an A. And if Zoe got one, too, it wouldn't be so terrible. After all, they were the two smartest girls in Mrs. Schraalenburgh's class.

Cricket and Zoe remain competitors, but can they become friends too? You can find out by reading the rest of Teacher's Pet.

Making the grade

When Mrs. Schraalenburgh gave Cricket a B– on her book report, she also wrote a paragraph explaining why. What grade would you give *Teacher's Pet*? Give a grade to the story, and then write a paragraph explaining why you gave that grade.

Johanna Hurwitz

Read, read, read. That's what Johanna Hurwitz did with every free minute when she was a child. She loved reading so much that she decided she would one day become a librarian. That way she could get paid for being around books all day.

Hurwitz did become a librarian. But instead of just reading books, Hurwitz started writing them too. Now she writes great books like this one:

- *The Hot & Cold Summer*
  Buddies Derek and Rory don't want a girl named Bolivia hanging around them all summer.

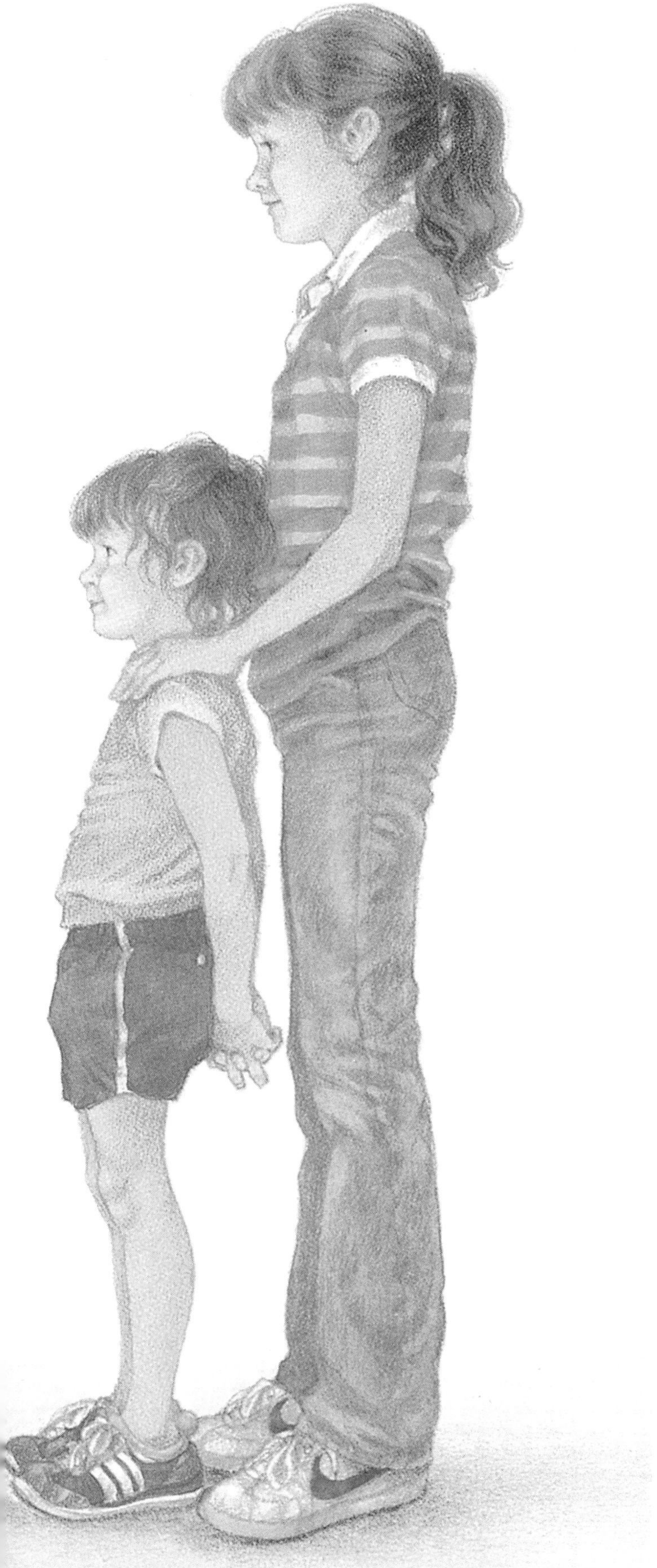

MAKING ROOM FOR UNCLE JOE

by Ada B. Litchfield with illustrations by Gail Owens

Mom looked really serious as she read us the letter from Uncle Joe's social worker.

Uncle Joe is Mom's younger brother. He has Down's syndrome. People with Down's syndrome are mentally retarded and need help taking care of themselves. After Uncle Joe was born his mother died, and no one else in the family could give him the care he needed. That's why he had been in a state hospital school for such a long time.

Uncle Joe had been happy at his school. But now it was closing, the letter said, and the people who lived there had to find other homes. Uncle Joe would have to live with us for a while. We were his only family.

"The social worker says she's looking for an apartment for Uncle Joe, but they are hard to find," Mom explained. "So your dad and I think Joe should stay with us until — "

"He'd better find an apartment fast," my older sister, Beth, shouted. "We can't have a retarded person living here forever!"

"But he won't be here forever, Beth," I said. "It's just until he finds another place."

"You keep out of this, Dan," Beth told me. "It might as well be forever. I won't be able to have any of my friends here. What will they say when they see Uncle Joe creeping around? They'll make fun of him and of me, too."

"Now Beth, stop that," Dad said. "No real friend would ever make fun of you for doing somebody a kindness. Besides, Uncle Joe won't bother you and your friends."

"Good grief," Beth said. "Doesn't anyone see how embarrassing this will be for all of us?" She burst into tears and ran out of the room.

"Let her go," Dad said when Mom tried to call Beth back. "She needs to think things over."

I needed to think things over, too. Suppose Uncle Joe *was* a nuisance? Suppose he hung around me all the time? Suppose he messed with my baseball cards?

"Dan, helping Uncle Joe is something our family has to do together," Dad said, as if he were reading my thoughts. "Your mother and I will appreciate any help you and Beth and Amy can give us."

"I'll help Uncle Joe," Amy said.

Amy is only five and a half. What kind of help could she be?

"I'll help, too," I said, trying to sound cheerful. But to tell the truth, I didn't feel cheerful at all.

I felt worse when I talked to my friend Ben the next day.

"Down's syndrome, eh?" Ben said with a know-it-all look on

his face. "You should be upset. I saw a TV program about people with Down's syndrome. Their eyes slant and their noses look squashed in." He showed me with his fingers what he meant. "Does your uncle look like that?"

"I don't remember," I said. "I only saw him once when I was little. My mom and dad always visited without us kids."

"Doesn't matter," Ben said. "All retarded people are funny looking and most of 'em drool. You'll probably have to wipe his chin all the time."

"A fat lot you know!" I shouted.

I didn't know if what Ben said was true or not, but it made me mad just the same. I didn't think it was a very helpful thing for a friend to say.

When I got home, I found Mom and Dad moving furniture around. They had moved the TV from the family room into the living room and the record player into Beth's room.

"We're making room for Uncle Joe," Mom said when she saw me. "You're just in time to help."

Dad and I brought an extra bed up from the basement into the family room. Uncle Joe would sleep there.

"Whew," said Mom when everything was in place. "The social worker just called to say Uncle Joe will be here tomorrow. I wish we'd known sooner."

Tomorrow!

Beth was sitting on the back porch with her hands over her face. I could tell she'd been crying.

"I had to cancel my slumber party for tomorrow night," she told me between sobs.

"Why?" I asked. "Did Mom make you?"

"No," she said. "But how can I have the girls over with *him* around?"

"I don't know," I said. I understood how Beth felt.

Early the next day, Mom and Dad drove to the state school to bring Uncle Joe home. All morning, Amy and Beth and I waited at the front window, watching for them to return. Finally, about noon, we saw our car turn into the driveway. In a few minutes, Mom and Dad came up the walk. Behind them came a short man carrying a suitcase and a small blue bag.

As soon as Beth saw them, she left the window and went into her bedroom.

Uncle Joe came into the house very slowly. His cap was on crooked. He was wearing a jacket with sleeves too short for his arms. His pants were too long for his legs. I was glad to see he wasn't drooling. But to tell the truth, his eyes did slant a little, and his nose did look a little squashed in.

He looked around at everything in the room and at Amy and me. Then he smiled, showing a gap between his small, even teeth.

"Hi," he said. "My name's Joe. What's . . . uh . . . yours?"

"This is Dan," my father said. "And here's Amy."

Amy made a little bow, and I bobbed my head.

"And, oh, yes," Dad said, "there's one more." He left the room and came back holding Beth by the arm.

"This is Beth," Dad said.

"Hello, Beth," Uncle Joe said. "You're pretty."

"Thank you," said Beth. She looked surprised.

Dad took Uncle Joe's suitcase into the family room. But Uncle Joe wouldn't let him take the blue bag. Instead, he brought it over to me.

"This is my bowling ball," he said, holding the bag up almost in my face. "My friend Ace gave it to me. Can you bowl?"

"I don't know," I said. "I never tried."

"That's okay," he said. "I'll . . . uh . . . show you."

Soon after that we all sat down for lunch. All except Uncle Joe, that is. He sat in a chair by the china cabinet, holding his bowling ball on his lap.

"Come sit here, Joe," Mom said, pointing to the empty chair beside Amy. "Put that bowling ball down somewhere and come eat."

"No," Uncle Joe said, shaking his head. "I don't want to. I can't eat without my friend Ace. I miss Ace. I need a friend with me . . . uh . . . when I eat lunch."

He hung his head and looked sad. Nobody seemed to know what to do, except Amy. She slid out of her chair, went over to Uncle Joe, and put her hand in his.

"I'll be your friend, Uncle Joe," she said. "You can eat with me." And she pulled him to the table.

It was a terrible meal. Amy chatted away, but nobody else seemed to know what to say. Uncle Joe dribbled catsup on the tablecloth and forgot to use his napkin. The mustard from his hot dog got all over his face. Beth watched him in disgust.

Then Amy spilled her milk. "See?" she said cheerfully. "Everyone spills sometimes." I think she was trying to make Uncle Joe feel better.

That was the beginning of Amy's friendship with Uncle Joe. As soon as we finished lunch, she showed him her library book. Every day after that, Uncle Joe and Amy spent a lot of time together with their heads bent over Amy's books. I don't think he always knew if she read the right words or not, but he listened carefully anyway, nodding his head. And showing off for someone made Amy very happy.

Every night Uncle Joe would sit on the stairs with Amy while she told him bedtime stories. He'd laugh and clap his hands and join in when she came to something like the huff and puff part in "The Three Little Pigs." When he said, "Time for bed, Amy," she scooted off without any fuss.

Yes, Amy and Uncle Joe got along fine right away, but for the rest of us, having Uncle Joe around wasn't easy.

He had to be reminded to wear his glasses, comb his hair, take a shower, and things like that. And somebody had to see that he put on matching socks.

When he ate, he always left bits of food all over the table and floor. He did like everything Mom cooked though, and he always said, "Mmmm . . . good!" no matter what we had for dinner. Mom liked that.

Most of the time Uncle Joe was cheerful, but sometimes he sat in his room or on the back porch just staring into space. Then even Amy couldn't cheer him up. He'd just mutter something about being a no-good dumbhead who couldn't take care of himself.

Uncle Joe offered to help around the house, but he often seemed to get directions mixed up. Usually he was more trouble than help.

One day Dad asked him to weed the garden. I was supposed to help, too. By the time I got out to the yard, Uncle Joe had already started — and he had pulled up as many flowers as he had weeds! When I told him what he'd done, he was really upset.

"It's not your fault, Uncle Joe," I said over and over. "Nobody showed you which plants not to pull up."

But Uncle Joe was so mad at himself he disappeared into his room and wouldn't come out.

We didn't know what to do. Finally Mom got the idea that I should take him bowling. I didn't want to go, but before I knew what was happening, Uncle Joe had come out of his room wearing his bowling jacket and carrying his blue bag.

All the way to Bowl-a-rama, I hoped none of my friends would see us. I hadn't seen any of them — even Ben — for a few weeks. I guess I was afraid they would make fun of Uncle Joe. I didn't want them staring and saying things like "How's Danny Dan and the retard man?"

But we didn't see anyone I knew, and as soon as we started bowling I forgot about everything else.

Uncle Joe was a good bowler. Sometimes he got a spare. And sometimes he got a strike.

Me? I was lucky if I knocked down any pins at all.

"It's okay, Danny," Uncle Joe kept saying in his slow way. "I . . . uh . . . know you can do it. You'll get a strike. Just . . . uh . . . keep trying."

And I did. I got a strike. On the very last frame, all the pins went down — whack, whack, whack — just like that!

We both shouted and jumped up and down.

Everyone around us looked. But I didn't care. I didn't even care when I saw Ben and two other guys from my school watching us.

At first, they just stared and nudged each other. I could tell they were looking for something to laugh at.

When they finally came over to us, I introduced them to Uncle Joe.

"I'm glad to meet you . . . Ben . . . and John . . . and Eli," Uncle Joe said. He shook each of their hands and smiled at them. They looked down at the floor and shuffled their feet, but Uncle Joe didn't seem to notice.

"Would you like to bowl with us?" he asked.

They all nodded yes. Ben and Eli had bowled before, but John hadn't. Uncle Joe showed him how to hold the ball and encouraged him the way he had encouraged me.

In no time at all, everybody seemed to forget that Uncle Joe had Down's syndrome. We were all just trying to knock down bowling pins. We were all just having fun.

After that, Ben and my other friends started coming over to the house again. They were always kind to Uncle Joe, and he loved to talk with them.

And after a while, things seemed to go better at home. Mom and Dad took more time showing Uncle Joe how to do simple jobs. Uncle Joe began to be a real help around the house. He could carry in groceries and help put them away. He liked to peel carrots and potatoes for dinner. He helped wash and polish the car. He helped Amy put the new bell on her tricycle, and he helped me paint a display rack for my baseball cards.

And Uncle Joe was good at weeding, once he knew which plants to leave alone. One day I went out with him to be sure he didn't pull out the flowers. But I think my checking up on him hurt his feelings. "You don't have to watch me, Danny," he told me. "This is my job, and I . . . can do it by myself."

I didn't watch anymore, but I stayed outside anyway. I liked being out in the backyard with Uncle Joe. Sometimes after he finished his work we tossed a Frisbee around for a while.

But what about Beth?

For a long time, Beth acted almost as if Uncle Joe didn't exist. He never bothered her, but sometimes he would sit quietly in the living room and listen while she practiced her piano lesson. Once he clapped, but that startled her so much he never did it again.

Then one day, when he thought no one was around, Uncle Joe sat down at the piano and played "Chopsticks."

Everyone in the family came running, and we clapped so loudly for him that he played it again.

"My friend Ace showed me how to do that," Uncle Joe said, grinning.

Beth went over to the piano. "I know how to play another part of that piece," she said. She sat down next to Uncle Joe and taught him how to play "Chopsticks" as a duet.

Later, Beth showed Uncle Joe how to play other tunes. Sometimes he played them over and over so many times we all got tired of listening, but we felt good because Beth was being kind to Uncle Joe. She started inviting her girl friends over again, and one day I heard her tell a friend that she was giving Uncle Joe piano lessons. I think Beth liked being a teacher, and I know Uncle Joe liked being her pupil.

By the time spring came, things had settled down into what Mom called a "comfortable routine."

Then another letter came from Uncle Joe's social worker.

Mom read the letter to us. It said that Uncle Joe would be leaving. Everything had finally been arranged. Uncle Joe would share an apartment with two other men in the city. He would work at a sheltered workshop close to where he lived.

A sheltered workshop is a place where handicapped people are taught to do special jobs. They sort nuts and bolts, put together small motors, package things to send through the mail, or do other simple tasks. The work is easy enough for them, and they are paid for doing it.

At first, Uncle Joe seemed pleased. He had Mom read the letter again and again.

I was sure he felt good about having a place of his own and a job of his own. He wanted to take care of himself.

I was sure my parents felt good about not having to be responsible for Uncle Joe anymore.

We would all be glad to have the family room back again so we could entertain our friends there.

We'd always known that Uncle Joe would be leaving sometime. So why did everyone look so sad that night at dinner?

"I'm going to miss you, Uncle Joe," Amy said. She burst into tears.

"I'll miss you, too," said Uncle Joe. He began to look very unhappy.

"Who will listen to me practice for my recital now?" Beth said. Tears were running down her cheeks, too.

"And who will teach me new songs?" Uncle Joe asked her, looking sadder than I had ever seen him look before.

"Hey, I'm not going to cry about this," I said to myself, taking a drink of water. But there was a lump in my throat, and I choked so badly I had to leave the table.

I knew I was going to miss Uncle Joe something awful.

When I came back, even my father looked as if he'd been crying. He cleared his throat and blew his nose.

"Listen," he said at last, "your mother and I have been talking this over for quite a while. We thought you all might be pretty upset if Joe leaves. We don't see why Uncle Joe has to live somewhere else if he doesn't want to. We are his family. I can drive him to that workshop every day on my way to the office, and he can take the bus back. What do you say, Joe? Would you like to stay with us?"

Uncle Joe looked thoughtful for a long time. He pulled at his hair. Then he started to grin. "I want to stay here. Yes, I do. . . . I can work hard and . . . uh . . . pay for my food. I want to stay here all the time forever with my family."

"Then it's settled," Mom said. "I'll call the social worker right away and tell her we'd all like Uncle Joe to stay with us."

"Yippee!" shouted Amy. She climbed into Uncle Joe's lap and gave him a big hug.

And Uncle Joe? He looked so happy nobody cared that he had forgotten to comb his hair. Or that there was a mess of crumbs around his plate and more on the floor. We all knew that in many ways Uncle Joe is a neat guy.

We were glad he had come to stay with us . . . all the time, forever.

"I Used to Think..."

Before they got to know Uncle Joe, Dan and Beth were uncomfortable with the idea of his staying with them. But after getting to know Uncle Joe, they realized how foolish their worries were.

Write a poem about Uncle Joe as either Dan or Beth might write it. Write four verses, each of which begins

"I USED TO THINK ____________
BUT NOW I ____________"

Ada B. Litchfield

Ada B. Litchfield hopes people will learn something from reading her books. Maybe people will gain "a little better understanding and compassion" for others if they read a book like *Making Room for Uncle Joe*, she says.

Among the other books Litchfield has written are the following:

- *A Cane in Her Hand*
  A girl who is nearly blind learns that there are different ways of seeing.
- *Words in Our Hands*
  This book describes the daily life of a boy whose parents are deaf.

Justin, a city boy, is going to a festival with his grandpa, who lives on a ranch and bakes delicious biscuits.

JUSTIN and the ★ best biscuits ★ in the world

from the book by Mildred Pitts Walter
illustrated by Brian Pinkney

When Justin awoke, Grandpa was already up. Justin jumped from Grandpa's big bed. *The festival starts today*, he thought. Quickly he put on his clothes and joined Grandpa in the kitchen.

Already a fire crackled in the big stove. While Justin put eggs on to boil for breakfast, Grandpa got busy making biscuits from ingredients he had placed on the table the night before. Grandpa planned to enter the Best Biscuit Competition at the festival.

The rules stated that all biscuits entered must be in the judges' hands by eleven o'clock that morning.

"Can you cook them there?" Justin asked.

"Oh, no. We must cook them at home," Grandpa answered.

"But who will say cold biscuits are good, Grandpa?"

"Why, that's something to think about, son. Hm-m-m. Maybe we should arrive at the festival at five minutes before eleven."

At ten-thirty, Justin and Grandpa raced to the fairgrounds where the festival took place each year. The biscuits, in a heavy hot iron skillet, carefully wrapped in towels to help keep them hot, rested in the back of the truck.

The streets were crowded with people from the town and from neighboring farms. Banners waved all over announcing events. Colorful posters with bucking broncos splashed BILL PICKETT RODEO ads everywhere. People moved up and down streets, car horns honked, friends greeted one another. Justin wished his best friend, Anthony, was with him for the fun.

Traffic slowed them down. Ten-forty-five: a clock at a savings and loan bank flashed the golden numbers. Justin wondered if they would make it. They were not near the fairgrounds and they had only ten minutes more.

Grandpa kept his eye on the road, driving carefully, and seemingly not a bit worried. But the traffic now moved more slowly than ever.

Soon they reached a stretch of road that led out of town into the country. Grandpa picked up speed. Still Justin worried that they might be late.

Finally the long metal building near the rodeo stands came in view. Its round domelike shape glistened in the late summer

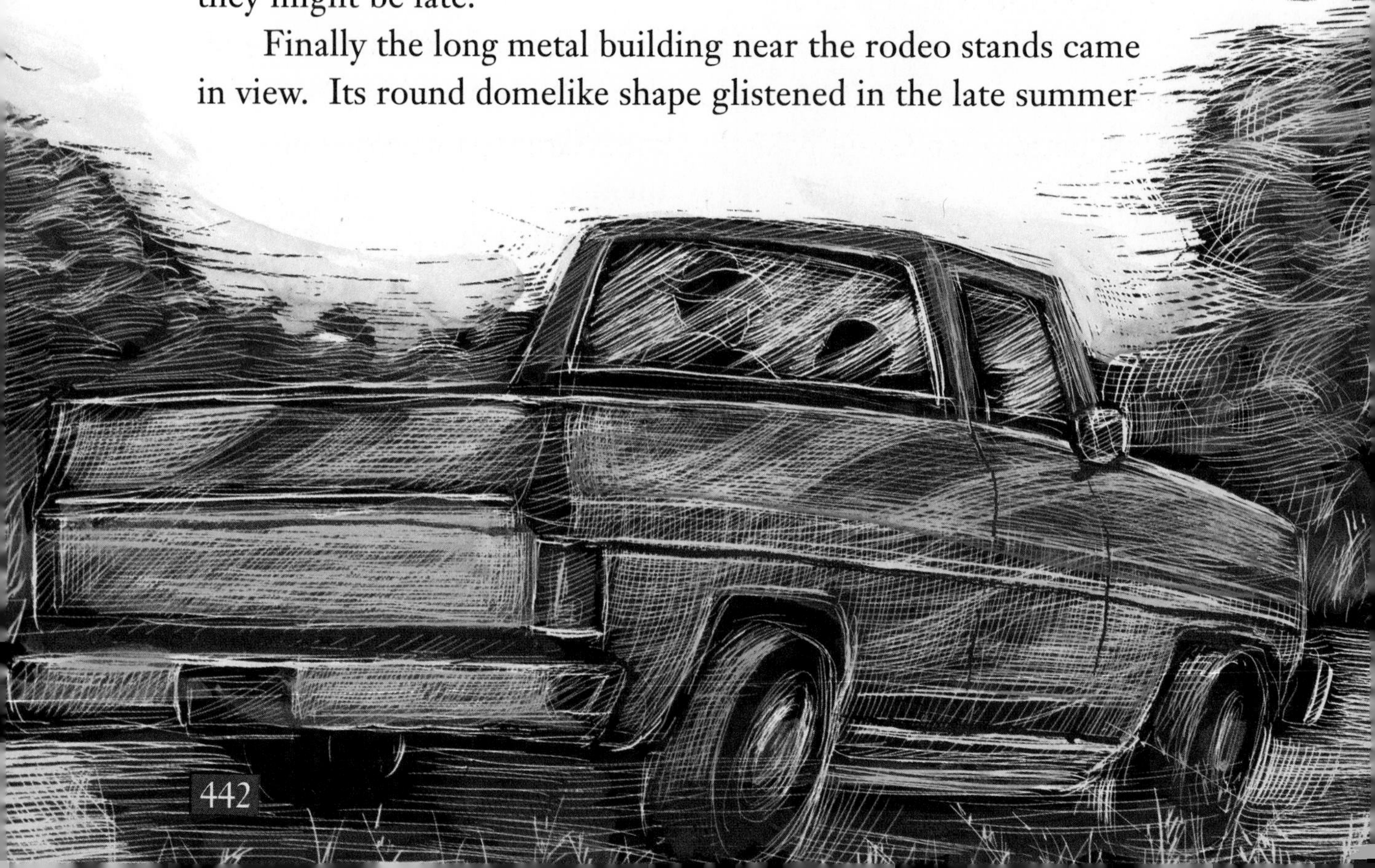

sun. Quickly, Grandpa parked the truck and carefully removed the biscuits from the skillet and placed them on a paper plate. He covered them with a gleaming white napkin and rushed inside.

Justin grabbed a lone biscuit left in the skillet. It was still warm and ever so delicious. While eating it he ran after Grandpa, who was already nearing the far end of the long building. Justin pushed through the crowd after him, hoping Grandpa was not late.

At ten-fifty-nine, Grandpa handed his biscuits to a pleasant-looking lady. She sat behind a table with covered plates of biscuits around her. "You just made it," she said, and smiled at Grandpa.

"I'm glad, too," Grandpa said, returning the lady's smile as he filled out an entry form.

"The judges will announce their decision this evening," the lady said.

"That late?" Justin asked. "They'll be cold, Grandpa."

The lady laughed. "The judging will begin in a minute. It's the decision that will come later."

Justin smiled, relieved. He wished he could get a glimpse of some of the biscuits there under cover. But whose biscuits could taste better than Grandpa's? He knew Grandpa would win.

They moved with the crowd looking at things that had been made by people in the town. All kinds of needlework, quilts, knitted sweaters, scarves, and afghans on display looked inviting. Some had already been judged. Blue, red, and white ribbons announced first, second, and third prizes. Justin wished he could take his mama a beautiful quilt with a big green-and-gold star in the center. But none of those lovely things were for sale.

There were so many things displayed: photography, woodwork. A big model airplane floating from the ceiling surprised Justin. *Wow!* he thought, *that'll get a blue ribbon.*

Soon they came to the display of desserts. Justin had never seen so many scrumptious-looking pies, cakes, brownies, and cookies. He thought of his sister, Hadiya, and wished she had entered. She'd win for sure.

The pie-eating contest was just about to start. The judges stood ready to determine who could eat the most pie the fastest. Justin stretched up as tall as he could, waving his hand, trying to attract a judge's attention. He knew he could eat a lot of pie. A judge pointed at him. He entered the competition. A whole chocolate pie in front of him did not dim his enthusiasm.

Quickly he ate one piece, two, three, but when he glanced at a boy next to him, he almost choked with surprise. A whole pie had been downed, and all but one piece of another.

If only he hadn't eaten so many biscuits for breakfast, he thought as he finished the last piece on the plate. Another pie was plopped in front of him. But before he could finish the first piece of it, the buzzer sounded. Time up! The boy next to him had eaten all but one piece of his second pie. He won only second place, though. The winner had eaten two whole pies!

"You did good," Justin said to the winner next to him.

The boy sighed, held his stomach, then placed his head on the counter.

"Don," a lady said, putting her hand on his shoulder. "You all right?"

"Oh-h-h-h, Ma," Don said.

"We had better move on, Justin," Grandpa said, and led Justin through the crowd.

Justin felt nothing but stuffed. He thought of the boy called Don and was glad the buzzer rang before he had a chance to eat more of that pie. He and Grandpa wandered through the big barnlike building looking at prize-winning carrots, pumpkins, squash, and tomatoes.

Then they decided to go home and feed the animals. Later, they would return for the judges' decisions and the big dance in the pavilion.

Darkness crept over the plains. Justin, ready to go back to the fairgrounds, waited for Grandpa downstairs. He wondered what was keeping him so long. Grandpa had finished showering before him, and Justin had been ready to go for a long time. Justin was anxious to get back. Other contests might be going on.

Finally Grandpa came down the stairs so dressed up that Justin stood surprised. Never had he seen Grandpa looking so sharp. The suede vest he wore had deep fringe on a yoke in the back and front.

His light beige shirt, fitted beige pants, and belt with a big silver buckle were just right with the rich brown vest.

While riding in the truck, Justin sniffed a strange but nice fragrance. Surely Grandpa hadn't put on that smelly stuff Mama forced on him, Justin thought. Now he was glad Anthony was not there. What would he think about Grandpa wearing that stuff? Another whiff came Justin's way. *It's not so bad, though,* he decided. But he liked Grandpa best when he smelled like work, sweet grass, soap — stuff like that.

They arrived just in time for the cake-baking contest. One contestant had entered fifteen cakes — every one a different flavor. Some of them looked too pretty to eat, Justin thought. The judges thought they were perfect. The woman who had baked them won a blue ribbon in every category.

A girl as young as Hadiya won second place for her lemon chiffon cake. Justin clapped and clapped for her.

Then the judges came to announce the winner for the best biscuits. The lady chosen to do the honors wore a big flower on her bosom and one on her hat. She seemed nervous and dropped all the ribbons. *Why doesn't she hurry up,* Justin thought. His stomach felt weak, his hands were cold. He was now worried that maybe Grandpa would not win.

"First place winner," the lady said in a loud, excited voice, "Phillip Ward, Junior!"

Justin let out a yell. Grandpa smiled and rushed up to get a shiny blue ribbon and a certificate. "The Best Biscuits in the World," the certificate said.

Later at the dance, all the ladies crowded around Grandpa. Many wanted his recipe. Justin stood by holding the blue ribbon and certificate as Grandpa danced, dance after dance with a different partner. He didn't know if the best biscuits or that smelly stuff had wowed all those ladies.

The story doesn't end here. You can find out how Justin learns to make Grandpa's secret biscuit recipe by reading the rest of Justin and the Best Biscuits in the World.

"Add a Pinch of Salt . . ."

Maybe Grandpa will become so famous for his biscuits that he'll be asked to appear on a talk show on public television. With two partners, act out the show based on this **TV TIMES** entry.

7 PM ❸ TALKING WITH BETTY; 30 min. The cooking cowboy, Phillip "Grandpa" Ward, shows how to make his award-winning biscuits; interview with Justin about participating in a pie-eating contest; tips by Grandpa on selecting men's cologne.

Mildred Pitts Walter

Whether it's a boy who wants to fly or a girl who loves rock and roll, Mildred Pitts Walter writes about real people. Some of her characters, like Justin, are learning about growing up. Others, like Mariah in *Mariah Loves Rock*, are having trouble at home. But all are like people you might know.

Where does Mildred Pitts Walter get her story ideas? Some come from her experiences as a teacher. Others come from her travels. *Brother to the Wind*, her book about a boy who dreams of flying, was inspired by a trip to Africa.

CHASING AFTER ANNIE

by Marjorie Weinman Sharmat
with illustrations by Marc Simont

May 3 **Richie**

Dear Journal,
I think Annie Alpert likes me. She probably thinks I'm the greatest! Because of my muscles, my A's, and my famous fish scrapbook. Annie likes everything about me including a few things she doesn't even know about yet.

May 3 **Annie**

Dear Diary,
I can't stand Richie Carr. I totally dislike him. More than bugs, more than itches, more than liver. Bugs don't brag, itches don't brag, liver doesn't brag. But Richie Carr brags all the time.

May 4 **Richie**

Dear Journal,
The way I can tell Annie likes me is because she pretends so hard that she doesn't.

Today I saw her walking to school. So I chased after her, kind of slowly of course. Then I yelled, "Annie!"

She dropped a book. How about that? I ran to pick it up. "Hey, Annie," I said. "Let me do that."

"I can pick up my own book," she said.

"There's a special way to pick it up," I said. "Bend your knees and keep your back straight. I know these things. I'm an athlete."

"That's not all you are," Annie said.

DID YOU HEAR THAT, JOURNAL? Annie must have been checking up on me. She must have found out I can play chess, spell *microgroove* without checking the dictionary, as well as high dive.

Annie Alpert likes me so much she can't stand it!

May 4 **Annie**

Dear Diary,
Well, I almost told Richie Carr off today. He made me drop a book and then he bragged when he tried to pick it up. How can anyone brag about picking up a book? Richie Carr can.

On my way home from school I told Frances what happened. "Isn't Richie Carr the worst braggart in the world?" I said.

"I think Richie Carr likes you," she said.

"Hmmpph!" I said.

Then when I got home, Mom told me that Fritz was lost. The back gate was open and he ran out after another dog and didn't come back.

I wish Richie Carr would get lost.

Come home, Fritz.

May 5 **Richie**

Dear Journal,
Annie is down today. I mean *down*. She didn't even do her Annie Walk, where she hops every few steps or twirls in circles and laughs. I saw her in school, and she looked like somebody sad and droopy. Her dog ran away and Annie likes that dog almost as much as she likes me. That's a whole lot, Journal.

So I'm going to look for Annie's dog. Who else can Annie count on? And I'll *find* him. Because when Richie Carr does something, he does it right.

May 5 Annie

Dear Diary,
Maybe I'll never see Fritz again. Maybe some people took him into their house and they're moving to California and so Fritz is, too. If Fritz comes home, I'll never make him take a bath again.

May 6 **Richie**

Dear Journal,
Tired! That's me. I've been looking and looking for Annie's dog. I mean I looked an hour and a half today for that creature. I, Richie Carr, have been to alleys, parks, stores, dumps, delicatessens, parking lots, and garbage cans.

Still, Annie said *thanks* to me today. What happened was that I saw Annie in an alley. I said, "I'm looking for Fritz, too." And that's when Annie said, "Thanks!"

May 6 Annie

Dear Diary,
Mom and Dad put an ad in the newspaper about Fritz being lost. But I'm saving up my allowance so I can go to California and look for Fritz. Every day I think of something else I loved about him. Today it's his tail. I don't know why Richie Carr is looking for Fritz. How could someone like *him* be a dog person?

May 7 **Richie**

Dear Journal,
I've increased my dog hunt. Three hours! I added meat markets to my looking places, and also under the benches of the school cafeteria. I even drew a picture of Fritz, because I draw very well. I put it up at school under LOST.

May 7 **Annie**

Dear Diary,

It's been 3 days now, and I'm still looking for Fritz. Richie Carr is, too. He's strange, Richie is. I was at the supermarket asking if anyone had seen a black-and-white dog with a long tail and a sad face and there was Richie. "A very sad face," Richie said.

Oh, and Richie draws pretty good.

May 8 **Richie**

Dear Journal,

No. 1: A sore knee.

No. 2: A hole in my sneakers.

No. 3: Sweat. Sweat. Sweat.

These are the things I've gotten so far looking for Fritz. The sneakers were guaranteed to last through 75 baseball games. I wish I had worn them out that way.

P.S. I think Fritz got married or something.

May 8 Annie

Dear Diary,
Richie has been walking a little funny. Should I tell him to look in his socks for a pebble?

May 9 Richie

Dear Journal,
You won't believe what happened today.

Zitts came over in the morning and said, "Guess what I'm getting today."

I answered, "A skyscraper."

And Zitts said, "Wrong. A dog."

Then Zitts asked me to go to the animal shelter with him and his dad to help pick out a dog. Well, I've had enough of looking for a dog this week. So I almost said no. ALMOST. What if *Fritz* was at the dog shelter! I went with Zitts and his father. I've never seen so many dogs at one time in my life! I've never heard so many yelps and barks and dog sounds. And I've never felt so sorry for so many dogs. All behind bars and wanting to get out.

"You can have any one you want, Zitts," his dad said. "Except for the big monsters."

Zitts kept looking at one dog, then another, then another. At last he said, "*That* one!"

That one was brown and white with a bushy tail. I didn't know what kind of dog it was. Zitts's dad went to get someone in charge.

Suddenly I saw something that made me stop. Stop like a red light, Journal.

Right there at that animal shelter I found Fritz!!!!

Black except where he was white, sad face, long tail.

I ran after one of the people in charge. Then I pointed to Fritz. "That dog belongs to my friend," I said. "He ran away a few days ago."

“No, he didn’t,” said the lady. “That dog has been here for almost a month.”

“Nuts,” I said. But I kept staring at that dog. I was getting an idea! I could take him to Annie and hope she thought he was Fritz. After all, a dog is a dog. And Annie needed any Fritz she could get. It was perfect. This sad, droopy dog would get a new home. Annie would be happy again. She would have Fritz back.

Then I began to wonder. Do dogs have warts and moles and scars and stuff like people? Could Annie tell the difference between the dogs? Maybe Fritz had a pimple that I didn’t know about that Annie knew about. Still, he’d been gone for a few days. Who knows what a dog can get and get rid of?

I wanted this dog, Journal. Now, how to take him home?

It was easier than you'd think.

Zitts's dad had to sign a paper and pay a few dollars for Zitts's dog. (Zitts's dog in its previous life was named Brussels Sprouts. Zitts changed it to Wolf right then and there.) I said to Zitts's dad, "My mother and father want me to pick out a dog, too."

"No they don't," said Zitts's dad.

"Yes they do," I said. "They told me that if I found one I wanted, I could bring it home. And I found one."

"No they don't," said Zitts's dad again. He wasn't exactly listening.

"I love that black-and-white dog," I said.

"Love is what counts," said the animal shelter person.

I also had a dollar with me, and I told Zitts's father I'd pay him the rest next week. Then Zitts started with his *Please, please, Pops* routine that he's famous for in our neighborhood because it works.

Zitts's dad signed for two dogs.

I held my breath when Zitts saw my dog. Would he notice how much he looked like Fritz? But Zitts was too busy with Wolf.

My dog's name in his (yes, it was a *his,* I had forgotten to think about that) previous life was Duchess. Wild. How could a boy dog get the name of Duchess?

"What are you going to name your dog?" Zitts asked on the way home.

"Brussels Sprouts," I said.

"Brussels Sprouts? That's stupid," Zitts yelled. "That's why I took my dog. I figured he must have had a stupid life with stupid people who would name him Brussels Sprouts. I want to give this dog a new life. Right, Wolf?"

Wolf and my dog were panting and drooling and moving around in the backseat. It was a crazy ride home. When we got to my house, I rushed out of the car and pulled my dog after me.

I started to walk to Annie's house. I had to give this dog — *return* him — to Annie right away. Before my mother and father knew I had him.

50

That walk to Annie's was the best walk ever. Because I, Richie Carr, was returning Fritz to Annie. Well, maybe it wasn't exactly Fritz, but it was close enough. All dogs have wet noses and fleas and they sniff and they wag their tails. Annie would think it was Fritz and she'd be so happy she couldn't stand it.

But what if Annie just knew that this sad long thing following me down the street was in real life Duchess? Duchess of the dog pound. Poor Annie. Without a Fritz.

Duchess followed close behind me. He seemed to like me. He should. I was getting him a new home, and a lot of instant love.

I rang Annie's doorbell. Nobody answered. I rang five times. Duchess barked. Uh-oh, I hoped his bark was like Fritz's. I hadn't thought about that.

I left a note at Annie's house. It was a super note. I knew she'd call me as soon as she read it. Then Duchess and I went home.

I tried to sneak Duchess up to my room.

"Who is that?" my mother asked.

Some question.

"I'm showing Duchess my room," I said.

"What if she …?" my mother asked. My mother hadn't noticed that Duchess was a he.

"Duchess is a he and he's housebroken," I said. (The lady at the animal shelter told me he was. She also said Duchess was friendly, very good-natured, intelligent, obedient, and wonderful with children. She said the exact same thing about Zitts's dog. I think it's a commercial.)

"Well, you have to clean your room if she messes it," my mother said. "Whom does she belong to?"

"He didn't tell me," I said.

The rest of the day I waited for Annie to call me. Duchess slept most of the time. At suppertime I left Duchess in my room and went downstairs. My mother didn't ask about him. I guess she thought he'd left.

"EEEEEK!"

That was my mother when she felt something warm and furry rubbing against her leg. It was Duchess. Then Duchess made this little puddle on the floor. Trouble, Journal. It went like this.

"Get rid of her at once!": my mother.

"Out! Out!": my father.

"I have to keep him a little longer," I said. "Just a little longer."

"Why?": my mother.

"Why?": my father.

"Because.": me.

I cleaned up the puddle.

Then I took Duchess for a long walk. He needed it. When we got home Duchess went up to my mother as if he liked her. This made a big hit, Journal. My mother bent down and patted Duchess and said, "Well, she is cute."

Duchess sat down and waited for lots of pats.

My father said, "Yes, she's a nice dog."

I hadn't even thought about Duchess that way. Cute, nice — who cares? I only thought about the Duchess who was going to be Fritz. We all gave him a few pats because he expected them. Then my father said, "Time to take her home."

My father didn't know that Duchess was a he or that Duchess's home was our home. At least for the night. Because Annie hadn't called. I waited until my mother and father were watching TV and then I snuck Duchess upstairs to my room.

Well, I tried to keep that dog from barking. I tried to keep my rug dry. I tried to sleep with a wet nose near my face. There was more, but I can't write another word except to say that my father discovered Duchess at half past one in the morning and that belongs in my next day, Journal.

May 9 **Annie**

Dear Diary,

Today I thought about Fritz's ears, both of them. They were always warm, and sometimes they quivered. Except for that, it was the same old Saturday stuff. Visited with Aunt Fan and Uncle Mack. Came home smelling of cigar smoke. Found a dumb note from Richie Carr. It said, BIG IMPORTANT NEWS! CALL ME. He probably wants to show me a new fish picture. Ho hum. I'm going to bed.

May 10 **Richie**

Dear Journal,

My father isn't the kind of father who would send a dog away in the middle of the night. He's the kind of father who would take away my allowance for a week instead. I guess that's fair. Except my allowance was going to pay back Zitts's dad.

Anyway, my father said, "I am too tired to ask you why you have this dog in your room, why it isn't home, where its home is, where you got it, and will it be gone by tomorrow morning." My father drooped out of the room.

Duchess climbed up on my bed. And we fell asleep.

In the morning Duchess and I went out. My mother and father said, "Good-by, Duchess," as if they felt that *good-by* was the key word.

I went straight to Annie's house. I rang her bell. Duchess was standing behind me. Annie answered the door. This was it!!!

"Guess who I found," I said.

Annie saw Duchess. She looked surprised. Then she squealed. She ran past me and hugged Duchess. Duchess yelped. Annie has a boa constrictor hug. "Oh, Fritz!" she cried. "You're back, you're back, you're back! I love you, I love you, I love you!"

Do you have to tell dogs things three times? Annie patted Duchess and looked him all over. This was the test! Warts, moles, what would Annie find that Duchess had that Fritz didn't have? Or what did Fritz have that Duchess didn't have? Annie said, "He smells funny."

I hadn't thought of that. I said, "Well, who knows where he's been?" I felt on top of things, like I knew everything.

Then Annie asked, "Where did you find Fritz?"

I hadn't thought of that either. Dummo! I said, "It was tough. Tough. But anyone who can spell *microgroove* without checking the dictionary can find a dog."

"But *where,* Richie?"

"*There,*" I said, pointing backward. "Way over there."

"What was he doing?"

"Well, he was just sort of being a dog. You know."

I guess Annie knew. No more questions.

"Well, thanks a lot, Richie," she said.

I, Richie Carr, knew that *thanks a lot* means more than thanks a lot. I knew that Annie was thinking I'm the greatest. I knew that Annie wanted to kiss me. But Duchess came over for pats.

When I left Annie's house, Duchess started to follow me.

Annie had to run after him and grab him. I turned around. Annie was holding Duchess. And Duchess was squirming to get free. They both were sorry to see me go.

May 10 Annie

Dear Diary,

I got Fritz back! Richie Carr found him. Fritz smells funny, and we have to housebreak him all over again. Do dogs forget things like that? I guess so.

I'm not sure Fritz loves me anymore.

May 11 **Richie**

Dear Journal,

Went to school. Saw Annie twice. She smiled at me both times.

May 11 **Annie**

Dear Diary,

Can't figure out Fritz. The smell won't go away, after two baths. He jumps up on furniture, and he chews socks. And I'm tired of cleaning up the puddles. Frances called it a "personality change." I didn't know dogs had that.

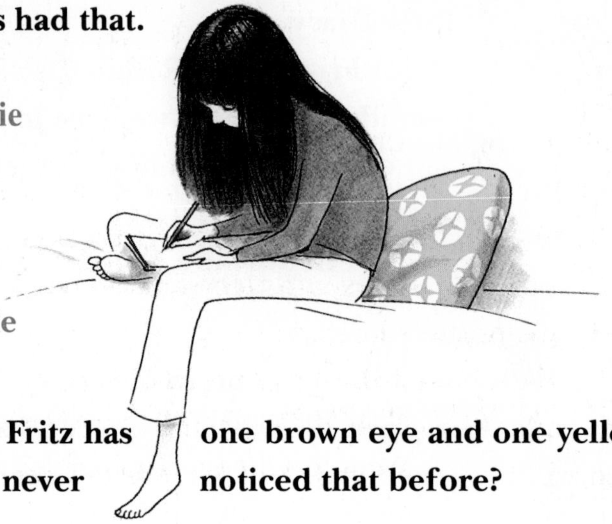

May 12 **Richie**

Dear Journal,

Three smiles!!!

May 12 **Annie**

Dear Diary,

I just noticed that Fritz has one brown eye and one yellow eye. How come I never noticed that before?

May 13 **Richie**

Dear Journal,

Today was boring. My mother and father talked about Duchess. "A sweet thing," my mother said. I think they like him better now that he isn't here. So do I. Why is that? Maybe they miss him. Maybe I miss him.

May 13 **Annie**

Dear Diary,

Dumb is what I am.

That's why I never noticed that Fritz has a funny bump on his leg that won't wash out in his bath.

May 14 **Richie**

Dear Journal,
Saw Annie five times in school. Got five smiles. Five out of five. Something big is happening!

May 14 **Annie**

Dear Diary,
I've been thinking about Richie. I'm going to buy him a nice present for finding Fritz. Maybe a game or a book. Maybe a book about high divers. That would make Richie feel good because he is one. When I think of bugs and itches and liver, I will no longer think of Richie at the same time.

But I'd better ask him some more questions about finding Fritz. That might help me know why Fritz seems so strange. I don't suppose it will help me figure out why his tail seems shorter.

May 15 **Richie**

Dear Journal,
Hooray! How do you spell that? Maybe it's hurrah. Who cares? Here it is in big letters.

ANNIE TOLD ME SHE BOUGHT ME A PRESENT AND SHE WANTS ME TO GO TO HER HOUSE TOMORROW TO GET IT.

This is really it. I hope Duchess will be at the door to meet me, because I MISS him in big letters, too.

May 15 **Annie**

Dear Diary,
The high diver book cost me two weeks' allowance. I bought a thank-you card, too. Fritz almost threw up over the present after I gave him his favorite dinner. I guess his favorite dinner isn't his favorite dinner anymore.

May 16 **Richie**

Dear Journal,
I almost left a blank page for today. Blank is better than what happened to me. I got all dressed up to go to Annie's house to get my present. I wore my shark T-shirt. This was Richie Carr Day. A present for Richie Carr. Annie *liking* Richie Carr a lot. And no more chasing after Annie. Annie was chasing after Richie Carr, sort of. Buying me a present. Asking me over.

I thought about Annie and me all the way to her house. How much I wanted her to like me. How hard I tried. Like finding Fritz for her.

Then it hit me. Right in the stomach. On the way to Annie's house. I didn't find Fritz. All I did was play a trick on Annie, that's what I did. I was phony Richie Carr. Pretending Duchess was Fritz. And now I was getting a present for a dirty trick. I wanted to go back home. Maybe Annie liked Richie Carr, but I didn't. Even worse, poor little Duchess liked me. I must be a great phony, fooling a dog. (I read somewhere that it's hard to fool dogs.)

Well, my feet kept walking toward Annie's house. When I got there, my fingers rang the bell. Annie answered. My feet walked inside.

Duchess ran toward me and jumped all over me. Then he sat down and waited for his pats. Annie was looking at me like I was an A on her report card. Like I was the greatest. She had my present in her hand. Then she held it in front of my eyes. She could hardly wait to give it to me.

But now (and I'm gritting my teeth as I write this) I had to *be* the greatest. By telling the truth, Journal, by telling the truth. Annie would hate me. But it was better than me hating me.

Duchess was sitting there watching us. Good. I needed a friend. I was getting up my courage. Annie looked so happy, so friendly, that I wanted to memorize that look forever, like the alphabet. She said, "Richie, I . . ."

She stopped. She was looking behind me. I looked behind me. The door was still open.

Coming up the walk, sniffing all the good old scents of home sweet home, was Fritz.

May 16 Annie

Dear Diary,
Two Fritzes! Got to think. Richie ran off. Odd.

May 17 **Richie**

Dear Journal,
Shock is a bad thing. Even *I* don't deserve shock.

Yes, it was Fritz, the genuine real one-hundred-percent Fritz.

First thing, he sniffed Duchess. Seeing them together made my eyeballs shudder. Then Fritz slunk up to Annie and cried. And cried.

I ran home. It wasn't a smart thing to do. But it felt very good.

I haven't mentioned today. I spent today trying to forget yesterday.

May 17 Annie

Dear Diary,
Number Two is *my* Fritz. I knew it right away. But I have to be very fair about this. Just because Number One Fritz was wrecking my house isn't why I decided against him. There's the smell, the bump, the eyes, the tail. The bark is a little off, too, when I think about it.

So who is he and where did Richie get him? And why did Richie run off? I wonder if stores take back books and thank-you cards.

May 18 **Richie**

Dear Journal,
I think I died today. I was in school. And Zitts comes up to me. And Annie comes up to me at the same time.

Zitts asks, "How is Brussels Sprouts?"

Annie asks, "Who is Brussels Sprouts?"

"An ugly vegetable that shouldn't have been born, ha ha," I say. And I walk away.

Zitts and Annie keep on talking. Did I die on the spot?

May 18 **Annie**

Dear Diary,

Are you ready for weird? Here it is. Zitts told me that Richie got a dog from the animal shelter. He named it Brussels Sprouts. Zitts said that I'd be just crazy about Brussels Sprouts. I thought it was a vegetable joke when he said it. Now I'm not sure.

Here's some sad news. I was saving it until last.

My folks say I can't have two dogs. Number One Fritz has to go. But where?

May 19 **Richie**

Dear Journal,

I'm not dead yet, but I'm getting there. Soon. Zitts says his dad wants to talk to me. Something about honor and owing money. And Frances says Annie wants to talk to me. Something about Fritzes Numbers One and Two.

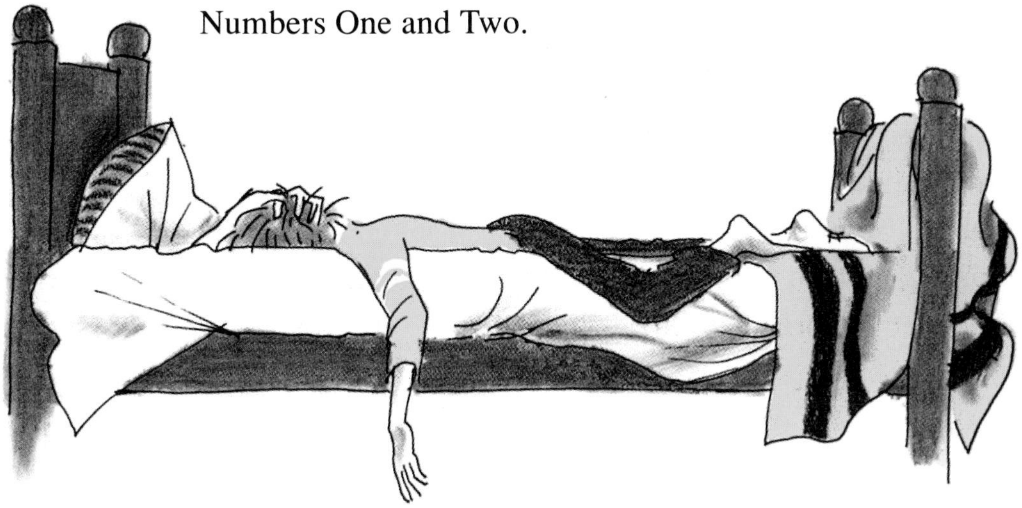

May 19 **Annie**

Dear Diary,

Decision. Tomorrow I'm going over to Richie's house with Fritz Number One and Fritz Number Two. There's something fishy going on. With Brussels Sprouts. With Richie running away. With two Fritzes. Tomorrow will be a big day.

May 20 **Richie**

Dear Journal,
What happened today? I finally died.

May 20 **Annie**

Dear Diary,
I hate Richie Carr. More than bugs, more than itches, more than liver.

May 21 **Richie**

Dear Journal,
What happened yesterday?

When Annie and Fritz and Duchess came over after school, Annie didn't even say hello. She looked like one of those characters in comic books who can turn into something else, some kind of monster. She looked like she was turning.

I invited her and the dogs inside. Duchess came over and sat for pats. Annie asked, "Where did you find the dog you said was Fritz? Why did you run away when the real Fritz came home? Who is Brussels Sprouts? Do you have a big secret?"

Just then my mother peeked into the room. Duchess ran over for pats. My mother said, "Nice Duchess. Good Duchess." Then my mother left.

Now Annie had a new question. "Duchess? *Duchess?*" It was all over.

"Duchess is Brussels Sprouts is Number One Fritz," I said. "I got him from the animal shelter. I got him because he looks like Fritz and I wanted to find Fritz for you."

Now Annie was out of questions. And into statements. "Richie Carr, you're rotten," she said. And she picked up Fritz and left.

Duchess came over to me for more pats. Well, somebody likes me.

May 21 **Annie**

Dear Diary,
I'm still too mad to write anything.

May 22 **Richie**

Dear Journal,
I want to write something good right away so I'll tell you that I paid Zitts's father the minute I got my allowance. Also, I told Zitts everything. Then I told my mother and father everything. I think they're getting a lecture ready for me. But I don't care because they're letting me keep Duchess. I have plenty of cleaning up to do, but I'm getting busy training him. I take him for long hikes. I love him. He loves me, too. I don't even have to *try* to impress him.

May 22 **Annie**

Dear Diary,
I keep thinking about the dirty trick Richie Carr played on me.

May 23 **Richie**

Dear Journal,
Duchess is the best dog in the world and sometimes I think I'm lucky, but not very. I won't mention Annie because I don't want to.

May 23 **Annie**

Dear Diary,
A perfect day because I didn't see Richie Carr. I guess he's busy with his new dog Duchess.

May 24 Richie

Dear Journal,
No puddles today.

May 24 Annie

Dear Diary,
Today I saw Richie Carr playing with Duchess. Duchess rolled over for stomach rubs and Richie gave him at least nine. You'd almost think that Richie was some kind of good person if you didn't know better.

May 25 Richie

Dear Journal,
Still no puddles.

May 25 Annie

Dear Diary,
Guess who I saw again. He was walking along, kicking pebbles, talking to Duchess, not showing off. I must be crazy but I almost liked him when I looked at him. Maybe Richie is a dog person just like me. Maybe the next time I see him, or the time after that, I'll speak to him.

May 26 Richie

Dear Journal,
Annie spoke to me! She said, "Hello." And we walked together down an alley. I told her I was training Duchess and that Duchess already knows what *sit* means. Annie patted Duchess and I patted Fritz.

Well, it's a start. Richie Carr may rise again.

May 26 **Annie**

Dear Diary,
I'm sure, I'm positive, that there are worse people in this world than Richie Carr.

Today we went for a walk. It was nice. Maybe someday I'll look at the fish scrapbook he keeps talking about.

May 27 **Richie**

Dear Journal,
Annie came over today. I only had to ask once. She looked at every fish in my scrapbook. She went wild over my piranha. Then we raced around the block twice with Fritz and Duchess. Annie said to me, "Richie, you're a dog person!"

I, Richie Carr, am a dog person? Annie Alpert *really* likes me, Journal.

And I haven't even told her yet that I can multiply 3,000 by 464 in my head and get the right answer!

DOG DAYS

May 16 was the day the real Fritz came home and the fake Fritz (Duchess) was exposed. If the two dogs could talk, what would they say about each other? Write two journal entries for that day: one by Fritz and one by Duchess.

Marjorie Weinman Sharmat

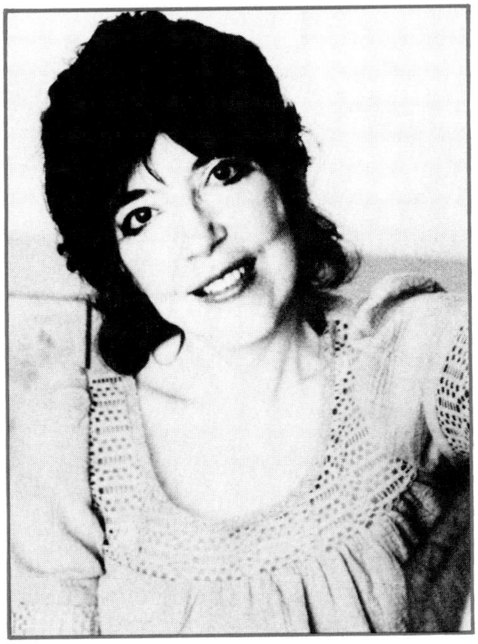

When Marjorie Sharmat was eight years old, she made up her own newspaper called *The Snooper's Gazette*. She filled it with news obtained by spying on grownups in the neighborhood. That was Sharmat's start as a writer.

Sharmat's early days as a spy and reporter may have prompted her to write *Mysteriously Yours, Maggie Marmelstein*, about a girl secretly writing for her school paper.

Sharmat often gets ideas for characters in her stories from people and sometimes pets in her own life. In fact, Fritz, the dog in *Chasing After Annie*, was named after her own dog.

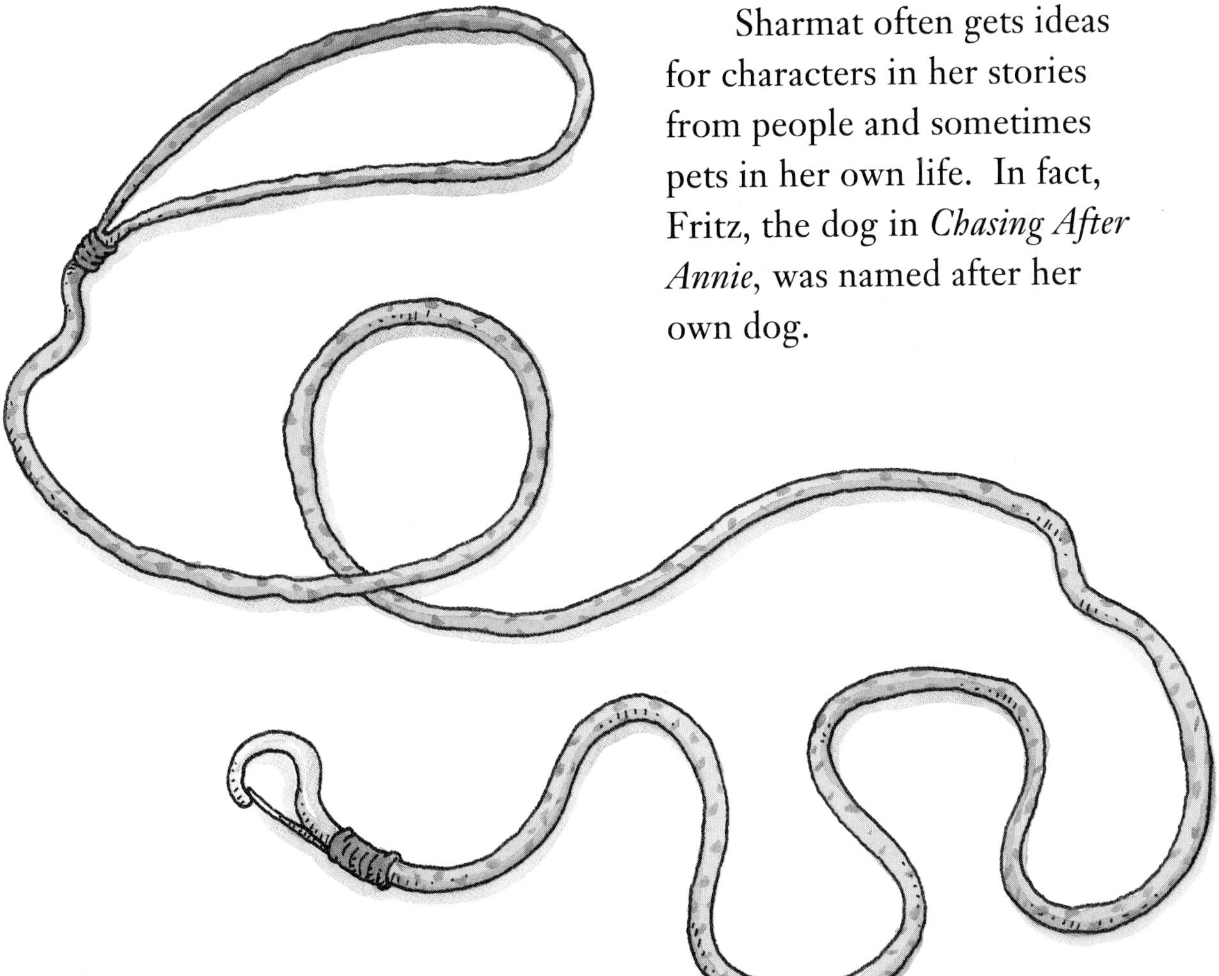

Take a peek at these books

The Secret Moose *by Jean Rogers*

Gerald is the only one to see the moose in his yard one morning. He never dreams what will happen when he follows this secret creature.

Staying Nine *by Pam Conrad*

Heather Fitz likes being nine years old. In fact, Heather likes being nine so much, she refuses to turn ten.

The Hundred Penny Box *by Sharon Bell Mathis*

Each penny means another special memory shared by Michael's great-great-great Aunt Dew.

Your Former Friend, Matthew
by LouAnn Gaeddert

Gail and Matthew have always been best friends — until Matthew returns from summer camp.

The Chalk Box Kid *by Clyde Robert Bulla*

Gregory discovers a hidden talent and earns the nickname "the chalk box kid."

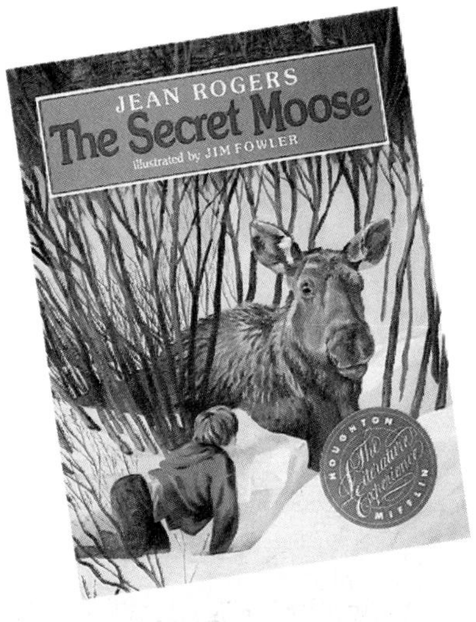

Glossary

Some of the words in this book may have pronunciations or meanings you do not know. This glossary can help you by telling you how to pronounce those words and by telling you the meanings with which those words are used in this book.

You can find out the correct pronunciation of any glossary word by using the special spelling after the word and the pronunciation key that runs across the bottom of the glossary pages.

The full pronunciation key opposite shows how to pronounce each consonant and vowel in a special spelling. The pronunciation key at the bottom of the glossary pages is a shortened form of the full key.

FULL PRONUNCIATION KEY

Consonant Sounds

b	**b**i**b**	k	**c**at, **k**i**ck**, pi**que**	th	pa**th**, **th**in
ch	**ch**ur**ch**	l	**l**id, need**l**e	*th*	ba**th**e, **th**is
d	**d**ee**d**	m	a**m**, **m**an, **m**u**m**	v	ca**v**e, **v**al**v**e, **v**ine
f	**f**ast, **f**i**f**e, o**ff**, **ph**ase, rou**gh**	n	**n**o, sudde**n**	w	**w**ith
g	**g**a**g**	ng	thi**ng**	y	**y**es
h	**h**at	p	**p**o**p**	z	ro**s**e, si**z**e, **x**ylophone, **z**ebra
hw	**wh**ich	r	**r**oa**r**	zh	gara**g**e, plea**s**ure, vi**s**ion
j	**j**u**dg**e	s	mi**ss**, **s**au**c**e, **s**ee		
		sh	di**sh**, **sh**ip		
		t	**t**igh**t**		

Vowel Sounds

ă	p**a**t	î	d**ea**r, d**ee**r, f**ie**rce, m**e**re	ou	c**ow**, **ou**t
ā	**ai**d, th**ey**, p**ay**	ŏ	p**o**t, h**o**rrible	ŭ	c**u**t, r**ou**gh
â	**ai**r, c**a**re, w**ea**r	ō	g**o**, r**ow**, t**oe**	û	f**i**rm, h**ea**rd, t**e**rm, t**u**rn, w**o**rd
ä	f**a**ther	ô	**a**lter, c**au**ght, f**o**r, p**aw**	yo͞o	ab**u**se, **u**se
ĕ	p**e**t, pl**ea**sure	oi	b**oy**, n**oi**se, **oi**l	ə	**a**bout, sil**e**nt, penc**i**l, lem**o**n, circ**u**s
ē	b**e**, b**ee**, **ea**s**y**, s**ei**ze	o͝o	b**oo**k	ər	butt**er**
ĭ	p**i**t	o͞o	b**oo**t		
ī	b**y**, g**uy**, p**ie**				

STRESS MARKS

Primary Stress ′	*Secondary Stress* ′
bi•ol•o•gy [bī **ŏl′**ə jē]	bi•o•log•i•cal [bī′ə **lŏj′**ĭ kəl]

A

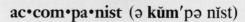

ac•com•pa•nist (ə **kŭm**′pə nĭst) *n.* A performer, such as a pianist, who plays an instrument for the lead performer: *The singer sang while her* ***accompanist*** *played the piano.*

ac•cuse (ə **kyo͞oz**′) *v.* To blame for wrongdoing: *The police officer* ***accused*** *Mr. Curry of stealing.*

ag•gra•vat•ing (**ăg**′rə vāt′ĭng) *adj.* Annoying or irritating. "I was aggravating" means I was getting on your nerves.

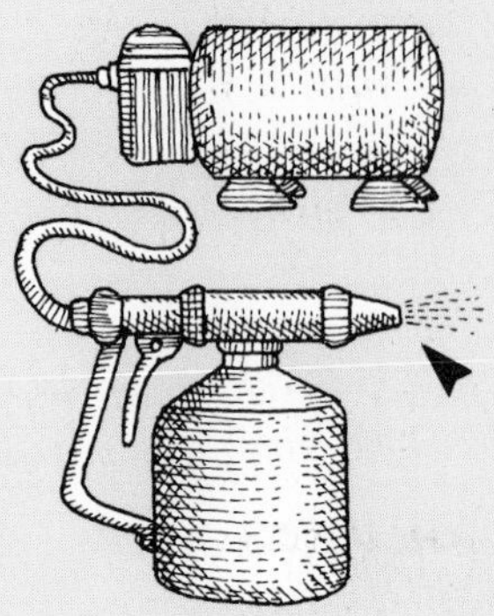

airbrush

air•brush (**âr**′brŭsh′) *n.* A tool that uses compressed air to spray paint or other liquids on a surface.

an•i•mal shel•ter (**ăn**′ə məl **shĕl**′tər) *n.* A place for homeless animals to stay: *Richie went to the* ***animal shelter*** *to find a pet that needed a home.*

an•i•ma•tor (**ăn**′ə mā′tər) *n.* A person who draws the pictures for an animated cartoon.

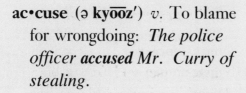

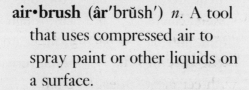

an•nounce (ə **nouns**′) *v.* To make known to people officially: *The judges will* ***announce*** *the winner's name this afternoon.*

anx•ious (**ăngk**′shəs) *adj.* Feeling nervous or afraid about something uncertain: *Ellen felt* ***anxious*** *about her grade on the math test.*

ap•pre•ci•ate (ə **prē**′shē āt′) *v.* **1.** To be grateful for: *I* ***appreciate*** *your cheering me up when I was feeling sad.* **2.** To recognize the worth or importance of something.

ar•mor (**är**′mər) *n.* A hard protective covering: *The hard shell of a turtle is* ***armor*** *that protects it from its enemies.*

au•then•tic (ô **thĕn**′tĭk) *adj.* Real; true; genuine. If something is authentic, it is real and not a fake.

AUTHENTIC

To the ancient Greeks, an *authentes* was a master. An authentic piece of work was "created by the master," not copied.

B

bar•gain (**bär**′gĭn) *v.* To try to agree about a price for something: *If I* ***bargain*** *with the landlord, maybe he will lower the rent.* — *n.* An agreement between two sides about a payment or trade.

ă pat / ā pay / â care / ä father / ĕ pet / ē be / ĭ pit / ī pie / î fierce / ŏ pot / ō go / ô paw, for / oi oil / o͝o book /

bis•cuit (**bĭs′kĭt**) *n.* A small cake of baked dough.

bliz•zard (**blĭz′**ərd) *n.* A very heavy snowstorm with strong blowing winds: *Two feet of snow fell before the* ***blizzard*** *was over.*

bluff (blŭf) *n.* A high, steep hill, cliff, or river bank. — *v.* To fool someone with a false show of strength or confidence: *Peter said he had solved the case, but he was* ***bluffing****.*

brag•gart (**brăg′**ərt) *n.* Someone who speaks with too much pride about him or herself in an attempt to show off: *Amy was a* ***braggart*** *when she said that she was smarter than us.*

C

ca•reer (kə **rîr′**) *n.* The kind of work that a person chooses to do; a profession: *Marian chose a* ***career*** *as a singer.*

car•toon•ist (kär **tōō′**nĭst) *n.* A person who sketches or draws cartoons: *Mickey Mouse was drawn by the* ***cartoonist****, Walt Disney.*

ca•tas•tro•phe (kə **tăs′**trə fē) *n.* A disaster that causes great damage and often loss of life: *Scientists think a great* ***catastrophe*** *may have killed the dinosaurs.*

cat•e•go•ry (**kăt′**ə gôr′ē) *n.*, *pl.* **categories.** A division that names a particular kind; class: *In the baking contest there was one* ***category*** *for cake and another for pie.*

cel•lu•loid (**sĕl′**yə loid′) *n.* A clear shiny material used for making animated motion pictures: *A cartoonist draws the characters for animated movies on sheets of* ***celluloid****.*

cer•tain•ty (**sûr′**tn tē) *n.*, *pl.* **certainties.** The feeling of being sure. "The boy said it with certainty" means he felt sure of what he was saying.

cham•pi•on•ship (**chăm′**pē ən shĭp′) *n.* The award for a person or team that is accepted as the best of all: *The Pirates beat the Orioles and won the baseball* ***championship****.*

cliff (klĭf) *n.* A high, steep, or overhanging section of rock or earth.

BISCUIT

A biscuit was once a bread that was baked twice. *Biscuit* comes from two old French words, *bis* and *cuit*, meaning "twice-cooked."

CHAMPIONSHIP

The old Latin word for battle-field, *campus*, is in the word *championship*. Today's champions win battles on playing fields.

cliff

o͞o boot / ou out / ŭ cut / û fur / *th* the / th thin / hw which / zh vision / ə ago, item, pencil, atom, circus

cli•mate (**klī′**mĭt) *n.* The weather that usually occurs in a place: *People who live in a cold **climate** need to dress warmly.*

com•mand (kə **mănd′**) *n.* An order or direction: *The conductor gave the **command** and the band began to play.*

com•pe•ti•tion (kŏm′pĭ **tĭsh′**ən) *n.* A contest or other test of skill and ability: *A **competition** was held to decide who made the best biscuits.*

CONVINCE

When you convince your friends of something, you win them over. The Latin word *vincere* means "to win."

com•pet•i•tor (kəm **pĕt′**ĭ tər) *n.* A person or group that tries to be more successful than another: *Walt Disney tried to make better animated movies than his **competitors**.*

con•cert (**kŏn′**sûrt′) *n.* A performance of music given by one or more singers or musicians: *Thousands of people filled the stadium to hear the singer's **concert**.*

con•sent (kən **sĕnt′**) *v.* To agree or give approval: *If she does **consent** to marry him, they will become husband and wife.*

con•tract (**kŏn′**trăkt′) *n.* An official paper that shows the conditions of an agreement: *According to the **contract** you must pay me one thousand dollars.*

con•vince (kən **vĭns′**) *v.* To make someone believe something; persuade: *Sam said he had done his best, but the teacher was not **convinced**.*

D

de•cay (dĭ **kā′**) *v.* To rot away: *The flesh of the dinosaurs **decayed**, so now we have only their bones to study.*

de•ci•pher (dĭ **sī′**fər) *v.* To make out the meaning of something that is hard to understand or is not clear: *After the note fell in a puddle, the words were difficult to **decipher**.*

de•code (dē **kōd′**) *v.* To change from code into the original language: *The detective tried to **decode** the puzzling message.*

de•cree (dĭ **krē′**) *v.* To give an official order or decision: *The gods have* ***decreed*** *that the merchant's daughter must marry Taro.*

de•duce (dĭ **do͞os′**) *v.* To figure out by reasoning: *The detective tried to* ***deduce*** *from the clues where the missing baseball was.*

de•duc•tion (dĭ **dŭk′**shən) *n.* The drawing of a conclusion by reasoning: *Meg's list of* ***deductions*** *showed what she had learned about the clues.*

de•sire (dĭ **zīr′**) *n.* A strong wish; a longing: *Roberto's* ***desire*** *to play baseball was like a hunger for food.*

de•tect (dĭ **tĕkt′**) *v.* To discover or notice something: *I* ***detect*** *a dimple in your cheek whenever you smile.*

de•tec•tive (dĭ **tĕk′**tĭv) *n.* A person whose work is gathering information about crimes and trying to solve them.

de•ter•mine (dĭ **tûr′**mĭn) *v.* To find out definitely: *The judges will* ***determine*** *the winner of the contest.*

de•test (dĭ **tĕst′**) *v.* To dislike very much. "They detest each other" means they hate each other.

dis•ap•pear (dĭs′ə **pîr′**) *v.* To pass out of sight; vanish: *If Treehorn* ***disappears,*** *no one will be able to see him.*

dis•guise (dĭs **gīz′**) *n.* Clothes and often make-up worn to hide one's identity or to look like someone else: *Paddington wore a* ***disguise*** *so no one would guess who he was.* — *v.* To change the appearance with a disguise so as not to be recognized.

du•et (do͞o **ĕt′**) *n.* A musical piece for two voices or two instruments: *The two girls sang a* ***duet*** *together.*

E

ef•fort (**ĕf′**ərt) *n.* **1.** The use of physical or mental energy to do something: *Cricket put a lot of* ***effort*** *into her book report because she wanted to get a good grade.* **2.** An attempt; a try.

DETECT, DETECTIVE

Detect comes from the Latin word *detectus*, meaning "uncovered." A good detective uncovers hidden facts.

o͞o **boot** / ou **out** / ŭ **cut** / û **fur** / *th* **the** / th **thin** / hw **which** / zh **vision** / ə **ago, item, pencil, atom, circus**

el•o•quent (ĕl′ə kwənt) *adj.* Using language in a clear, forceful, and effective way: *The man's speech was so **eloquent** that he talked many people into voting for him.*

em•bar•rass•ing (ĕm **băr′**əs ĭng) *adj.* Causing to feel uncomfortable and nervous: *It was **embarrassing** for me when you started to snore in the middle of the movie.*

en•cour•age (ĕn **kûr′**ĭj) *v.* To give hope or confidence to: *John didn't think he could bowl very well, but Uncle Joe **encouraged** him to try.*

en•hance (ĕn **hăns′**) *v.* To make greater in value or beauty: *Cricket thought a fancy cover would **enhance** the look of her book report.*

en•thu•si•asm (ĕn **thōō′**zē ăz′əm) *n.* A very strong, positive feeling for something; strong interest: *The boy showed his **enthusiasm** by yelling words of support.*

e•qual (ē′kwəl) *n.* Someone who has the same rights and privileges as another. To accept someone as an equal is to feel that person should have the same rights as you.

ex•pe•di•tion (ĕk′spĭ **dĭsh′**ən) *n.* A journey made for a definite purpose: *The scientists went on an **expedition** to look for the bones of dinosaurs.*

ex•tinct (ĭk **stĭngkt′**) *adj.* No longer existing in living form: *Woolly mammoths once lived on earth but today they are **extinct**.*

F

fair•ground (**fâr′**ground′) *n.* An open space of land where fairs or exhibitions are held: *When the family saw the big striped tents they knew they had found the **fairgrounds**.*

fes•ti•val (**fĕs′**tə vəl) *n.* A day or time of celebrating; a holiday: *Every year the people celebrated the end of summer with a big **festival**.*

fierce (fîrs) *adj.* **1.** Wild; dangerous: *The **fierce** expression on Taro's face scared the merchant.* **2.** Very strong or extreme.

ford (fôrd) *n.* A shallow place in a body of water, such as a river, where one can cross: *The horses were able to swim across the river at the **ford**.*

ă pat / ā pay / â care / ä father / ĕ pet / ē be / ĭ pit / ī pie / î fierce / ŏ pot / ō go / ô paw, for / oi oil / ŏŏ book /

fran•ti•cal•ly (**frăn′tĭk lē**) *adv.* Done in excitement from fear or worry: *Afraid of freezing in the storm, the children* ***frantically*** *gathered wood for a fire.*

G

gen•u•ine (**jĕn′yo͞o ĭn**) *adj.* Not false; real: *Annie could tell that this dog was the* ***genuine*** *Fritz, and not a fake.*

gos•sip (**gŏs′əp**) *n.* **1.** Stories and news, often not true, that people repeat; rumors. **2.** A person who likes to tell and hear such stories and news.

grad•u•al•ly (**grăj′o͞o əl ē**) *adv.* Happening little by little: *The dinosaurs may have died off* ***gradually****, over a long period of time.*

grove (**grōv**) *n.* A group of trees with open ground between them.

guide (**gīd**) *n.* Someone or something that shows the way, directs, or teaches: *The* ***guide*** *led us safely through the jungle.*

H

Hall of Fame (**hôl ŭv fām**) *n.* A group of persons judged outstanding in a sport or profession: *Roberto Clemente is in baseball's* ***Hall of Fame*** *because he was one of baseball's greatest players.*

hes•i•tate (**hĕz′ĭ tāt′**) *v.* To pause or hold back because of feeling unsure: *Ann* ***hesitated*** *because she could not decide what to do first.*

hon•or (**ŏn′ər**) *n.* A sign of someone's excellence or worth; a mark of respect: *One of the* ***honors*** *the singer received was a medal from the queen of England.*

hum•ble (**hŭm′bəl**) *adj.* Not thinking or speaking too highly about one's own talents or accomplishments: *The man is so* ***humble*** *that he never talks about his wealth.*

I

im•pa•tience (**ĭm pā′shəns**) *n.* A feeling of not being able or willing to put up with something calmly: *When she was interrupted, the princess sighed with* ***impatience****.*

FRANTICALLY

People who move around frantically act as if they have a fever. The word comes from an old disease called *phrenitis*, which meant "a fever of the brain."

grove

HUMBLE

Humble comes from the Latin word *humus*, meaning "the ground." To be humble once meant "to lower yourself to the ground."

o͞o **boot** / ou **out** / ŭ **cut** / û **fur** / *th* **the** / th **thin** / hw **which** / zh vision / ə **a**go, it**e**m, penc**i**l, at**o**m, circ**u**s

INVESTIGATE

Investigate goes back to the Latin word *vestigium*, or "footprint." A detective who investigates a mystery is following footprints.

lizard

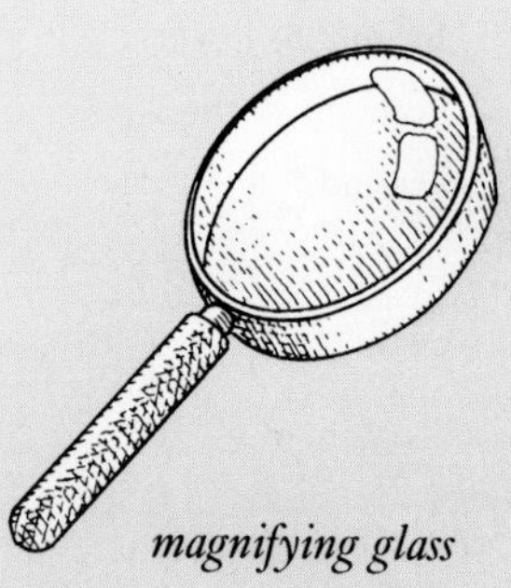

magnifying glass

im•pos•si•ble (ĭm **pŏs′**ə bəl) *adj.* **1.** Difficult to deal with or put up with: *My baby sister is **impossible** when she doesn't get her way.* **2.** Not capable of happening or existing.

im•press (ĭm **prĕs′**) *v.* To have a strong, favorable effect on someone's mind or feelings: *Mendel was so **impressed** by the stranger that he decided to rent him the room.*

in•field (**ĭn′**fēld′) *n.* The part of a baseball field that includes the bases and the area inside them: *If the pitcher had not caught the ball, it would have gone out of the **infield**.*

in•ning (**ĭn′**ĭng) *n.* One of nine divisions of a baseball game during which each team comes to bat: *Both teams came to bat in the eighth **inning** and scored a run.*

in•struc•tions (ĭn **strŭk′**shənz) *n.* Directions; orders: *According to the **instructions**, the first player to reach the blue square is the winner.*

in•ves•ti•gate (ĭn **vĕs′**tĭ gāt′) *v.* To look into carefully: *The detective decided to **investigate** the mystery.*

L

land•lord (**lănd′**lôrd′) *n.* A person who owns property, such as a house or apartment, that is rented out: *Mendel became a **landlord** after he rented a room to the stranger.*

lick•ing (**lĭk′**ĭng) *n.* A punishment of being hit or struck again and again.

liz•ard (**lĭz′**ərd) *n.* An animal that has a scaly body, four legs, and a long tail: *The largest **lizards** the world has known are the dinosaurs.*

lurch (lûrch) *v.* To move suddenly or heavily forward or to one side: *The wagon **lurched** to one side and we tumbled to the floor.*

M

mag•ni•fy•ing glass (**măg′**nə fī′ĭng **glăs**) *n.* A lens that makes things look bigger.

ma•jor leagues (**mā′**jər lēgz) *n.* A group of the highest class of professional baseball teams in the United States: *The young pitcher dreamed of playing on a team in the **major leagues** some day.*

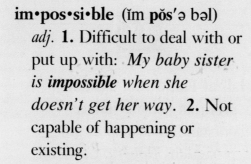

ă pat / ā pay / â care / ä father / ĕ pet / ē be / ĭ pit / ī pie / î fierce / ŏ pot / ō go / ô paw, for / oi oil / o͝o book /

match (măch) *n.* Someone or something that is equal or nearly equal to another. "She met her match" means she met someone who has the same ability she has.

mem•o•ry (**mĕm**′ə rē) *n., pl.* **memories.** The power or ability to remember: *The girl closed her eyes and named all the states from* ***memory****.*

might•y (**mī**′tē) *adj.* **mightier, mightiest.** Great in size, strength, or importance: *Other dinosaurs ran for cover when they saw the* ***mighty*** *Tyrannosaurus coming.*

mis•tress (**mĭs**′trĭs) *n.* A woman or girl in a position of authority, control, or ownership: *Charlotte is the dog's* ***mistress*** *because she takes care of him.*

mon•soon (mŏn **so͞on**′) *n.* A wind in southern Asia that brings heavy rain from the ocean: *During the season when the* ***monsoon*** *blows, the rain falls almost every day.*

O

ob•nox•ious (əb **nŏk**′shəs) *adj.* Extremely unpleasant: *The princess spoke in an* ***obnoxious*** *way when she didn't get what she wanted.*

on pur•pose (ŏn **pûr**′pəs) *idiom.* Not accidentally; for a reason: *Treehorn's parents wondered if he was shrinking not by accident but* ***on purpose****, just to be different.*

or•ches•tra con•duc•tor (**ôr**′kĭ strə kən **dŭk**′tər) *n.* A person who leads or conducts a group of musicians who play various instruments.

orchestra conductor

outfield (**out**′fēld′) *n.* The grassy part of a baseball field outside the bases: *Roberto ran to the edge of the* ***outfield*** *and caught the ball before it went over the fence.*

P

part•ner (**pärt**′nər) *n.* One of two or more persons joined in a business: *When the job became too hard for one person, the detective worked with a* ***partner****.*

o͞o **boot** / ou **out** / ŭ **cut** / û **fur** / *th* **the** / th **thin** / hw **which** / zh vi**sion** /
ə **a**go, it**e**m, penc**i**l, at**o**m, circ**u**s

pa•thet•ic (pə **thĕt′**ĭk) *adj.* Causing one to feel pity, sorrow, or sympathy: *The little boy seemed* ***pathetic****, sitting alone on the bench weeping.*

pavilion

pa•tient (**pā′**shənt) *adj.* Putting up with trouble, delay, or pain without complaining or getting angry: *Roberto asked the Pirates to be* ***patient*** *and give the new player time to get used to the team.*

pa•tron (**pā′**trən) *n.* The guardian or protector of a nation, place, person, or group: *Ujigami is the town's* ***patron*** *because the people believe he protects them.*

PERSONALITY

In ancient Greek drama, a *persona* was the special mask an actor wore. In time it led to *personality*.

pa•vil•ion (pə **vĭl′**yən) *n.* A building with open sides that is used at parks or fairs for entertainment or shelter.

per•son•al•i•ty (pûr′sə **năl′**ĭ tē) *n.*, *pl.* **personalities.** All the kinds of behavior and feelings a person has that make that person different from everyone else. A "personality change" is a change from the way someone usually acts.

prairie

prai•rie (**prâr′**ē) *n.* A wide area of flat or rolling land with tall grass and few trees.

pre•tend (prĭ **tĕnd′**) *v.* **1.** To make believe. **2.** To put on a false show: *Annie really likes me, but she* ***pretends*** *she hates me.*

pre•vi•ous (**prē′**vē əs) *adj.* Coming before something else; earlier: *I am a teacher now, but my* ***previous*** *job was playing baseball.*

priv•i•lege (**prĭv′**ə lĭj) *n.* A special right or permission given to a person or group: *Having special* ***privileges*** *means being allowed to do things that others cannot do.*

pro•duc•tion (prə **dŭk′**shən) *n.* The act or process of making something. The production costs are the money needed for making a movie.

pro•fes•sion•al (prə **fĕsh′**ə nəl) *adj.* Performing an activity as a job, for money. A professional singer is someone who is paid for singing.

prof•it (**prŏf′**ĭt) *n.* The amount of money left after the costs of operating a business have been subtracted from all the money earned: *I earned thirty dollars, but I spent ten dollars on the job, so my* ***profit*** *was twenty dollars.*

pro•ject (prə **jĕkt′**) *v.* To cause light to throw a picture on a screen: *I flipped the switch and the cartoon of Mickey Mouse was **projected** on the screen.* (**prŏj′**ĕkt′) — *n.* A special study or experiment.

proof (pro͞of) *n.* Evidence or facts that show that something is true: *The fact that Meg solved the mystery was **proof** that she was a good detective.*

pros•per•ous (**prŏs′**pər əs) *adj.* Enjoying or marked by wealth or success. Someone who is prosperous-looking looks successful or wealthy.

py•thon (**pī′**thŏn′) *n.* A very large snake of Africa, Asia, and Australia, which coils around and crushes the animals it eats.

R

rea•son (**rē′**zən) *v.* **1.** To talk or argue in order to make sense of something: *The detective **reasoned** that if it snowed last night, the thief must have left footprints.* **2.** To use the ability to think clearly.

rec•i•pe (**rĕs′**ə pē) *n.* A set of directions for preparing food: *The biscuit **recipe** calls for two cups of flour.*

rep•tile (**rĕp′**tīl′) *n.* One of a group of cold-blooded animals that are usually covered with scaly skin: *Snakes, turtles, and dinosaurs are all **reptiles**.*

re•sem•blance (rĭ **zĕm′**bləns) *n.* Similarity in looks; likeness. Family resemblance means that the members of the family look a little like each other.

re•spon•si•ble (rĭ **spŏn′**sə bəl) *adj.* **1.** Having a duty or obligation: *I am **responsible** for my little brother when we go to the movies.* **2.** Being the cause of something: *Who is **responsible** for this mess?*

roam (rōm) *v.* To move or wander over an area: *Dinosaurs **roamed** from place to place in search of food.*

rou•tine (ro͞o **tēn′**) *n.* The usual or regular way of doing things. A comfortable routine means a regular way of doing things that you are satisfied with.

PROJECT

The Latin word *projectus* means "thrown forward." Moving pictures are thrown forward when we project them on a screen.

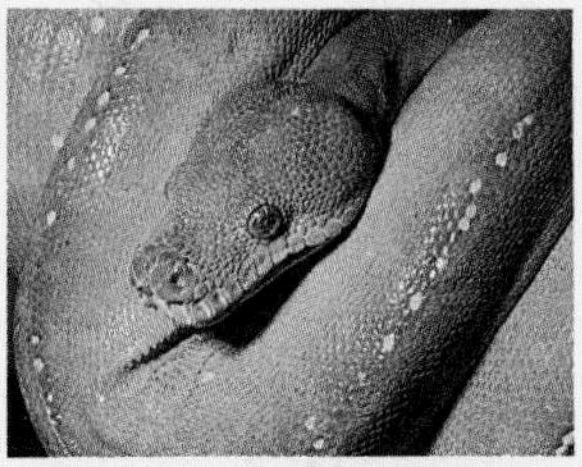

python

REPTILE

Reptiles get their name from the Latin word *reptilis*, which means "creeping."

ROUTINE

Routine comes from the French word *route*, which means "a road that is well-traveled."

o͞o **boot** / ou **out** / ŭ **cut** / û **fur** / *th* **the** / th **thin** / hw **which** / zh **vision** /
ə **ago, item, pencil, atom, circus**

ru•ins (**rōō'**ĭnz) *n.* The remains of a building that has been destroyed or fallen into pieces from age: *Scientists can learn about the past from the* ***ruins*** *of old buildings.*

S

sam•u•rai war•ri•or (**săm'**ōō rī' **wôr'**ē ər) *n.* A member of a special class of people in Japan who were experienced in war or fighting.

scal•y (**skā'**lē) *adj.* **scalier, scaliest.** Covered with the small, thin plates that form the skin of a fish or reptile: *The* ***scaly*** *skin of a lizard feels bumpy to the touch.*

scan•dal (**skăn'**dl) *n.* Harmful talk or gossip: *The story about the king caused a* ***scandal*** *that turned people against him.*

scene of the crime (sēn ŭv thə krīm) *n.* The place where an unlawful activity occurred. When there is a bank robbery, the bank is the scene of the crime.

scoun•drel (**skoun'**drəl) *n.* A very wicked person: *The man with the fine manners was really a* ***scoundrel.***

scowl (skoul) *n.* An angry frown: *We could tell the boy was angry from the* ***scowl*** *on his face.*

se•cure (sĭ **kyŏŏr'**) *v.* To hold or fasten tightly: *The thief was* ***secured*** *by rope so that he could not escape.*

se•lect (sĭ **lĕkt'**) *v.* To choose; pick out: *Before the game begins, each player* ***selects*** *a card from the pile.*

se•ries (**sîr'**ēz) *n.* A number of similar things that occur in a row or follow one another: *Walt Disney could make a* ***series*** *of drawings look like a mouse dancing.*

shirk (shûrk) *v.* To avoid doing something one ought to do: *You were* ***shirking*** *when you should have been helping us clean the room.*

shock (shŏk) *n.* Something sudden that disturbs or upsets the mind or feelings: *The loss of their homes was a terrible* ***shock*** *to the people.*

ă pat / ā **pay** / â care / ä father / ĕ pet / ē **be** / ĭ pit / ī **pie** / î fierce / ŏ pot / ō **go** /
ô paw, for / oi **oil** / ŏŏ book /

short•cut (**shôrt′kŭt′**) *n.* A shorter, faster route than the usual one: *If you use the **shortcut**, you can get home in half the time it usually takes.*

shrine (shrīn) *n.* A place where people may worship or remember an important person or event.

shuf•fle (**shŭf′**əl) *v.* To walk slowly, while dragging the feet: *Treehorn was **shuffling** along because his shoes were too big for his feet.*

spir•i•tu•al (**spĭr′**ĭ cho͞o əl) *n.* A religious folk song of African-American origin.

sta•di•um (**stā′**dē əm) *n.* A large building, often without a roof, where athletic events are held.

stag•ger (**stăg′**ər) *v.* To move unsteadily: *The logs were so heavy they caused Mary to **stagger** as she carried them.*

sud•den•ly (**sŭd′**n lē) *adv.* Happening or arriving without warning: *The storm came **suddenly**, before anyone was ready for it.*

sus•pect (**sŭs′**pĕkt′) *n.* A person who, without proof, is thought to be guilty of a crime: *The boy was a **suspect** because he was in the building around the time the skates were stolen.*

swift•ly (**swĭft′**lē) *adv.* Very fast: *Pushed along by the windy storm, the clouds moved **swiftly**.*

swirl (swûrl) *v.* To move or spin round and round: *As the wind blew, the snow **swirled** in circles on the ground.*

stadium

T

tal•ent (**tăl′**ənt) *n.* A natural ability to do something well: *Marian had a great **talent** as a singer, but she had to develop it with study and practice.*

tar pit (tär pĭt) *n.* A hole in the ground that was once filled with a thick, dark, sticky substance: *Most animals who fell into **tar pits** could not get out.*

tell•tale (**tĕl′**tāl′) *adj.* Indicating or revealing information: *The footprints were a **telltale** sign that someone had been there.*

TAR PIT

Tar comes from *treow*, an old English word for "tree." In those days tar came from the wood of trees.

o͞o **boot** / ou **out** / ŭ **cut** / û **fur** / *th* **the** / th **thin** / hw **wh**ich / zh vi**s**ion / ə **a**go, it**e**m, penc**i**l, at**o**m, circ**u**s

ten•ant (**tĕn′**ənt) *n.* A person who pays rent to use or live on property that is owned by another person: *Mendel's new **tenant** made his home in Mendel's shop.*

trace (trās) *v.* To copy by following lines seen through thin paper: *The animator copied the cartoon rabbit by **tracing** it onto another piece of paper.*

trunk

trip (trĭp) *v.* **1.** To trap or catch in a mistake: *The thief was **tripped** when he lied about where he had been.* **2.** To strike the foot against something and stumble.

trot (trŏt) *v.* To run slowly; jog: *As the wagon rolled along, the dog **trotted** to keep up with it.*

trunk (trŭngk) *n.* The long, flexible snout of an elephant, used for grasping and feeding.

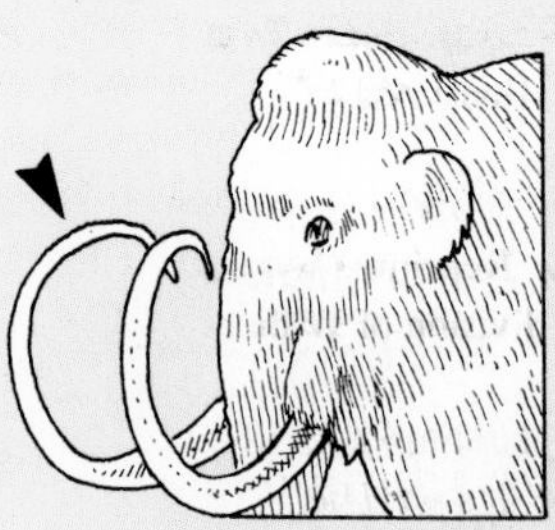
tusk

tset•se fly (**tsĕt′**sē flī) *n.* A bloodsucking African fly whose bite gives disease to human beings.

tusk (tŭsk) *n.* A long, pointed tooth, usually of a pair, reaching outside of the mouth of certain animals: *The mammoth's **tusks** grew out in two long curves.*

W

weap•on (**wĕp′**ən) *n.* Something that is used in defense or attack: *The tiger's **weapons** are its sharp teeth and claws.*

whirl•ing (**hwûrl′**ĭng) *adj.* Spinning quickly: *The **whirling** snow blew around and around.*

World Se•ries (wûrld **sîr′**ēz) *n.* The series of baseball games played each fall between the championship teams of the American League and the National League.

ă pat / ā pay / â care / ä father / ĕ pet / ē be / ĭ pit / ī pie / î fierce / ŏ pot / ō go / ô paw, for / oi oil / o͝o book / o͞o boot / ou out / ŭ cut / û fur / *th* the / th thin / hw which / zh vision / ə ago, item, pencil, atom, circus

Acknowledgments

For each of the selections listed below, grateful acknowledgment is made for permission to excerpt and/or reprint original or copyrighted material, as follows:

Major Selections

The Boy of the Three-Year Nap, by Dianne Snyder, illustrated by Allen Say. Text copyright © 1988 by Dianne Snyder. Illustrations copyright © 1988 by Allen Say. Reprinted by permission of Houghton Mifflin Company.

"The Case of the Missing Roller Skates," from *Encyclopedia Brown: Boy Detective*, by Donald J. Sobol. Copyright © 1963 by Donald J. Sobol. Reprinted by permission of the publisher, Lodestar Books, an affiliate of Dutton Children's Books, a division of Penguin Books USA, Inc.

"A Changing Nation," from *America: Past and Present* by David C. King and Charlotte C. Anderson. Copyright © 1980 by Houghton Mifflin Company. Reprinted by permission of Houghton Mifflin Company.

Chasing After Annie, by Marjorie Weinman Sharmat, illustrated by Marc Simont. Text copyright © 1981 by Marjorie Weinman Sharmat. Illustrations copyright © 1981 by Marc Simont. Reprinted by permission of Harper & Row, Publishers, Inc.

"Farmer Boy," from the book by Laura Ingalls Wilder, illustrated by Garth Williams. Text copyright © 1933 by Laura Ingalls Wilder; copyright © renewed 1981 by Roger L. MacBride. Pictures © 1953 by Garth Williams. Reprinted by permission of Harper & Row, Publishers, Inc., and Lutterworth Press.

Farmer Schulz's Ducks, by Colin Thiele, illustrated by Mary Milton. Text copyright © 1986 by Colin Thiele. Illustrations copyright © 1986 by Mary Milton. Reprinted by permission of Harper & Row, Publishers, Inc.

Jumanji, by Chris Van Allsburg. Copyright © 1981 by Chris Van Allsburg. Reprinted by permission of Houghton Mifflin Company.

"Justin and the Best Biscuits in the World," from the book by Mildred Pitts Walter. Copyright © 1986 by Mildred Pitts Walter. Reprinted by permission of Lothrop, Lee & Shepard Co., a division of William Morrow & Co., Inc.

"Little House on the Prairie," from the book by Laura Ingalls Wilder, illustrated by Garth Williams. Text copyright © 1935 by Laura Ingalls Wilder, copyright © renewed 1963 by Roger L. MacBride. Pictures copyright © 1953 by Garth Williams, copyright © renewed 1981 by Garth Williams. Reprinted by permission of Harper & Row, Publishers, Inc., and Methuen Children's Books, London.

Making Room for Uncle Joe, by Ada B. Litchfield. Text copyright © 1984 by Ada B. Litchfield. Illustrations copyright © 1984 by Gail Owens. Reprinted by permission of Albert Whitman & Co.

Marian Anderson, by Tobi Tobias (Thomas Y. Crowell). Text copyright © 1972 by Tobi Tobias. Reprinted by permission of Harper & Row, Publishers, Inc.

Meg Mackintosh and the Case of the Missing Babe Ruth Baseball, by Lucinda Landon. Text copyright © 1986 by Lucinda Landon. Reprinted by permission of Little, Brown and Company.

"The Mysterious Girl in the Garden," from the book by Judith St. George. Text copyright © 1981 by Judith St. George. Reprinted by permission of G. P. Putnam's Sons.

"On the Banks of Plum Creek," from the book by Laura Ingalls Wilder, illustrated by Garth Williams. Copyright 1937 by Laura Ingalls Wilder, copyright © renewed 1965 by Roger L. MacBride. Pictures copyright © 1953 by Garth Williams, renewed © 1981 by Garth Williams. Reprinted by permission of Harper & Row, Publishers, Inc. and Methuen Children's Books, London.

"Paddington Turns Detective," from the book *Paddington on Stage*, by Michael Bond and Alfred Bradley, illustrated by Peggy Fortnum. Text copyright © 1974 by Alfred Bradley and Michael Bond. Illustrations copyright © 1974 by William Collins Sons & Co., Ltd. Reprinted by permission of Houghton Mifflin Company and Lemon, Unna & Durbridge Ltd.

Roberto Clemente, by Kenneth Rudeen (Thomas Y. Crowell). Text copyright © 1974 by Kenneth Rudeen. Reprinted by permission of Harper & Row, Publishers, Inc.

The Shrinking of Treehorn, by Florence Parry Heide, illustrated by Edward Gorey (Holiday House, 1971). Text copyright © 1971 by Florence Parry Heide. Illustrations copyright © 1971 by Edward Gorey. All rights reserved. Reprinted by permission of Holiday House and Penguin Books Ltd., London.

The Sign in Mendel's Window, by Mildred Phillips, with illustrations by Margot Zemach. Text copyright © 1985 by Mildred Phillips. Illustrations copyright © 1985 by Margot Zemach. Reprinted by arrangement with Macmillan Publishing Company.

Strange Creatures That Really Lived, by Millicent Selsam. Text copyright © 1987 by Millicent Selsam. Reprinted by permission of Scholastic, Inc.

"Teacher's Pet," from the book by Johanna Hurwitz. Copyright © 1988 by Johanna Hurwitz. Reprinted by permission of Morrow Junior Books, a division of William Morrow & Co., Inc.

Tyrannosaurus, by Janet Riehecky. Copyright © 1988 by The Child's World, Inc. Reprinted by permission of The Child's World, Elgin, IL, Jane Buerger, President.

"Walt Disney: Master of Make-Believe," from the book by Elizabeth Rider Montgomery. Copyright © 1971 by Elizabeth Rider Montgomery. Reprinted by permission of Arthur Julesberg.

Wild and Woolly Mammoths, by Aliki. Copyright © 1977 by Aliki Brandenberg. Reprinted by permission of Harper & Row, Publishers, Inc.

Poetry

"Donkey," by Eloise Greenfield, from *Under the Sunday Tree.* Illustrated by Mr. Amos Ferguson. Paintings copyright © 1988 by Amos Ferguson and text copyright © 1988 by Eloise Greenfield. Reprinted by permission of Harper & Row, Publishers, Inc. and Marie Brown Associates.

"Dreams," by Langston Hughes, from *The Dream Keeper and Other Poems.* Copyright © 1932 by Alfred A. Knopf, Inc., and renewed 1960 by Langston Hughes. Reprinted by permission of Alfred A. Knopf, Inc. and Harold Ober Associates Incorporated.

"Fossils," by Lilian Moore, from *Something New Begins.* Copyright © 1982 by Lilian Moore. Reprinted with permission of Atheneum Publishers, an imprint of Macmillan Publishing Company.

"Gertrude," by Gwendolyn Brooks Blakely from *Bronzeville Boys and Girls.* Copyright © 1956 by Gwendolyn Brooks Blakely. Reprinted by permission of Harper & Row, Publishers, Inc.

"Hold Fast Your Dreams," by Louise Driscoll, from *The New York Times.* Copyright © 1918 by The New York Times Company. Reprinted by permission.

"The Mastodon," by Michael Braude, from *Dinosaurs and Beasts of Yore,* edited by William Cole. Copyright © 1979 by Michael Braude and William Cole.

"Poor Old Lion," from *Aesop's Fables,* retold by Tom Paxton, illustrated by Robert Rayevsky. Text copyright © 1988 by Tom Paxton. Illustrations copyright © 1988 by Robert Rayevsky. Reprinted by permission of Morrow Jr. Books, a division of William Morrow and Co., Inc., and Wendy Lipkind Agency.

"S'no Fun," by William Cole, from *Dinosaurs and Beasts of Yore,* edited by William Cole. Copyright © 1979 by Michael Braude and William Cole.

"There once was a Plesiosaurus," author unknown, from *Laughable Limericks.* Copyright © 1965 by Sara and John E. Brewton (Harper & Row, Publishers, Inc.).

"Tyrannosaurus," by Jack Prelutsky, from *Tyrannosaurus Was a Beast.* Copyright © 1988 by Jack Prelutsky. Reprinted by permission of Greenwillow Books (a division of William Morrow & Co., Inc.).

"What If . . .," by Isabel Joshlin Glaser. Used by permission of the author, who controls all rights.

Quotations from Authors/Illustrators

Marian Anderson (pg. 336), quotation from *American Heritage,* Vol. 28, no. 2. Copyright © 1977 by The American Heritage Publishing Co., Inc.

Michael Bond (pg. 331), quotation from *Something About the Author Autobiography Series,* Vol. 3. Copyright © 1987 by Gale Research, Inc. Reprinted by permission of the publisher.

Walt Disney (pg. 336), quotation from *The New York Times,* December 16, 1966.

Florence Parry Heide, Donald J. Sobol (pps. 73, 330), quotations from *Something About the Author,* Vols. 32, 31. Copyright © 1983 by Gale Research, Inc. Reprinted by permission of the publisher.

Allen Say (pg. 147), quotation from "The Boy of the Three-Year Nap," from *The Horn Book Magazine,* March/April 1989, pps. 174–175. Reprinted by permission of The Horn Book, Inc., 14 Beacon St., Boston, MA 02108.

Millicent Selsam (pg. 123), quotation from *Books Are by People* by Lee Bennett Hopkins. Copyright © 1969 by Scholastic, Inc. Reprinted by permission of Scholastic, Inc.

Laura Ingalls Wilder (pg. 191), quotation from her speech, Detroit, MI, 1937 from the collection of the Herbert Hoover Presidential Library. Copyright © 1982 by Roger L. MacBride. Reprinted by permission of Roger L. MacBride.

Margot Zemach (pg. 187), quotation from *Something About the Author,* Vol. 21. Copyright © 1980 by Gale Research, Inc. Reprinted by permission of the publisher.

Additional Acknowledgments

"My Visit with Laura Ingalls Wilder" (pg. 259), by Garth Williams. Printed by permission of Garth Williams.

Roberto Clemente (pg. 400), quotation from *Who Was Roberto? A Biography of Roberto Clemente,* by Phil Musick. Copyright © 1974 by Associated Features Inc. Reprinted by permission of Doubleday, a division of Bantam, Doubleday, Dell Publishing Group, Inc.

"Who Stole the Jewels?" (pg. 328) from *The Spy's Guidebook,* by Falcon Travis et al. Reprinted by permission of Usborne Publishing Ltd., London.

Theme Books

The Theme Books shown on Extended Reading pages are available from Houghton Mifflin Company and are reprinted with permission from various publishers. Jacket artists for these books are listed below.

Cam Jansen and the Mystery of the Television Dog, by David A. Adler. Jacket art by Susanna Natti, copyright © 1981 by Susanna Natti.

Dinosaur Hunters, by Kate McMullan. Jacket art by John R. Jones, copyright © 1989 by John R. Jones.

Farmer Boy, by Laura Ingalls Wilder. Jacket art by Garth Williams, copyright © 1953 by Garth Williams.

Flat Stanley, by Jeff Brown. Jacket art by Tomi Ungerer, copyright © 1964 by Tomi Ungerer.

The Lion and the Stoat, by Paul O. Zelinsky. Jacket art by Paul O. Zelinsky, copyright © 1984 by Paul O. Zelinsky.

The Secret Moose, by Jean Rogers. Jacket art by Jim Fowler, copyright © 1985 by Jim Fowler.

Take Me Out to the Airfield! by Robert Quackenbush. Jacket art by Robert Quackenbush, copyright © 1976 by Robert Quackenbush.

Additional Recommended Reading

Houghton Mifflin Company wishes to thank the following publishers for permission to reproduce their book covers in Extended Reading lists.

Coward-McCann, Inc., a member of the Putnam Publishing Group:
The Monsters Who Died: A Mystery About Dinosaurs, by Vicki Cobb. Jacket art by Greg Wenzel, copyright © 1983 by Greg Wenzel.
Thomas Y. Crowell, an imprint of Harper & Row, Publishers, Inc.:
Mary McLeod Bethune, by Eloise Greenfield. Jacket art by Jerry Pinkney, copyright © 1977 by Jerry Pinkney.
Follett Publishing Co., a division of Modern Curriculum Press:
All-of-a-kind Family, by Sydney Taylor. Jacket art by Helen John. Copyright © 1951 by Follett Publishing Company, renewed © 1979 by Ralph Taylor.
Harper & Row Publishers, Inc.:
The Boy Who Wanted a Family, by Shirley Gordon. Jacket art by Charles Robinson, copyright © 1980 by Charles Robinson; *Sarah, Plain and Tall*, by Patricia MacLachlan. Book design by Constance Fogler, copyright © 1985.
Holiday House:
Martin Luther King, Jr.: Free At Last, by David A. Adler. Jacket art by Robert Casilla, copyright © 1986 by Robert Casilla.
Alfred A. Knopf, Inc.:
Mystery of the Plumed Serpent, by Barbara Brenner. Cover art by Judy Clifford, copyright © 1981 by Judy Clifford; *Blackberries in the Dark*, by Mavis Jukes. Jacket art by Thomas B. Allen, copyright © 1985 by Thomas B. Allen.
J. B. Lippincott Company:
Talk About a Family, by Eloise Greenfield. Jacket art by James Calvin, copyright © 1978 by James Calvin.
Little, Brown Books:
The Enormous Egg, by Oliver Butterworth. Published in association with The Atlantic Monthly Press. Jacket art by Louis Darling, copyright © 1956; *The Young Detective's Handbook*, by William Vivian Butler. Published in association with the Atlantic Monthly Press. Jacket art by Lucinda Landon, copyright © 1981 by Little, Brown and Company.
Gregory S. Paul:
The News About Dinosaurs, by Patricia Lauber. Jacket art by Gregory S. Paul, copyright © 1989 by Gregory S. Paul.
Penguin Books Ltd.:
Grandma Moses: Painter of Rural America, by Zibby Oneal. Cover painting, *In the Studio*, by Grandma Moses, courtesy Sidney Janis Gallery.
Random House:
The Chalk Box Kid, by Clyde Robert Bulla. Jacket art by Thomas B. Allen, copyright © 1987 by Thomas B. Allen. *The Great Cheese Conspiracy*, by Jean Van Leeuwen. Jacket art by Imero Gobbato, copyright © 1969.
Scholastic Inc.:
Helen Keller, by Margaret Davidson. Jacket art by Jimenez. Copyright © 1969 by Scholastic Inc.
Troll Associates:
Lou Gehrig, Pride of the Yankees, by Keith Brandt. Jacket art by John Lawn, copyright © 1986.

Credits

Program design Carbone Smolan Associates

Cover design Carbone Smolan Associates

Design 12–75 Landesberg Design Associates; **76–125** Pronk & Associates; **126–189, 190–261, 270–333** Carbone Smolan Associates; **406–477** Joshua Hayes

Illustrations 13–15 Lynne Buschman; **16–31** Chris Van Allsburg; **34–51** Alexander Farquarson; **54–72** Edward Gorey; **76–77** John Gurche; **78–79** Alan Barnard; **80** (inset) Greg Douglas; **80–81** Courtesy of Byron Preiss Visual Publications, Inc., copyright Bill Stout; **83** Greg Douglas; **84** (top) Steve Van Gelder; (bottom) John Sibbick/courtesy of Salamander Books; **86** John Sibbick/courtesy of Salamander Books; **87** C. R. Knight; **88** Ian Carr; **89** John Gurche/courtesy of Smithsonian Institution; **92–104** Aliki Brandenberg; Paper reliefs by Margo Stahl; **105** Ian Carr; **108** Alan Barnard; **108–109** (bottom) American Museum of Natural History, restoration by Ferguson; **109** (top) Margo Stahl; **110** (top right and bottom) Greg Douglas; **113** (top) Greg Douglas; **114** Greg Douglas; **115** The Macmillan Illustrated Encyclopedia of Dinosaurs and Prehistoric Animals; **117** Barb Massey; **120–121** Bing Chapelle; **124–125** Julie Ebberly; **127–129** Kristina Rodanas; **127–128** (calligraphy) Grace Peters; **130–145, 147** Allen Say; **149–163** Mary Milton; **164** Chris Demarest; **165** Mary Milton; **166–167** Robert Rayevsky; **169** Amos Ferguson; **170–185, 187** Margot Zemach; **188–189** Kristina Rodanas; Calligraphy by Grace Peters;

194–218, 222–242 Garth Williams; **243** Carolyn Vibbert; **246–256** Garth Williams; **257** Carolyn Vibbert; **260–261** Ellyn Siegel; **266** (map) Precision Graphics; **274–296** Hilary Mosberg; Handwriting by Marsha Goldberg; **297** Amy Wasserman; **298–299** Kathleen Dunne McCarthy; **300–316** (line drawings) Peggy Fortnum; **318–326** Paul Van Munching; **328–329** Kathleen Dunne McCarthy; **332–333** Paul Van Munching; **335** Linda Phinney; **339–355** (lettering) Tom Canty; **344–347** Olive Jar Animation; **359** Barbara C. Morse; **362–379** (borders) Linda Phinney; **380–381** Margery Mintz; **384** Pat Rossi; **402–403** Linda Phinney; **404–405** Margery Mintz; **407** Joshua Hayes; **408–409** Renée C. Williams; **410–423** George Courage; **424–438** Gail Owens; **439** Joshua Hayes; **440–449** Brian Pinkney; **450–474** Marc Simont; **475** Renée C. Williams; **476–477** Joshua Hayes; **480** Joe Veno/Gwen Goldstein; **486** (top) Pam Levy; **486** (bottom) Joe Veno/Gwen Goldstein; **488** (top) Pam Levy; **488** (bottom) Joe Veno/Gwen Goldstein; **492** (bottom) Joe Veno/Gwen Goldstein

Photography **32** Richard Howard/People Weekly © 1989, The Time Inc. Magazine Co., All Rights Reserved; **33** Susan Lapides; **52** (top center and right) Topham/The Image Works; **53** (top) A. C. Cooper Ltd. Copyright Reserved to Her Majesty Queen Elizabeth II; (bottom left and right) Courtesy of Judith St. George; **73** (left) Courtesy of Florence P. Heide; (right) AP/Wide World Photos; **74–75** Kevin Burke; **85** Royal Ontario Museum, photo by Ian Chrysler; **90–91** (top) John Lei/OPC; (bottom) Chip Clark/Smithsonian Institution; **91** (top right) Chip Clark/Smithsonian Institution; **92–104** Artwork photographed by See Spot Run; **106** Tass from Sovfoto; **107** (top left) Novosti from Sovfoto; (top right) Craig Aurness/West Light; (bottom) Sheriden Photo Library; **110** (top left) Chip Clark/Smithsonian Institution; **111** Royal Ontario Museum; **112** (top) Chip Clark/Smithsonian Institution; (bottom) Royal Ontario Museum, photo by Ian Chrysler; **113** Courtesy of George O. Polnair, Jr., Berkeley Amber Laboratory; **116** Jonathan Blair; **118–119** Royal Ontario Museum, photo by Ian Chrysler; **122** (left) Courtesy of Janet Riehecky; (right) Courtesy of Aliki Brandenberg; **122–123** (background) Royal Ontario Museum, photo by Ian Chrysler; **123** Courtesy of Robert Selsam; **146** (all) Courtesy of Diane Snyder; **147** Richard Allen, courtesy of Houghton Mifflin Company; **186** (top) Courtesy of Mildred Phillips; (bottom) Courtesy of Four Winds Press, imprint of Macmillan Publishing Co.; **187** Courtesy of Kaethe Zemach-Bersin; **191** Bettmann Newsphotos; **192** Laura Ingalls Wilder — Rose Wilder Lane Museum and Home; **220** (background) Aubrey Sherwood Collection, De Smet, S.D.; (bottom left) Laura Ingalls Wilder — Rose Wilder Lane Museum and Home; (bottom right) Laura Ingalls Wilder Memorial Society; **221** (exterior photos) Leslie A. Kelly; (interior photos) Laura Ingalls Wilder Memorial Society; **244** Laura Ingalls Wilder Memorial Society; **244–245** (background) Laura Ingalls Wilder — Rose Wilder Lane Museum and Home; **245** Laura Ingalls Wilder Museum — Rose Wilder Lane Museum and Home; **263** "On the Road" by Thomas Otter. The Nelson-Atkins Museum of Art, Kansas City, Missouri (Nelson Fund); **265** Culver Pictures; **267** Santa Fe Railroad; **268** (center) Solomon D. Butcher Collection/Nebraska State Historical Society; (bottom) Culver Pictures; **271, 272, 317, 327** Kurt Mundahl; John Lei/OPC; **330–331** (background) Kurt Mundahl; **330** (top) Courtesy of Lucinda Landon; (bottom) Courtesy of Donald J. Sobol; **331** Courtesy of Houghton Mifflin Company; **336–337** Steve Nelson/Fay Foto, Inc.; **336** (left) © The Walt Disney Company/RKO Radio Pictures, Inc.; (right) The Lester Glassner Collection; **337** The Pittsburgh Pirates; **338** © The Walt Disney Company/RKO Radio Pictures, Inc.; **340–341** Steve Nelson/Fay Foto, Inc.; **351** © The Walt Disney Company; **353** © The Walt Disney Company/RKO Radio Pictures, Inc.; **357–358** © The Walt Disney Company; **360–361** Roy Bishop/Stock Boston; **361** © The Walt Disney Company; **363** The Lester Glassner Collection; **364** (top left) The Lester Glassner Collection; (top right and bottom left) Culver Pictures; (bottom right) Paul Cordes/Culver Pictures; **369** AP/Wide World Photos; **370** Culver Pictures; **372** FPG; **373** The Lester Glassner Collection; **375** (all) UPI/Bettmann Newsphotos; **376** Lisa Larsen/LIFE Magazine/Time Inc.; **377** UPI/Bettmann Newsphotos; **379** AP/Worldwide Photos; **382–383** (baseball cards) Copyright The Topps Company, Inc.; (photo) Steve Nelson/Fay Foto Inc.; **385** (left) Sybil Shelton/Peter Arnold, Inc.; (right) Jacques Janqoux/Peter Arnold, Inc.; **387** Courtesy of Diana D. Zorilla; **389** La Presse; **392–393** The Pittsburgh Pirates; **395–396** AP/Wide World Photos; **397** National Baseball Library, Cooperstown, N.Y.; **399** National Baseball Hall of Fame; **400** Ciudad Deportiva Roberto Clemente Inc.; **401** The Pittsburgh Pirates; **402** Peter Liddell/The Seattle Times; **403** Courtesy of Kenneth Rudeen; **423** Allen A. Raymond; **439** Courtesy of Ada B. Litchfield; **449** Bert Andrews; **475** Andrew Sharmat; **481** Biological Photo Service; **485** Stephen G. Maka; **487** Morton Feinberg/The Picture Cube; **489** Biological Photo Service; **491** Dan Kelley/The Picture Cube; **492** (top) Stephen G. Maka

End Matter production by Publicom, Inc.